The Design and Construction of British Warships 1939-1945

Mainly LCTs assembled at Southampton prior to D-Day, 1944

The Design and Construction of British Warships 1939-1945

The Official Record

Landing Craft and Auxiliary Vessels

Edited by

D K Brown RCNC

CONWAY
MARITIME PRESS

Records of Warship Construction © Crown Copyright 1996
Reproduced by permission of the Controller of Her Majesty's Stationery Office
© Introduction and notes D K Brown 1996

First published in Great Britain in 1996 by
Conway Maritime Press,
an imprint of Brassey's (UK) Ltd,
33 John Street,
London WC1N 2AT

British Library Cataloguing in Publication Data
Design and Construction of British Warships, 1939-45:
Official Record – Vol. 3: Landing Craft and Auxiliary Vessels
 I. Brown, D. K.
 623.8250941

ISBN 0 85177 675 2

Typesetting and page make-up by TypeBright, Burton upon Trent
Printed and bound by Butler and Tanner Ltd, Frome

Contents: Landing Craft and Auxiliary Vessels

Introduction

At the end of World War I, the Naval Construction Department of the Admiralty produced a two-volume history of its wartime activities. Though originally 'Confidential', copies of this work can be found in a few libraries and have proved invaluable to historians. When World War II came to an end in August 1945 it was decided to produce a similar record but, though largely complete, it was never printed or issued, even internally. A number of chapters were slightly re-shaped and published as papers to the Institution of Naval Architects in 1947. In 1983 a carbon copy of the typescript came to light and a few copies were made for naval libraries and it is from these that the current work has been produced. There are indications on the original that one or two chapters were never completed, notably the introduction on the effect of naval limitation treaties (now covered briefly in the introduction to Volume I)

and on wartime damage to ships. This book is published as it was written and no attempt has been made to correct any errors there may be (except obvious spelling mistakes), though manuscript notes suggest that it was very carefully checked. A limited number of footnotes have been added to supplement the information given, mainly as references to other sources. The second volume of a three-volume series, this book incorporates Chapters 9 to 16 of the original manuscript. Volume 1 covers Major Service Vessels, and Volume 3 covers Amphibious Warfare Vessels and the Fleet Train.

With rare exceptions, the text mentions only those designs which were actually built and the many designs progressed but abandoned are not mentioned. Few records remain of these designs which are frequently the 'missing link' between apparently unrelated ships which entered service.

ROYAL CORPS OF NAVAL CONSTRUCTORS IN 1945

Director of Naval Construction – C S Lillicrap, Esq, CB, MBE

Deputy Directors of Naval Construction – A P Cole, MBE (*act*) – (*a*) W G Sanders, MBE (*act*) and
L C Williamson (*act*), Esqrs

Director of Warship Production – S A McCarthy, Esq (*act*)

Director of Contract Work (Ships) – (*a*) C Hannaford, Esq, MBE (*act*)

Director of Contract Work (Supplies) – C J W Hopkins, Esq, MBE (*act*)

Assistant Directors of Naval Construction – F Hickey (*act*) and (*a*) A W Watson, MBE, Esqrs

Deputy Director of Dockyards – G A Bassett, Esq (*act*)

‡ *Senior Staff*

Bartlett J L (ADNC) (*act*),
Blackman, F T, MCD (*act*) (*tempy*),
Curphey, E S, MBE (*Assistant D of D*) (*act*),
Davies, W J A, OBE (*Assistant DWP*)
Forbes, W A D (ADNC) (*act*),
Gawn, R W L (Supt, Haslar),
Holt, N G, CBE (ADNC) (*act*),
Horley, A E (WPS NW Area)
Hudson, G, MBE (MCD) (*act*),

(*a*) Joughlin, J C, CBE (*Assistant DCW (s)*)
Kennett, E G (MCD) (*act*),
McCloghrie, G OBE (ADNC) (*act*),
Mathias, J E (*WPS Scottish Area*) (*act*),
Mathias, T L (ADNC) (*act*),
Merchant, C F (*Assistant D of D*) (*act*),
Moon, J E P (MCD) (*act*),
Offord, D E J, (*Superintendent, Undex, Rosyth*),
Payne, S, MBE (MCD) (*act*),

Pengelly, H S (ADNC) (*act*),
Shepheard, V G (ADNC) (*act*),
Stanley, H (*WPS North East Area*) (*act*),
Stantan, A G W (ADNC) (*act*),
Steed, F H (ADNC),
Sutcliffe, F (MCD) (*act*),
(*a*) Walker, J F, MBE (MCD)
Wallond, W H (*WPS NW Area*) (*act*),
(*a*) Woollard, L, MA (ADNC), Esqrs

‡ *Chief Constructors.*

(*a*) Adams, A (*act*),
Baker, R (*act*),
Bentley, T H (*act*),
(Bessant, J L, BSC (*act*),
Constr Capt F G Bogie, (*FNCO East Indies Station*),
Bryant, G (*act*),
Cannon, S R (*act*) (*Deputy WPS, Scottish Area*)
Carter, L T (*act*),
Chapman, J H B (*act*),
Constr Capt E F Craggs, BSC, *Lyness* (*act*),
Constr Capt V W Hall (*act*), (*tempy*) *For duty in Australia*
Hatchard W J (*act*),
Constr Capt S I Hill, *Colombo* (*act*),
Holt, W J (*act*),

W H Jackman, (*act*),
John, W G (*act*),
Johnson, H T (*act*),
King, I E, CBE (*act*),
Leddra, C H (*act*),
Lemmon, A T
McCammon, G W R MBE (*act*),
Mann, H R, OBE (*act*), (*tempy*),
May, H (*act*), (*Deputy WPS, NE Area*)
Constr Capt A J Merrington, OBE, BSC (*SCO Staff of ANCXF*) (*act*),
Monk, R J (*act*),
Narbeth, J H, BSC (*Eng*) (*act*),
Newnham, H E (*act*),
(*a*) Nicholls, A CBE, OBE,
(*a*) Noble, W E,
Constr Capt Paige, C V (*Bombay*) (*act*),

Constr Capt G W Pamplin (*Staff of RAFT*) (*act*),
Peake, H S (*act*), (*Deputy WPS NW Area*)
Perrett, W R (*act*),
Perry, C H, BSC (*act*),
Pound, F J A (*act*),
Richards, R H (*act*),
(*a*) Scott, C
Skinner, H E, OBE, BSC (*act*),
Sims, A J, OBE (*act*),
Constr Capt D W Smithers (*FNCO Mediterranean Fleet*) (*act*),
Stevens, L G (*act*),
Sutherby, F S (*act*),
Trevan, S N (*act*),
Watson, H J (*act*),
Watson, S H (*act*) Esqrs
Constr Capt R H Wright, *Kilindini* (*act*),

Tempy. Chief Constructors, H J Cox,

‡ *Senior Constructors*

Penwill, C H (*act*),
Pether, R P (*act*),

Sherwin, C E (*act*), Esqrs

‡ *Tempy. Senior Constructors*

Mitchell, C C H P,

P G Rouse, BA, MINA (*Supt of Conversions*),

Whiting, W R G, MBE, MA Esqrs

‡ *Constructors.*

Andrew, W R, (*M Eng*) (*act*),
Barrett, L J (*act*),
Brooks, L J (*act*),
Chislett, H W J (*act*),
M C Dunstan (*act*),
Contr Com G S Ferris, BSC (ENG) (*act*) (*Lent to RIN*)
French, A W (*act*),
Gibbons, A J T (*act*),
Hancock, N (*act*),
Harrington, J W (*act*),
Constr Capt A N Harrison (*Lent to Royal Canadian Navy*),
Constr Com W R N Hughes (*Staff of VA(D)*) (*act*),

Constr Com L Kirkpatrick (*act*),
McCalin, E (*act*),
Mason, H R (*act*),
Matthews, F W (*act*),
Constr Com J R F Moss (*act*),
Mowatt, H M, BSC (*act*),
Newton, R N (*act*),
Constr Com S J Palmer, (*duty in Australia*) (*act*),
Perry, W G (*act*),
Constr Com T H Pilfold, (*duty at SHAEF*) (*act*),
Pound, E C, BSC (ENG) (*act*),
Purvis, M K (*act*),

Rayner, L W A (*act*),
Rogers, F C C,
Spanner, W F (*act*),
Constr Com J F Starks, (*Staff Admiral (S)*) (*act*),
Stewart, A, BSC (*act*),
Stunden, G J (*act*),
Tabb, H J (*act*),
Thorpe, T (*act*),
Tozer, R E (*act*),
Constr Com J E S Vincent, (*Freetown*) (*act*),
Vosper, A J (*act*),
Wood, R K, BSC (ENG) (*act*),

---

‡ *Arranged alphabetically*   (*a*) *Re-employed*   (*act*) *Acting*   (*tempy*) *Temporary*

‡ Temporary Constructors

Allen, T E,
Baker, D M,
Bedford, C A,
Constr Com J A Bonnyman, MBE (*duty in India*),
Boulton, T J,
Brookshaw, S W,
Bugler, A R,
Burrell, L W J,
Bush, F R,
Campaign, H H,
Chandler, C,
Coombes, L C,
Corfield, W A H,
Constr Com N J Coscoros,
Constr Com J Craig (*Staff of C-in-C, EIS*),
Constr Com R G Craig (*duty in Australia*),
Cross, T S,
Crossley, E,
(*a*) Cumbe, E. R,
(*a*) Daniels, S G,
Davey, S J,
Dwelly, E,
Eddey, J F J,
Grant, R C,

Constr Com F W Gray (*N Africa*),
Grinyer, A L,
Hankins, P H,
Constr Com A C Hardy,
Harris, C H L,
Hickish, J R,
Holloway, A H E,
Jago, E G,
Jeffery, W A,
Kicks, E,
King, P,
Langford, A T,
Littlejohns, F,
Constr Com C Lloyd-Roberts (*India*),
McMurray, M, BSC,
Mann, W J,
Martin, F J,
Matthews, A J,
Constr Capt J A Mavor (*PBCO, Italy*),
Mitchell, A BSc
Morley, F,
(*a*) Morris, R,
Constr Com H H Mutch (*Colombo*),
Nancarrow, G C,
New, H J C,

Norrington, E C,
North, D H,
O'Keeffe, W,
Osborne, A H,
Patridge, A,
Patterson, A P, BSC
Payne, R L,
Constr Com N H Perkin,
Phillips J,
Pitcher, H A,
(*b*) Sears, F H,
Sedgwick, H E,
Smart, F J,
Constr Com W B Strang (*Staff of ANCXF (PH)*),
Thomas, A W,
Tillett, F L,
Turner, F,
(*a*) Turner, H A,
Constr Com A G Wearn (*Italy*),
Webb, W J,
Wolfe, A J M,
Wyatt, R,
Young, F, Esqrs

‡ Assistant Constructors, First Class

Constr Lieut-Com R Anscomb,
Constr Lieut-Com I McD Black, (*Staff of C-in-C, EIS*)
E C S Hepden, Esq

Constr Lieut-Com D R King,
Constr Lieut-Com R F Lofft, (*For special duty*),

Constr Lieut-Com E P Skinner (*Staff of C-in-C, BPF*),
Constr Lieut-Com W H Winn,

‡ Assistant Constructors, Second Class

Austin, A A,
Bell, L G,
Boulter, G J (*act*) (*tempy*),
Brinton, L J,
Brokensha, E A,
Chatten, H R P,
Cope, A J,
Dale, S D,
Constr Lieut-Com R J Daniel, (*Staff of RA(D), BPF*),
Davis, S M, M.ENG,
Evans, K G,
Constr Lieut-Com L H Evans, (*Staff of C-in-C, BPF*),

Farrell, K P,
Constr Lieut-Com J H Froud, (*For duty in Australia*),
Gibbons, E S,
Gundry, N E (*act*),
Hawkes, R,
Honey, N W,
Constr Lieut-Com R H Howorth,
Jolliffe, F V,
Constr Lieut-Com D B Kimber,
Constr Lieut J C Lawrence (*Staff of C-in-C, Med*),
Constr Lieut-Com C G Nace (*Staff of C-in-C, EIS*),

Constr Lieut A H Matthews (*duty in Australia*), (*act*),
North, E R (*act*),
Oldridge, C P (*act*),
Padbury, A E W,
Phillips, A E W,
Constr Lieut D S Radford (*Staff FOCT*),
Reeves, A E, (*act*),
Revans, J T,
Warren, W G,
Wood, E F,
Yearling, F H J, Esqrs

‡ Temporary Assistant Constructors

Blake, G D,
Crawford, J B,
Davies, J B,
(*a*) Froude, W,
(*a*) Hackney, G,

Lawson, D F,
Lees, J A H,
Constr Lieut L A Oliver,
Peel, R W,
Robinson, L M C,

Spanner, D C,
Lieut-Com P J Thornycroft,
Constr Lieut R J Tirard,
Watson, R H M,
Williams, F, Esqrs

‡ Temporary Acting Assistant Constructors

Constr Lieut-Com J P Allsopp,
Algate, E F,
Benoy, W H,
Chester, R,
Clews, C E,
Collecott, W B,
Davies, J J,
Dean, F D'A,
Dowden, A G,
Dunstall, J C,

Foot, F G,
Fuller, J V,
George, J,
Hastings, W A W,
Hosking, W H,
Jones, W,
King, J H,
Kingcome, F J,
Mason, T J,
(*a*) Merriman, T P,

Nightingall, V H,
Paradise, R,
Parsons, C H,
Price, J A,
Price, T L,
(*a*) Roberts, F C,
Rowe, J P,
Tippins, H G W,
Truscott, A G Esqrs

Honorary Member of the Corps
H B W Evans, Esq, MBE (*Assistant Constructor*)

---

‡ Arranged alphabetically   (*a*) *Re-employed*   (*b*) *On loan from other Government Departments*

(From Vol. III of the "Navy List" for July 1945 (corrected to 30 June)).

Key to Abbreviations and Terms

This book was written by naval constructors who probably expected that most readers would also be naval architects and other Admiralty officers who would be familiar with the many abbreviations and initials used. This glossary defines and explains most of them; though one or two sets of initials beat even the editor's 40 years of experience. Many of the entries relate to stability or strength and two short notes are included which explain the problems and define the terms used.

A   Aft

ACNS (W)   Assistant Chief of Naval Staff (Warfare)

Advance   The distance the ship moves in the direction of the original course during a turn.

AE   After End

AEW   Admiralty Experiment Works, at Haslar, near Portsmouth, where all hydrodynamic model testing was carried out.

Angle of max righting lever (GZ)   See Stability note.

Angle of vanishing stability   See Stability note.

AP   After perpendicular, at this date taken as the centre of the rudder stock.

AQ   Cannot be recognised. It clearly refers to cemented armour (C) and may be an error in the original.

BATM   British Admiralty Technical Mission – in Washington, USA.

BD   Between Deck. Of gun mounting refers to mountings, mainly twin 4.5in, worked from a gun bay between decks.

Bending Moment   See Strength note

BP   Between perpendiculars (of length) The fore perpendicular (FP) was the intersection of the design waterline with the stem, AP as above.

BTU   British Thermal Unit – an old, Imperial measure of heat.

Buster   A twin Bofors mount under development late in the war but never put into service, mainly because its weight of 20 tons was excessive.

C   Cemented, of armour. Armour with a very hard face produced by heating for a long period in contact with carbon.

Crush (of dock blocks)   During the war, most dock blocks were of timber which would compress (crush) under the weight of a ship.

D (quality), D1, D1HT   D Quality steel was a high strength steel introduced in the 1920s, D1 and D1HT were slight variations on D. It was not possible to make good, lasting welds on any of them.

DB   Double Bottom.

DC   Depth Charge.

DCHQ   Damage Control Headquarters, primary (1), secondary (2).

DCT   Director Control Tower.

Developed (blade) area   The total area of all blades outside the boss on the face of a propeller. (The face is the high pressure side, facing aft.)

Disc   The circle swept by the blades of a propeller.

Displacement   The total weight of a ship. Deep is fully laden, everything on board; standard is defined by the Washington Treaty, roughly deep without all liquids, water, fuel etc.

DTSD   Director of Tactical and Staff Duties. Responsible for co-ordinating the views of naval staff divisions and issuing the Staff Requirement for a ship.

DW   A development of D quality steel which could be welded.

Endurance   Normally given with fouling corresponding to the average effect, six months out of dock in temperate waters. This conventionally added 1/4% per day to the frictional resistance (20-25% in six months). The effect was doubled in tropical waters. The quoted endurance was a comparative figure only, and true endurance was much less.

Expansion joint   A long superstructure will be strained by the flexing of the main hull in a seaway. It can either be made strong enough to accept the resulting load or the superstructure can be divided into short lengths. The joints between these lengths are known as expansion joints and will have a splash-proof cover.

F   Forward (sometimes used for Freeboard).

°F   Temperature, degrees Fahrenheit

(fl)   Fluid, refers to the effect of liquid movement on metacentric height, see Stability note.

g   The acceleration due to gravity – 32.2 ft/sec^2 – used as a measure of acceleration.

GM   Metacentric height. See Stability note.

HA   High Angle (gun mounting).

HADT   High Angle Director Tower

HA/LA   Combined High Angle/Low Angle mounting

Haslar   Site of AEW (*qv*), the ship model tanks.

Hogging   See Strength Note.

HP   High Pressure, as of a high pressure turbine stage or of a compressed air system

HT   High Tensile steel. Usually used in this book to describe high strength steels earlier than D quality.

Inclining (experiment)   See stability – an experiment to measure GM.

Inertia (in^{2}ft^2)   See Strength note

Lbs (Plate thickness)   Naval architects have to be very conscious of weight and to keep this in mind, the thickness of plates was given in lbs/sq ft. A 1 inch thick plate weighed 40lbs per sq ft (approximately) and was referred to as '40lb' plate. A similar approach was used for sections such as angle bars which were described by their weight ft run.

lbs/in^2   Pressure or stress in pounds per square inch, can also be written as psi.

Legend   In submitting a design for approval, DNC would complete a standard 4-page form setting out the main particulars of the design. This form was known as the Legend and quantities such as displacement given thereon became the Legend Displacement. After the Washington Treaty, the Legend Displacement would be the Standard (Washington) displacement. Prior to Washington the Legend displacement would include some fuel, usually one third.

Length (Between perpendiculars BP), (Overall)   See BP, length overall was from the furthermost points forward and aft (excluding the ensign staff but including stern galleries).

LP   Low pressure.

Maximum righting lever, Max GZ   See Stability note,

Metacentric Height   See Stability note.

ML   Middle Line.

NC   Non Cemented armour. Lacking the hard face of cemented armour which could not be made in thin plates. NC was generally preferred for turret roofs of any thickness because of its toughness.

NMMPP   Non Magnetic Protective Plating, used near the magnetic compass.

OB   Outer Bottom.

Peace Tanks   Fuel tanks carried high up in the machinery spaces of destroyers. Only used in peace because of the risk of fire in war.

Pitch   The face of a propeller of the type used in World War II was part of a helical screw – like a wood screw. The pitch of the propeller is the distance such a screw would move forward along its axis if turned through one revolution without slipping (again as in wood rather than water).

Propulsive coefficient (PC)   This is not an efficiency. It is the ratio of the power required to tow the hull, without appendages (bilge keels, shaft brackets etc) and without propellers to the power put into the shafts by the engines. It is a very useful shorthand to the naval architect, particularly in giving a first estimate of power for a new ship by comparison with a similar, existing ship. However, definitions and usage differ and it is a trap for the unwary.

psi   Pounds per square inch.

Rabbetted   Two plates slotted together at their edges in similar fashion to 'tongue and groove' floorboards.

Range (of stability)   See Stability note.

rpm   Revolutions (of shaft) per minute.

Sagging   See Strength note.

Speed   This may be given at deep displacement or standard. For a destroyer, there would be about 5 knots difference. Speed is quoted with a 'clean bottom' – no fouling.

STAAG   Twin Bofors mounting introduced late in the war. Acronym for 'Stabilised Tachymetric Anti Aircraft Gun'.

Standard   Displacement as defined by Washington; also used for corresponding draught and freeboard.

Stress   See Strength note.

SWL   Standard Water Line – see Standard.

Tactical Diameter   The diameter of the turning circle of the ship; unless otherwise stated, is full rudder angle.

Trim   Difference in draught between bow and stern. It was usual to design for about 2ft trim by the stern which give good directional stability, sufficient draught for the propellers and would ensure that, in dry docking, the ship would settle on the blocks stern first, where the structure had been reinforced to take the heavy loads involved.

UD, UDk   Upper Deck.

UP   Unrotated Projectile. A rocket device which it was hoped would deter or even destroy attacking aircraft.

USK   Under Side of Keel.

Vote 8 cost   The cost without guns and stores.

WA   Warning Air (of Radar or, as it was then known, RDF – Radio Direction Finding).

WPS   Warship Production Superintendent.

WT   Wireless Telegraphy, radio using morse.

W/T   Water Tight.

Y   See strength note.

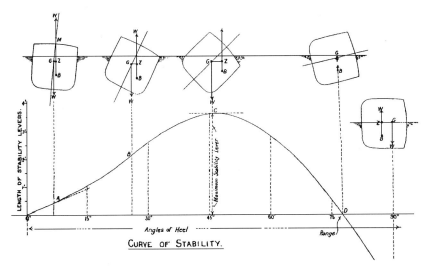

CURVE OF STABILITY.

Stability

To the naval architect, stability is a measure of the moment of force trying to bring the ship upright from a heeled position. The weight force acts downwards through the centre of gravity (G) which is (almost) a fixed point. The buoyancy force acts upwards through the centre of buoyancy (B) which is the centre of the underwater volume of the ship, which clearly moves as the ship is heeled.

The five small sections at the top of the diagram show how the centre of buoyancy B first moves outward as the ship is heeled, increasing the leverage bringing the ship upright and then, for extreme angles, moves back until the righting moment is zero and then becomes negative, causing capsize. Weight (W) equals buoyancy and hence the righting moment is measured by

$$\text{Weight (W) x GZ}$$

The stability characteristics were – and are – set out in the curve of stability or 'GZ curve' in which GZ, the righting lever, is plotted against angle of heel. The key parameters, which are given for each class in the text, are shown on the diagram.

Maximum stability lever, commonly called maximum GZ, defines the maximum steady heeling moment which the ship can withstand.

The angle at which the maximum GZ occurs is also important as if it is too small a sudden gust of wind may cause heel which exceeds the angle at which GZ is a maximum and lead to capsize (as in the loss of the *Captain* in 1870).

The extreme angle at which there is a positive righting moment is called the range. It is a less important parameter as, in a real ship, water will be pouring in down ventilators and other openings well before this angle is reached.

At small angles of heel (θ) GZ is given approximately by

$$GZ = GM. \sin(\theta) \quad - \text{See Diagram}$$

where GM is the metacentric height and θ is the angle of heel.

The values of most of the parameters used differ with changes in loading and are normally given for deep and light condition, the latter usually giving the worst results since the weight of fuel low down in the deep condition acts as ballast. It was frequently necessary to add water ballast if the ship approached the light condition. During World War II it was customary to base design values of GM, GZ etc on previous practice rather than on rigid standards. With the experience gained from operating a large navy this was a perfectly acceptable procedure, shown by the fact that no British warship was lost due to stress of weather. The chosen values would have to be justified in formal debate with increasingly senior – and experienced – officers concluding with the DNC himself, who was not easily satisfied.

In the first paragraph it was said that the centre of gravity (G) was (almost) fixed. The effect of liquids, fuel or water, which are free to move in partially filled tanks does cause some movement of G except in the light condition where there are no liquids. This movement can be calculated and an effective position of G determined. This is known as G (fluid) usually written in this book as Gfl. Care would be taken in the design to minimise the possible movement of liquids and operators were warned to minimise the number of partially filled tanks.

It is possible to measure metacentric height directly in an inclining experiment. Known weighs (w) are moved a specified distance (x) across the deck and the heel (θ) measured. Then

$$w.x = W.GM.\sin\theta$$

Since the position of M can be calculated precisely, that of G can be deduced.

Strength

Ships are loaded, even in still water, by the uneven distribution of weight and buoyancy along the length and this is made worse in waves. The worst case is when the ship is end on to waves of its own length and from a paper of 1870 by Edward Reed this was formalised into a standard calculation which was gradually refined. By World War II the waves considered were of the same length, crest to crest, as the ship with a height equal to 1/20 of the length.

Two conditions were considered:
Hogging with a wave crest amidships and the ends relatively unsupported and
Sagging with crest at either end.

The loading of the ship – stores, fuel etc – would be adjusted to give a worst case in either condition. (Note, in some tables the different displacement used for Hogging and Sagging is given.) With the ship 'balanced' (weight = buoyancy) on the wave it was a simple, if lengthy, task to calculate the differential vertical force, the difference between weight and buoyancy, at each point along the length. This could be integrated to give the bending moment from which the stress (load per unit area of cross section) in deck and keel could be obtained with a knowledge of the properties of the structural section.

The resistance of the section to bending is given by the 'moment of inertia' in which the area (in^2) of each longitudinally continuous member – plate or frame bar – is measured from the axis and multiplied by the square of this distance. Moment of Inertia (MI) or inertia has dimensions in^2 ft^2. In riveted ships 2/11 of the section in tension was deducted to allow for rivet slip.

When the ship is hogging, the deck will be in tension and the keel compressed whilst if sagging the deck will be compressed and the keel in tension. The neutral axis, roughly at half depth, is where there is no stress, either compressive or tensile, and the distance Y given in some tables is the distance of the deck or keel from this axis.

Such a calculation is an approximation to what happens in a real seaway but, given experience from many previous results for similar ships, its use can be quite reliable; indeed today's calculations, with a much greater theoretical background, are little different in principle. It was recognised that there were few long waves with a height of 1/20 their length and this was compensated for by accepting higher nominal stresses in long ships.

In ships of World War II the first warning of over-stressing was failure of rivets which was an all too common event, particularly in destroyers. However, there were no total failures of the structure of British ships as in some other navies. It should be noted that 'back breaking' was the commonest cause of sinking following action damage for destroyers and smaller ships. Appreciation of this problem led the designers to calculate stresses in battleships with all unarmoured structure destroyed.

For ships which are similar in both shape and loading it is reasonable to assume that bending moment is a constant fraction of Displacement x Length (= W.L/k where k is a constant derived from the previous ship) and reference will be found to estimates 'based on previous ships' in which this approximation has been used.

The tables usually give, both for hogging and sagging, values of bending moment and the stresses amidships in deck and keel. In one or two cases, stresses are calculated at other points along the length. There would also be a large number of calculations of the strength of detail portions of the hull and of items such as the rudder stock, shaft brackets, machinery seats etc but these are not reported in the book.

Mullion Cove was converted into a heavy-hull repair ship whilst building at Sunderland in 1944-5. She was intended to repair damage beyond the capability of existing repair ships.

CHAPTER 17

Fleet Train

Editorial Note

The problems of finding and converting suitable ships were even more difficult than for the ships of Chapter 16. On the one hand, the number of ships required to support the Pacific Fleet was much greater whilst, on the other hand, the demands for ships to feed the liberated but starving people of Europe were also great. In consequence, some of the ships were not very suitable[1] whilst it took longer than desirable to set up the Fleet Train. That it was possible at all says much for the efforts of Canadian and British yards whilst the support of the Fleet depended greatly on the generosity of the USN.

The Fleet Train

The war against Japan called for an entirely new conception of naval warfare, in that our naval forces were called upon to take the offensive not only tens of thousands of miles from the United Kingdom but thousands of miles from their nearest base.

It was thus impossible during operations for HM ships to replenish with fuel and stores from their bases, as all sheltered harbours within reasonable distance of the operational areas were, at that time, in enemy hands. So it was essential to replenish the fleet periodically at sea, and for this requirement the fleet train was formed.

As far back as 1936 a committee was set up in the Admiralty to consider the methods to be adopted for supporting a fleet at sea far in advance of the nearest base, and by 1939 we knew what we wanted. In the early years of the war, however, there was no immediate need for a fleet train and as every ship, both afloat and building, was needed to replace sinkings, it was only with the greatest difficulty that after the entry of Japan into the war a very modest start was made to build up the nucleus for the fleet train which would eventually and inevitably be required for an ocean war.

The first serious step was taken early in 1942 when five liners were taken up for conversion as repair ships or as depot ships for destroyers and submarines, but it was not until the summer of 1942 that attention was given to the detailed requirements of the fleet when operating in Far Eastern waters. At this time, plans for the prosecution of the war in Europe were well advanced and the Battle of the Atlantic well under control, but the only bases remaining in Allied hands in the Far Eastern theatre were those in Australia, and the American Pacific bases at Pearl Harbour, etc.

In September 1943 a panel was set up to consider the provision of floating base facilities and to make proposals for the types and numbers of the ships that would be required.

The types and numbers of ships estimated to be required were as shown:-

Requirements for Fleet Train

British Pacific Fleet			No required
Red Ensign			
Accommodation Ships	FO i/c		3
	NO i/c		5
	SRR(D)		4
	S/M crew		1
White Ensign			
Maintenance Ships	LC		4
	MC		2
	MTB		1
	LST		4
	Escort vessels		11
	DAS		2
Fleet Air Arm Ships			
	A/C engine repair		8
	A/C compt. repair		4
	Store ships		4
RAF Base for Flying Boats			8
Fleet Repair Ships			2
Hull Repair Ships			4
Minor LC Parent Ships			10
MTB Workshop Ships			3
MTB HQ and Parent Ships			3
Director of Sea Transport			
Hospital Ships			5
Issuing Ships	Armament supply		10
	Naval stores		7
	Victualling stores		15
Store Carriers			12
Fuel and FW Carriers			100
Motor Lighters for Stores and Ammunition			70
White Ensign			
Seaward Defence Ships			3

[1] Fisher, D. The Fleet Train in the Pacific War. Trans INA, 1953. Vice Admiral Fisher tells the story of the distiling ship, needed to supply fresh water, which was the only coal burner in the Train and hence had to be serviced by a collier. The collier's steam pipes leaked and she took most of the fresh water from the distiling ship so that the two ships sat quietly in a corner, servicing each other without contributing much.

These vessels were in addition to existing ships that would become available on the termination of hostilities in Europe, ie four repair ships, four MTB maintenance ships, four submarine depot ships, five minesweeper maintenance ships, fourteen armament supply issuing ships and two mine issuing ships.

It can be seen from these lists which include eighty-three major conversions that allowance was made for all sides of the fleet's activities, assuming that hardly any shore facilities would be available.

As new construction for the fleet train was out of the question, a number of preliminary investigations were made into the suitability of existing vessels both in and out of the Royal Navy. As far as the Naval vessels were concerned, very few would be suitable for the jobs required and most of these were usefully employed elsewhere.

Consideration now passed from planning the fleet's maintenance requirements to trying to cut down existing proposals and planning the conversion work, as it had become quite clear that the labour and shipyard berths required to convert the ships was the key to the situation. Inevitably the planned requirements of vessels had to be reduced to meet the practical proposition of the ships that could be made available, and the Admiralty commitment was reduced from eighty-three to forty-three major conversions.

A further outcome of the many discussions which took place was that as many ships as possible were to be converted in the UK, preferably during initial construction, but Canada should be asked to convert suitable ships under construction there, especially where a number of each type was required, and the United States asked to provide available types already under construction in that country.

As the war in the Far East progressed and bases were recaptured by the Allies, it was found that shore office facilities could be set up in a very short time. Consequently the number of accommodation ships for FO i/c and NO i/c were reduced and were later deemed unnecessary and removed from the programme altogether. Further ships were cancelled as the war progressed and in addition five were cancelled soon after the war with Japan ended.

In all, twenty-one major conversions were planned and carried out. They were:

Fleet Repair Ships	*Wayland, Ausonia, Artifex*
Heavy-duty Repair Ships	*Alaunia, Ranpura*
SRR(D) Accommodation Ships	*Lancashire, Southern Prince*
Hull Repair Ships	*Mullion Cove, Dullisk Cove*
A/C Maintenance Ships	*Perseus, Pioneer*
A/C Engine Repair Ships	*Beauly Firth*
A/C Component Repair Ships	*Holm Sound, Deer Sound*
Maintenance Ships	21 *Victory* Ships, *Kelantan, Corbrae*
Amenities Ships	*Menestheus, Agamemnon*
Seaward Defence Ship (Ark)	*Helvig*
Spare S/M Crew Accommodation Ship	*Aorangi*

Beauly Firth, *an aircraft engine repair ship of the Fleet Train. Built by Redhead and converted by Palmer.*

The remainder of the fleet train consisted of various types of storing ships for food, naval stores, ammunition etc. and large numbers of tankers for oil and water. In the main these were merchant ships adapted where necessary for the special cargoes, the work being carried out by the Ministry of War Transport. Several hospital ships also formed part of the fleet's retinue. Four Admiralty floating docks were also allocated to the British Pacific Fleet. Three were destroyer docks capable of lifting 2750 tons, and the other a cruiser dock - 15,500 tons lift.

Unfortunately these floating docks were not available for use in the forward areas until after the end of the war.

Repair Ships

Wayland (ex *Antonia*) - Fleet Repair Ship

In early 1939 a committee was set up to recommend the warship building and conversion programme that would be necessary to be carried out in the event of war. One fleet repair ship (*Resource*) was then in service, and two additional fleet repair ships were included in the conversion programme. The Cunard Liner *Antonia* and the Holt Liner *Patroclus* had been provisionally earmarked as suitable for the purpose and when war broke out the question of proceeding with these conversions was raised, action was however suspended because of the difficulty of supply of machine tools at that time. The requirements for one of these ships was later cancelled as shore facilities had in the meantime been provided at Scapa, and the conversion of *Antonia* was put in hand in November 1940, at HM Dockyard, Portsmouth. She was completed in September 1942 and renamed *Wayland*.

Leading particulars were:

Length overall	538ft 0in
Length between perpendiculars	520ft 0in
Breadth extreme	65ft 0in
Depth to upper deck	43ft 0in
Deep displacement as a repair ship	18,754 tons
Deep mean draught	26ft 11¼in
Power	8500shp
Max speed (deep)	14½kts
Endurance, 6 months out of dock in tropics	4500 miles at 12½kts
Fuel	1432 tons
Complement	26 officers, 569 crew

Machinery

Four geared steam turbines with twin screws.
   Propeller particulars:

two 3-bladed propellers	
diameter	18ft
pitch	18ft 9in
developed blade area	116sq ft

Distilling machinery with a total capacity of 200 ton/day was fitted and, in addition to the two 300kW generators already in the ship, three turbo generators each of 300kW were fitted.

Armament etc. fitted consisted of four 4in HA/LA in single mountings with fusekeeping clock control system, two 4-barrelled pom-poms and six Oerlikons. Magazines for these guns and the small arms ammunition were fitted out with the usual flooding and spraying arrangements.

Full base W/T equipment was installed and radar types 79 and 285 were fitted.

Protection

In view of the difficulty of obtaining armour, 120lb mild steel protection was fitted to crowns and ends of magazines. 20lb DIHT doubling was fitted to steering gear compartment, bridges, gun positions, etc.

Conversion

The major structural work carried out was as follows:

To adjust deck heights to suit workshops etc. portions of A, D and F decks were removed completely and other flats built as necessary and additional pillars and girders were fitted. The ship's sides between B and C decks were plated in over a length of about 190ft. All cargo hatches were plated in and made watertight. Minor bulkheads were fitted throughout the ship as required and gun and director supports built, trunks were fitted for transport of stores, materials, etc. to storerooms and shops without passing through intermediate spaces.

The existing cold and cool rooms were modified to suit Admiralty requirements (refrigerated stowage for the ship for forty-five days). Workshops fitted were: grinding machinery shop; heavy machine shop; light machine shop; foundry, smithery and plate shop; light plate shop; plumber's shop; welder's shop, coppersmith's shop; electrical shop; electrical test room; IC engine shop; MB engine test shop; tool room; pattern shop; woodworking shop; impregnating plant shop; painter's shop; sailmaker's shop; instrument repair shop; optical repair shop; ordnance shop; pneumatic tool stores and repair shop; covered working space.

Storage tanks for 10,000 galls petrol were fitted in the hold compartment with direct flooding arrangements from the sea.

Other items such as galleys, storerooms, heads, ventilation, water services, etc. were fitted to Admiralty requirements, the existing arrangements being utilised as far as possible. Tripod masts were fitted, but existing derricks, winches, anchor gear, etc. were retained as required.

The vessel was fitted out for service in the tropics.

Stability etc.

3000 tons of permanent ballast was provided and 1000 tons of water ballast carried in DB tanks to reduce freeboard and windage in the seagoing condition, for safer anchoring and to provide positive stability in a bilged condition. The vessel would take any two main transverse watertight compartments flooded.

The virtual metacentric height of *Wayland* in the deep condition was 2.18ft.

A standard longitudinal strength calculation gave the following results:

	Hogging	*Sagging*
Max bending moment	276,200tons ft	292,000tons ft
Stress in deck	6.79tons/in²	6.48tons/in²
Stress in keel	4.01tons/in²	4.95tons/in²

General

The bulkhead deck in this vessel was 'C' deck, but as the accommodation fitted was mainly on 'D' deck, side scuttles were fitted on this deck and a limited number in the sick bay on 'E' deck under. The accommodation provided was to the usual RN standards.

From reports of experience in service, the ship was satisfactory. Certain suggestions for improvements, such as the substitution of a crane for the main derrick and the improvement of the arrangements for internal transport of stores were made; these improvements were incorporated in later repair ships.

Artifex and Ausonia

In 1941 the approved programme included one new construction and three converted fleet repair ships, and the staff requirements for these ships called for workshops on the same scale as *Wayland*. This met normal requirements for maintenance and running repairs.

With the fall of Singapore the remaining combined resources in the Indian Ocean area were stated to be barely equivalent to one half of Portsmouth Dockyard. It was therefore considered essential that two repair ships of the 1941 programme should be capable of undertaking, in conjunction with a floating dock, sufficient structural repairs to enable a damaged ship to be steamed to a refitting port for final repair or, in the case of minor damage, to make her fit again for the fighting line. Also to undertake work at a base until proper shore facilities could be set up. This necessitated the fitting of larger constructive workshops such as smithery and plate shop, light plate shop, etc. and as these had to be fitted high in the ship to minimise transport of heavy plates and sections, the main effect was to reduce the space available for fleet facilities such as communications, sick bay, accommodation, etc. Approval was therefore given for the conversion of the Cunard liners *Aurania* and *Ausonia* to meet these requirements and the ships were terms 'base repair ships', instead of fleet repair ships. During the time the vessels were converting, however, the requirements were reduced by the elimination of facilities for base organisation and considerable omissions were approved, including all radar and armament except Oerlikons. The term applied to the function of these vessels was altered from 'base repair' to 'repair ships'.

The leading particulars of these ships were:

Length overall	538ft 0in
Length between perpendiculars	519ft 0in
Breadth extreme	65ft 3in
Depth to upper deck	43ft 0in
Deep displacement as a repair ship	19,016 tons
Deep mean draught	27ft 4in
Power	8500shp
Max speed (deep)	14½kts
Endurance	4500 miles at 12½kts
Fuel	1560 tons
Complement	32 officers, 560 men

Machinery

Four geared steam turbines with twin screws.
Propeller particulars:

two 3-bladed propellers	
diameter	18ft
pitch	18ft 9in
developed blade area	83.6sq ft

Distillers of a total capacity of 300ton/day, and in addition to the two 300kW generators already in the ship, one 300kW turbo and two 300kW diesel generators were fitted.

Armament fitted consisted of twenty-four 20mm Oerlikons (twenty only in *Ausonia*). Magazines for Oerlikon and small arms ammunition were fitted with the usual flooding and spraying arrangements. Magazines were also fitted out for 4in ammunition, but were not used as the 4in guns were eventually omitted.

Protection

Although the requirement for magazines was eliminated during the conversion, the structural work had been completed and 80lb NC protection was fitted to ends and crowns of magazines, 60lb mild steel to the steering gear compartment and splinter protection to bridges, guns, etc.

Conversion

The major structural work carried out was as follows:

To adjust deck heights to suit workshops etc. portions of E, C and promenade decks were removed completely and other flats built as necessary and additional pillars and girders were fitted. In particular to obtain sufficient space and deck height for the smithery and plate shops almost all the promenade deck had to be removed and to allow the shop to be covered by the overhead travelling cranes all existing pillars were removed and replaced by a few heavy ones in the middle line. The deck beams over were stiffened to take the increased span and fore and aft lattice girders fitted, and the side frames of the superstructure stiffened to withstand the increased racking forces due to the removal of the intermediate deck. All cargo hatches were plated in and made watertight. The ship's sides between promenade and boat decks were plated in over a length of about 220ft. Minor bulkheads were fitted throughout the ship as required, trunks were fitted for transport of stores, materials, etc. to storerooms and shops without passing through intermediate spaces.

The following fitting out work was undertaken: the existing cold and cool rooms were modified to suit Admiralty requirements. Workshops fitted were: grinding machine shop; heavy machine shop; light machine shop; engineer's fitting shop; foundry, smithery and plate shop; light plate shop; plumber's shop; welder's shop; coppersmith's shop; electrical shop; electrical test room; internal combustion engine shop; motor boat engine test shop; tool room; pattern shop; woodworking shop; covered working space; impregnating plant shop; painter's shop; sailmaker's shop; instrument repair shop; optical repair shop; pneumatic repair shop and store; ordnance workshop; LTO's workshop; radar workshop; Asdic repair and testing space; portable plant shop.

Other items such as galleys, storerooms, heads, ventilation, water services, etc. were fitted to Admiralty requirements, the existing arrangements being utilised as far as possible. Derricks, winches and anchor gear etc. were retained and an extra 10 tons derrick and three 4 tons electric cranes fitted.

These ships were fitted out for service in the tropics.

Stability

3500 tons of permanent ballast and 600 tons of water ballast (increased to 1180 tons as oil was consumed) was carried to reduce freeboard and windage in the seagoing condition, for safer anchoring and to provide positive stability in a bilged condition. The vessel took any two main transverse watertight compartment flooded.

Metacentric heights in the deep condition were:

Artifex	2.63ft (fl)
Ausonia	2.99ft (fl)

General

Accommodation in these ships was to usual RN standards. The bulkhead deck in this vessel was 'B' deck but, as the majority of the accommodation spaces were on 'C' deck, side scuttles and a limited number of watertight doors for through access were fitted on this deck.

Aurania, which was later renamed *Artifex*, was taken in hand at HM Dockyard Devonport in March 1942, and completed in May 1944. *Ausonia* was taken in hand at HM Dockyard Portsmouth in April 1942 and completed in May 1944. The vessels proved generally satisfactory in service and no As and As other than minor items were received.

Heavy Duty Repair Ships

Alaunia **and** *Ranpura*

On completion of *Artifex* and *Ausonia*, approval was given for a third conversion to be commenced and for a fourth ship to be converted in lieu of the new construction repair ship which had not been proceeded with.

The P&O liner *Ranpura* and the Cunard liner *Alaunia* were selected to be converted to the reduced requirements referred to above. The conversions were generally similar to *Artifex* and *Ausonia* except that minor improvements were made to workshops and the lifting facilities were increased by fitting one 10 tons and three 4 tons electric cranes. The same difficulties arose with

General arrangement of
the Heavy Duty Repair
Ship *Alaunia*

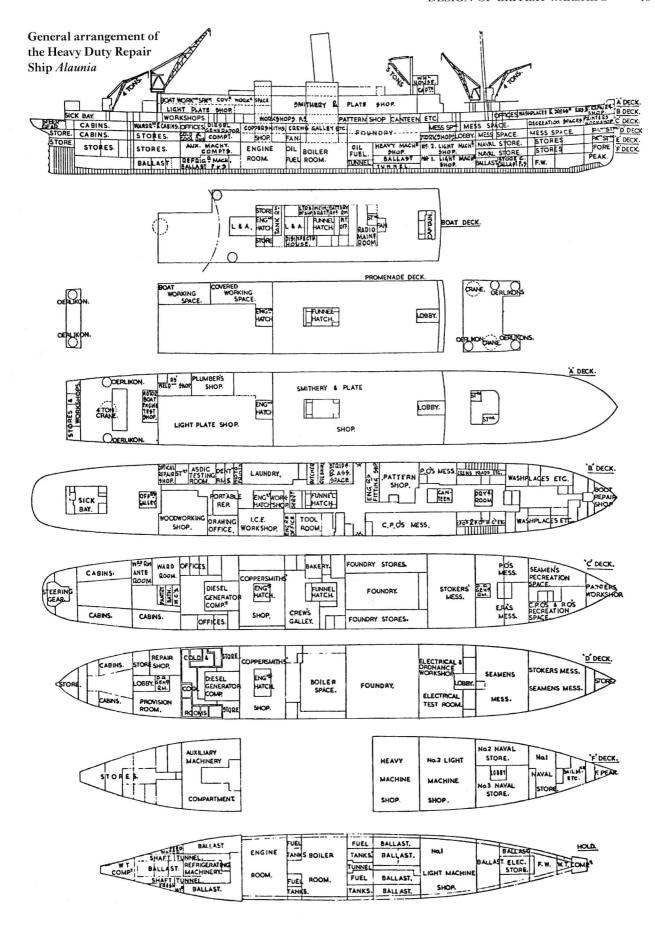

the siting of the smithery and plate shops as in the previous ships, and in the case of *Ranpura* involved the removal of a large portion of 'A' deck. 'B' deck was stiffened by fitting 35lb doubling and the side framing of the superstructure fitted and web frames fitted between 'B' deck and boat deck over. Fore and aft lattice girders were fitted under the boat deck and the engine and boiler casings stiffened to support the boat deck over.

Alaunia was a sister vessel to *Artifex* and *Ausonia*.

These ships were known as heavy duty repair ships and were the most capable repair ships in the Royal Navy. Owing to the large machine and workshops fitted they were unable to provide accommodation for the special repair ratings required to man the shops. Each vessel, therefore, needed an accommodation ship nearby to act as a floating hostel.

The leading particulars of *Ranpura* were:

Length overall	570ft 0in
Length between perpendiculars	547ft 0in
Breadth extreme	71ft 3in
Depth to 'C' deck	38ft 0in
Deep displacement as a repair ship	18,057 tons
Mean draught (deep)	24ft 1½in
Power	13,500shp
Speed (max)	15kts
Fuel	1766 tons
Endurance	3280 miles at full speed
Complement (including repair staff)	591 officers & men

Machinery

Twin screw reciprocating machinery.
  Propeller particulars:

two 3–bladed propellers	
diameter	19ft 6in
pitch	24ft 0in
developed blade area	120.6sq ft

Metacentric height in deep condition 4.2ft (fl)

Alaunia was taken in hand at HM Dockyard Devonport in May 1944 and completed September 1945.

Ranpura was taken in hand at HM Dockyard Portsmouth in May 1944 and completed January 1946.[2]

Accommodation Ships for Special Repair Ratings (Dockyard)

Lancashire

In the absence of shore bases in the Far East, requirements for the fleet train necessitated the fitting out of a certain number of ships as accommodation ships for special repair ratings (dockyard) to work in conjunction with fleet repair ships. These ratings, who were recruited from the various trades connected with warship repair, were accommodated in these vessels, and proceeded daily to work in the shops of the repair ships, on board warships in floating docks, or on board damaged warships at anchor in the neighbourhood.

The ship offered by the Ministry of War Transport for conversion was *Lancashire*, a mer-

Alaunia , a heavy duty repair ship converted at Devonport and seen soon after completion in September 1945.

[2] Mention might also have been made of the well equipped, US built *Assistance* and *Diligence*.

**General arrangement of *Lancashire*
as converted to a Accommodation
Ship for Special Repair Ratings**

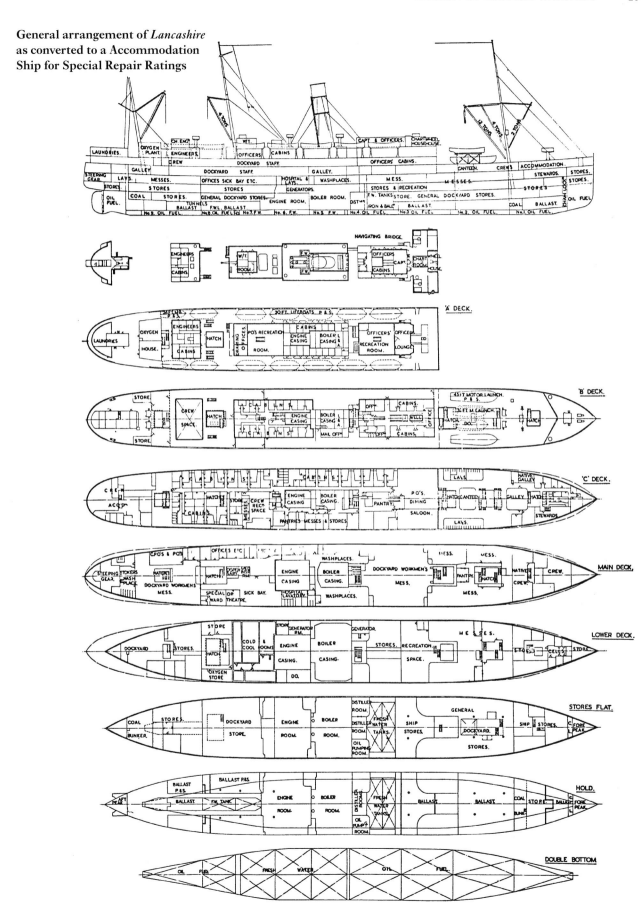

chant ship owned by the Bibby line. She was built by Messrs Harland & Wolff in 1917 and had a long record of service as a troopship.

The principal dimensions and particulars were as follows:

Length overall	502ft 3in
Length between perpendiculars	482ft 0in
Breadth moulded	57ft 0in
Depth to upper deck	35ft 0in
Deep displacement (as accommodation ship)	15,332 tons
Mean draught (deep) (as accommodation ship)	26ft 3in

Lancashire was taken in hand on 9 July 1944, the work of conversion being carried out by Messrs Grayson Rollo and Clover Dock Ltd at Liverpool and the vessel was completed, ready for sea, on 14 April 1945.

All modifications and additions required to convert this ship to her new service were made with the full concurrence of the owners and of the Classification Society concerned. The work was proceeded with, in the knowledge that the ship was to be run by Red Ensign Personnel, supplemented by a Royal Naval Administrative crew, the Special Repair Ratings (Dockyard) being classed as passengers. The demarcation of duties as between White and Red Ensign personnel was based on:

(a) the owners to be responsible for all messing, ie both White and Red Ensign;
(b) the owners to provide upper deck crew for working all lifting appliances, derricks, etc.;
(c) a Naval party to provide for running, care and maintenance of duty boats;
(d) armament to be RN responsibility;
(e) RN personnel to run oxygen plant.

The major structural alterations included the following items. An oxygen house was built aft on 'A' deck, No 6 hatch being partially plated over and a number of lifeboats and their davits being resited. The existing coal bunkers were gutted and the spaces made suitable for installing an additional four 50kW generators and two 100ton/day triple effect distiller plants. Two new bunkers were arranged at the forward and after ends of this ship to carry 200 tons of coal for culinary purposes. A new magazine was built forward of the officer's lounge on 'A' deck for the stowage of Oerlikon and Bofors ammunition.

Storerooms were fitted for the stowage of dockyard, naval and other stores, and a total of nearly 800 tons of dockyard and naval stores were provided for.

The existing cold and cool rooms were considered adequate for the ship's new service, but a number of domestic automatic refrigerators were arranged in enclosed messes.

The vessel was re-armed for her new service. The new armament consisted of fourteen hand-worked Oerlikons and two single Bofors.

The existing accommodation was re-arranged and provision was made for:

Red Ensign Crew	18 officers 230 ratings
White Ensign Administrative	3 officers 94 ratings
SRR(D) Ratings	20 officers 502 ratings

Owing to the type of ship, a large number of cabins were available, so a number were used as accommodation for CPO's and PO's dockyard ratings.

The existing sick bay also was re-arranged to provide a spacious bay with eighteen cots, a special isolation ward with four cots, an operating theatre, dispensary and medical inspection room.

The following amenities were provided:

(1) Recreation spaces for officers, CPO's and PO's and crew
(2) Bookshop and lending library
(3) Mail office
(4) Information office
(5) Barber's shop
(6) Tailor's shop
(7) Boot repair shop
(8) Canteen
(9) Laundry (hand worked)
(10) SRE rooms on deck 'B' and in crew's recreation space

Stability

To preserve stability *Lancashire* was ballasted with 3319 tons of sand or slag to a metacentric height of 2.9ft in the deep condition.

The ship proceeded to her Far Eastern station, arriving just prior to the cessation of hostilities with Japan.

Southern Prince

Another noteworthy vessel to join the fleet train was Messrs Prince Lines *Southern Prince*. This vessel which was taken over by the Admiralty shortly after the outbreak of the war was a twin-screw motor vessel of 10,917 gross tons, length 496ft 3in BP breadth, 64ft 7in depth 41ft 0in to upper deck, powered by engines developing about 11,000bhp and giving a speed of 16kts. She was taken in hand by Messrs John Brown, Clydebank and converted to a minelayer capable of carrying and laying about 550 mines.

The vessel was attached to the 1st Minelaying Squadron and carried out successfully many minelaying operations in enemy waters.

In April 1944 instructions were received to prepare the ship for duty as a flagship and to provide office and living accommodation for flag officers, British assault area and Naval party commanding D-day landing. The work consisted of building protected administrative offices, fitting more powerful wireless communication and providing additional accommodation, temporary wash-places, etc. This work was completed in time for the vessel to take part in the invasion of Europe.

In August 1944 it was decided that *Southern Prince* should be accepted for conversion to a dockyard accommodation ship for service in the Pacific; she was allocated to Harland & Wolff, North Woolwich, for conversion.

The conversion to SSR(D) involved a fair amount of structural work such as framing and plating up the aft end in way of mining doors and refitting the WT bulkheads which had been removed to give a clear deck for mine laying and also the removal of approximately 20,000 buoyancy barrels which were stowed in the holds forward and aft. Work was commenced about the end of September 1944 but towards the end of October instructions were received that *Southern Prince* was to transfer to Montreal to complete the conversion to SRR(D). The vessel sailed for Montreal in November 1944.

The requirements for the conversion were principally to provide suitable accommodation for dockyard personnel and carry materials and tools to enable the Pacific Fleet to be maintained in effective fighting condition. Accommodation was arranged for approximately 500 dockyard ratings and twenty officials in addition to the personnel required for administering and manning the vessel.

Additional bakery and galley equipment was provided, separate electric bakery and oil-fired galley being arranged to provide for the dockyard ratings and white crew. Special galley equipment for the native crew was also installed.

The refrigerated spaces available for the storage of foodstuffs were increased to about 10,000cu ft and additional refrigeration machinery fitted. A special enclosed ventilated potato and vegetable locker capable of storing about 20 tons of vegetables under tropical conditions was also fitted.

Store spaces were arranged for the stowage of between 900 and 1000 tons of materials, fittings and tools for after action repairs. A complete oxygen manufacturing plant supplied by the British Oxygen Company capable fo producing 500/c ft free oxygen per hour was fitted and a distilling plant of about 200 tons per day capacity supplied by Messrs Buckley and Taylor and fitted together with sufficient boiler capacity to provide the necessary steam. In addition recreation spaces, soda fountain, ice-cream bar, tailor's shop, boot repair shop, barber's shop, library and such amenities as were necessary to maintain a large body of men in good health and effective working condition in the Far East under war conditions were fitted.

The vessel completed her conversion at Montreal in October 1945.

The vessel was managed by the owners on behalf of the Admiralty, and manned by a commercial crew and sailed under the Red Ensign. On her return to England in September 1946 she was returned to trade.

Hull Repair Ships

Mullion Cove and *Dullisk Cove*
In order to provide adequate repair facilities for the fleet under war conditions, repair units for the fleet train were planned to consist of one repair ship working with one accommodation ship or shore establishment. It was considered that the existing fleet repair ships *Resource* and *Wayland* working alone did not possess sufficient capabilities, having inadequate workshops for structural work. In order therefore to provide the necessary facilities for fleet repair it was decided to include a special hull repair ship to work with each of these two vessels and the accommodation ships to form a repair unit.

Approval was given for the conversion of two PF(C) type merchant ships, which were then building, to hull repair ships to be capable of carrying out in conjunction with a fleet repair ship hull refitting work, minor hull damage repair, or temporary major hull damage repair to ships, preparatory to towing or steaming to a repair base. The two vessels selected were named *Mullion Cove* and *Dullisk Cove*. Arrangements were made for the main structural modifications required for the conversion to be incorporated by the shipbuilders during the building of the hull, and for the ships to be then transferred to another firm for fitting out. Arrangements were made by DMB Department for the additional structure such as decks and deck houses to be fabricated in the structural steel industry and forwarded to the shipbuilders. In addition to the usual general arrangements drawings, detailed drawings of the layouts of compartments, piping, and ventilation arrangements, etc. were supplied by DNC department.

The leading particulars of these ships were:

Length overall	447ft 9in
Length between perpendiculars	425ft 0in
Breadth extreme	56ft 3in
Depth to upper deck	38ft 0in
Deep displacement as hull repair ship	9,732 tons
Mean draught (deep)	19ft 6½in
Power	2500shp
Speed (max)	12kts
Oil fuel	933 tons
Endurance at 10½kts	5000 miles
Complement	19 officers, 204 crew

The major structural work undertaken was as follows: one new complete 3rd deck was fitted throughout the ship, a 4th deck fitted in one hold, and the necessary pillars and girders fitted. Large hatchways were cut to allow materials and repair work to be transported to and from the workshops. Minor bulkheads and deckhouses were fitted as necessary.

The following fitting-out work was undertaken: larger cold and cool rooms than those specified for the ships as a merchant ship were fitted. The following workshops were fitted: heavy plate shop (2); light plate shop (2); smithery, welding and plumber's shop; woodworking shop; electrical shop; engineer's workshop; pneumatic tool workshop; rigger's workshop; painter's workshop; general workshop. Items such as galleys, storerooms, heads, ventilation, water services, etc. were fitted to Admiralty requirements.

Hull Repair Ship *Mullion Cove* general arrangement

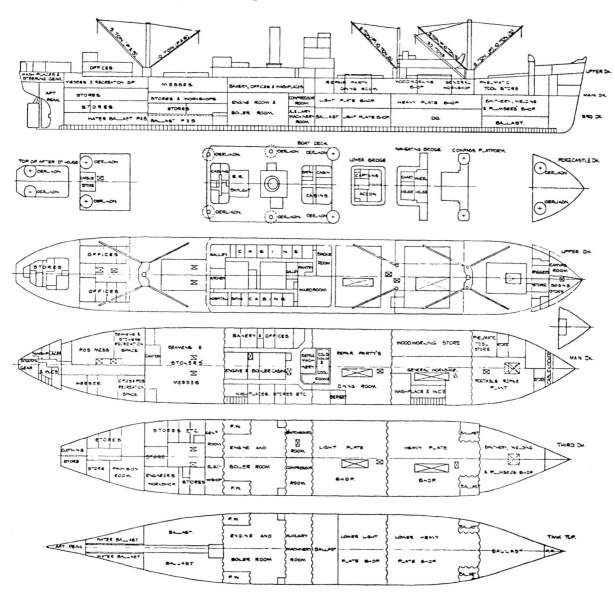

Five 5 tons derricks and five 10 tons derricks were also fitted.

Armament and Protection etc.
The ships were armed with fourteen Oerlikons and magazines fitted out. The only protection fitted consisted of plastic protective plating to the wheelhouse and 20lb protective plating to the bridge platform.

Machinery
These ships were single screwed with steam reciprocating engines developing 2500shp.

Propeller particulars:

diameter	16ft 6in
pitch	13ft 8in
developed blade area	100sq ft

The distilling machinery was of capacity 100ton/day, and two 150kW steam and two 200kW diesel generators were fitted.

Stability etc.
To reduce windage and freeboard in the seagoing condition, for safer anchoring and to provide positive stability in a bilged condition, 2250 tons of permanent ballast was fitted and up to 436 tons of salt water ballast was carried. The vessels' stability allowed of any two main adjacent watertight compartments to be flooded when at a mean draught not greater than 18ft 9in, but when at the normal deep draught of 19ft 6in the ship would not float with the two large compartments at the ends of the ship flooded.

The metacentric height in the deep condition was 3.78ft (fl).

The bulkhead deck in these vessels was the upper deck, but as the accommodation was generally fitted on the second deck side scuttles and watertight doors for through access were fitted at this level.

Accommodation was fitted to usual RN standards for the ship's complement, and a dining room to supply a midday meal to approximately 250 repair ratings. In addition sleeping facilities for 100 ratings were fitted should the ship be on detached duty. The vessels were fitted out for service in the tropics.

Mullion Cove was taken in hand for conversion while building by Messrs Bartram, Sunderland, in May 1944 and completed by Messrs Greenwell and Co, Sunderland, in July 1945. *Dullisk Cove* was taken in hand, while building by Messrs Short Brothers, Sunderland, in May 1944 and completed by Messrs Smiths Dock, North Shields, in June 1945.

Fleet Aircraft Maintenance Group

Towards the end of the Second World War it became increasingly evident that, in both peace and war, the provision of mobile aircraft maintenance facilities afloat would be necessary to enable aircraft embarked in aircraft carriers to be readily serviced, particularly in the absence of suitably equipped bases ashore.

These facilities were provided in a balanced number of maintenance ships, engine repair ships and component repair ships, which formed that part of the fleet train known as the fleet aircraft maintenance group (FAMG).

The group consisted of:

Perseus and *Pioneer*	- aircraft maintenance ships
Beauly Firth	- aircraft engine repair ships
Holm Sound and *Deer Sound*	- aircraft component repair ships

The FAMG provided the same range of maintenance facilities as an aircraft maintenance yard and could, if necessary, be divided into subgroups each specialising in a limited number of types of aircraft.

The ships were also capable of carrying bulk stocks of aircraft spare parts etc. over and above those held for their own specific functions; these stocks were drawn upon by the Air Store Issuing ships when necessary.

In view of the fact that the choice of ships for this group, materials and the availability of skilled labour were greatly limited by war conditions and observing that requirements were subject to frequent modifications, not only in the light of experience gained while the ships were being fitted out but also to meet new and modified types of aircraft, great credit was due to the Admiralty departments and to the shipbuilders who were concerned in this new venture in aircraft maintenance.

Aircraft Maintenance Ships

Pioneer and *Perseus*
These vessels were originally laid down as *Colossus* class light fleet carriers but were taken over during construction for completion as aircraft maintenance ships to form, together with the aircraft component repair ships and aircraft engine repair ships, the aircraft maintenance group of the fleet

Perseus in 1952.

train. This group was required to enable aircraft embarked in aircraft carriers to be readily serviced, particularly in the absence of suitably equipped bases ashore.

The functions of the aircraft maintenance ships were as follows:

(a) Maintenance work (generally carried out by the aircraft repair shops at a maintenance yard), including major inspections estimated to require not more than 1500 man hours, medium repairs, including fuselage repairs estimated to require not more than 1000 man hours, repairs by replacement of components, stripping and assembly of power plants.

(b) All functional tests of completed aircraft and their installations (radio, armament, etc.) other than those of compass swinging and flight testing.

(c) Minor engine and component repairs only were carried out in these ships as engine and component repairs were normally transferred to the engine and component repair ships respectively, the maintenance ships having been equipped with small ancillary workshops for this work.

The leading particulars of these ships were:

	Pioneer	*Perseus*
Length overall	690ft 5in	689ft 8in
Length between perpendiculars	630ft 0in	630ft 0in
Breadth at WL	80ft 2½in	80ft 4in
Breadth overall	108ft 3in	108ft 3in
Moulded depth (to flight deck at side)	61ft 9in	61ft 9in
Deep displacement	15,984 tons	16,475 tons
Mean draught	21ft 2in	21ft 7in
Power	40,000shp	40,000shp
Speed (max)	25kts	25kts
Endurance at 12kts	12,000mls	12,000mls
Oil fuel	3187 tons	3196 tons
Complement	47 officers, 942 men	58 officers, 974 men (including FAMG staff)

Machinery was the same as for the remainder of the *Colossus* class.

Armament was reduced to:
4-2pdr quadruple mountings
4-20mm powered twin Oerlikons
8-20mm single Oerlikons (hand worked)

Protection was limited to 15lb and 20lb protective plating fitted to island structure, guns and RU magazines.

In general design, of course, these ships were similar to the light fleet carriers, the main difference being in the internal arrangements which had been modified to suit their new role. Following is a list of the important modifications.

No arrangements were fitted to allow aircraft to fly on or off the flight deck; this allowed complete deletion of the operational flying facilities including operations room, aircraft direction room, radar display room, target indicating room, briefing rooms, ready rooms, meteorological office, the bridge mess room for flying personnel, balloon filling station, aircraft control room and flying control position.

A number of radar offices were omitted, as were the sponsors for guns, safety barrier controls, etc.

The following arrangements were fitted: aircraft workshops including battery charging room, engine stripping shop; engine assembly shop; carburettor and fuel pump shop; oleo and hydraulics shop; fabric worker's shop; metalworker's shop; machine shop; dope shop; propeller shop; oxygen producing and cylinder filling shop; woodworker's shop; instrument shop; blacksmith's, coppersmith's and welder's shop; electrical repair shop; sparking plug servicing shop; W/T test room; radar test rooms and armament workshop.

Facilities were provided to enable aircraft to be repaired in the hangar and on the flight deck.

Stores were arranged for aircraft spares including components, dope, electrical gear, aircraft spare parts, loose gear, dinghies, tyres, tools, metalworker's RU, propellers, engine and power plants, aircraft accessories, caustic soda and ground equipment.

Offices were fitted out for aircraft repair including air engineers, air engineer officer, writers, stores, air stores officer, drawing and publications, regulating, group AEO, air inspection, air electrical, air radio office and control and checkers.

In addition to existing arrangements the vessels were provided with an additional fixed crane and motor transport for handling and transporting aircraft.

Stability Particulars
From an inclining experiment carried out on *Pioneer* in January 1945, the following particulars were obtained:

	Deep Condition	*Light Condition*
Metacentric height	9.1ft	6.5ft
Max GZ	5.9ft	3.0ft
Angle of max GZ	39°	38°
Range	75°	61°
Displacement	15,984 tons	10,766 tons

The corresponding stability particulars for *Perseus* for deep and light displacements of 16,475 tons and 11,020 tons respectively were about the same as those quoted above.

1942 Programme

Ship	*Pioneer* (ex *Mars*)	*Perseus*
Builders	Vickers Armstrong Barrow	Vickers Armstrong Newcastle
Laid Down	2 Dec 1942	1 Jun 1942
Launched	20 May 1944	26 Mar 1944
Completed	8 Feb 1945	19 Oct 1945

General
Pioneer was fully employed on aircraft maintenance work in the Far East forward area during the last two months of the Japanese war; *Perseus* did not work under war conditions.

Aircraft Engine Repair Ship

Beauly Firth
To supplement the capacity of the maintenance ship for engine repairs *Empire Sarawak* - a PF(C) type cargo vessel - was taken over whilst on the slip for conversion to an aircraft engine repair ship. Two series of repair shops were fitted, one to deal with 'in line' engines and the other with 'radial' engines, the shops being arranged so that the engine passed from one stage of its overhaul to the next with the minimum of transport.

Particulars of this ship, which was renamed *Beauly Firth* were as follows:

Length overall	447ft 9in
Length between perpendiculars	425ft 0in
Moulded breadth	56ft 0in
Moulded depth	38ft 0in
Deep displacement	9773 tons
Mean draught (deep)	19ft 6½in
Power	2500ihp
Speed (max)	11kts
Fuel	836 tons
Complement	470 including 240 aircraft maintenance personnel

Machinery consisted of three oil-fired boilers and a reciprocating engine driving a single screw.

Propeller particulars	
diameter	16ft 6in
pitch	13ft 8in
developed blade area	100.5sq ft

Armament fitted consisted of twelve single 20mm Oerlikons.

The following workshops which were fitted in *Beauly Firth* contained the most modern equipment for aircraft engine repair: engine stripping shop; cleaning shop; viewing shop; in-line shop; radial shop; two assembly shops; accessory shop; machine shop; power plant assembly shop; electrical workshop; carburettor and fuel pump shop; sparking plug servicing shop; battery charging room; metalworkers' shop. In addition, adequate store spaces were available for engines awaiting repair and awaiting despatch.

**Internal arrangements of the Aircraft Engine
Repair Ship *Beauly Firth***

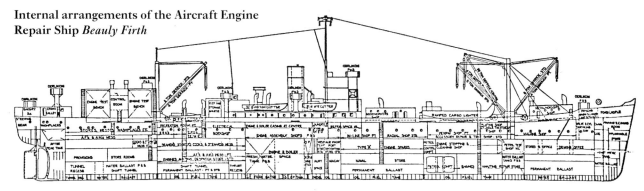

The complement of small craft carried for ship's use and aircraft repair work included two ramped cargo lighters for transporting aircraft engines.

The ships were fitted with recreation spaces including ice-cream and soda fountain and cinema, laundry, bakery, a cafeteria for men on shift-work, special offices for aircraft maintenance work and carried motor transport for shore work.

Stability
To preserve stability 2911 tons of slag and pig iron permanent ballast was fitted; also 151 tons of salt water ballast.

The resultant metacentric heights for the deep condition of 9773 tons and the light condition of 8948 tons were respectively 4.96ft (fl) and 4.26ft (fl).

General
Beauly Firth was built by Redhead & Sons, South Shields, and fitted out by Messrs Palmer's, Hebburn & Co Ltd. She was completed in June 1945.

Aircraft Component Repair Ships

Holm Sound and *Deer Sound*
Another PF(C) vessel - known as *Holm Sound* - was converted to an aircraft component repair ship. Its particular function was general maintenance work such as the repair of propellers, hydraulic fittings, oleo legs, instruments, electrical equipment, radio, bomb release gear and all aerofoils other than the fuselage, ie the type of work generally carried out by ancillary workshops of the maintenance yard and on aircraft workshop attached to a store depot. Another function was the manufacture of simple modification parts.

The leading particulars of *Holm Sound* were:

Length overall	447ft 9in
Length between perpendiculars	425ft 0in
Moulded breadth	56ft 0in

Moulded depth	38ft 0in
Deep displacement	9660 tons
Mean draught (deep)	19ft 4in
Oil fuel	852 tons
SHP	2500ihp
Max speed	11kts
Complement	610 including 360 aircraft maintenance personnel

Machinery
Single screw, three oil-fired boilers and reciprocating engines giving an ihp of 2500 and a speed of 11kts.

Propeller particulars:

diameter	16ft 6in
pitch	13ft 8in
developed blade area	100.5sq ft

Armament
Twelve single 20mm Oerlikon guns.

Stability
This ship was ballasted with 2744 tons of slag and pig iron to give a virtual metacentric height in the deep condition of 5.03ft. The metacentric height in the spent condition of 9092 tons (including 856 tons of SW ballast) was 5.02ft.

The workshops for aircraft maintenance, all of which were fitted with the most modern equipment, were as follows: radar workshop and test room; welding shops; metalworker's shop; smith's workshop; metallising shop; metal blade repair shop; propeller shop; oleo and hydraulic shop; propeller balancing shop; electrical repair shop; armament workshop; woodworker's shop; fabric worker's shop; normalising shop; mainplane shop; oxygen cylinder repair and test shop; machine shop; wireless workshop; instrument repair shop.

The complement of small craft carried for ship's use and aircraft repair work included two ramped cargo lighters for transporting damaged aircraft parts.

Deer Sound internal arrangement

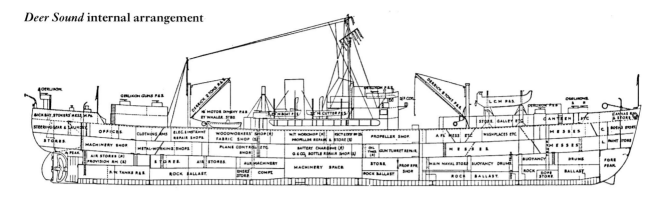

A second ship was converted to this service. She was *Deer Sound* (ex *Port Quebec*). Her function and conversion were the same as for *Holm Sound*.

The leading particulars of this ship were:

Length overall	451ft 0in
Length between perpendiculars	440ft 0in
Breadth (moulded)	59ft 4in
Depth (moulded)	39ft 9in
Deep displacement	10,698 tons
Mean draught (deep)	20ft 11in
Power	6700hp
Max speed	15kts
Diesel oil	511 tons
Complement	about 650 including 400 aircraft maintenance personnel

Machinery
Single screw and diesel engine giving a total of 6700hp and a speed of 15kts.

Armament
Thirteen single 20mm Oerlikons.

Stability
2300 tons of permanent ballast were fitted in this ship and nearly 500 tons of salt and fresh water ballast. This gave a virtual metacentric height of 2.69ft with a deep displacement of 10,698 tons; the spent condition of 10,021 tons had a metacentric height of 2.46ft (fl).

Both shops were fitted with recreation spaces including ice-cream and soda fountain, cinema, etc., laundry, bakery, air-conditioning in instrument repair shop, a cafeteria for men on shift-work, special offices for aircraft maintenance work and carried motor transport for shore work.

M/S and A/S Maintenance and Instructional Vessels

Kelantan
In considering the provision of adequate mobile units for maintenance of the fleet in the Far East until such time as our lost naval bases could be recovered, it was decided to provide facilities for the upkeep, maintenance and provisioning of 'LL' and Oropesa minesweepers in the forward areas. A vessel was required to keep the fleet of smaller vessels mobile and efficient and to accompany them to any area in which they were required to operate. Further, a requirement was that in addition to M/S maintenance, she should be provided with adequate instruction facilities and equipment in order that officers and ratings could be trained and kept up-to-date in all the latest developments of A/S installations.

Kelantan was selected as a suitable vessel for conversion to service as a M/S and A/S maintenance and instructional vessel. She was a twin-screw, oil-fired vessel built in 1921 by the Caledon Shipbuilding and Engineering Co, Dundee, for the Straits Steamship Co for trading in Far Eastern waters.

The vessel was lengthened by 30ft in 1924, the work being carried out in the Far East. She was brought home from Colombo in 1942 and the work of conversion to her new duties was carried out by Harland & Wolff, North Woolwich.

The leading particulars of *Kelantan* were:

Length overall	270ft 0in
Length between perpendiculars	260ft 4in
Breadth extreme	37ft 1in
Depth (to main deck)	10ft 6in
Deep displacement	2280 tons
Mean draught (deep)	10ft 7½in
Power	750shp
Oil fuel	150 tons

Complement	13 officers and 149 ratings including a maintenance staff of 3 officers and 49 ratings

Machinery
Diesel driven - one screw
  Propeller particulars:

diameter	7ft 6in
pitch	5ft 9in
developed blade area	17.5sq ft

Armament fitted consisted of one 4in HA/LA gun, seven Oerlikons and two Brownings, with ammunition including a quantity for the attached vessels.

The conversion included the following structural work: subdividing the main forward hold by steel watertight bulkheads; erection of raised forecastle with necessary stiffening for 4in HA/LA gun; fitting magazines; fitting Oerlikons and 4in gun; erecting steel divisional bulkheads in the after hold for victualling stores etc.; increasing officers' accommodation, crew's mess spaces and fitting new galleys and bakery; increasing stowage for fresh water and diesel oil; fitting arrangements for warping and securing minesweepers etc.

Workshops were provided, eg main machine workshop, woodworking shop, coppersmith's shop and foundry and smaller workshops.

Storerooms were also fitted for 'LL' stores and tails, spare 'LL' engines, Oropesa, A/S and E/S stores.

Instructional requirements were met by the fitting of an attack teacher room and a mass procedure teacher room.

A spacious, well-equipped sick bay for six cots with surgeon's examination room, dispensary and operations space was also provided.

A recreation space enclosed with curtains was fitted on the upper deck.

Kelantan was quite successful and did excellent work in connection with 'D' day operations. From technical observations and experience of ships officers, however, it was considered that a vessel of at least 30ft longer would have been preferred to meet all Departmental requirements and to provide increased facilities for the officers and crew under tropical conditions.

Corbrae

To supplement the services of *Kelantan* it was decided to convert another vessel for service as a M/S maintenance ship, and *Corbrae* was selected. She was originally built as a collier by the Burntisland Shipbuilding Company, and with

other similar vessels was purchased outright in the early days of the war for conversion to a 'magnet ship' for use against magnetic mines.

Leading particulars of the ship were:

Length overall		265ft 8in
Length between perpendiculars		257ft 0in
Beam		39ft 3in
Depth to upper deck		18ft 9in
Deep displacement		3343 tons
Draughts deep	F	12ft 9¼in
	A	18ft 2¾in
Power		770ihp
Oil fuel		334 tons

Before conversion could commence the magnets and associated equipment had to be removed. This chiefly comprised removing the main magnet and supporting structure - occupying almost the entire forward half of the ship and weighing 500 tons; the auxiliary magnet - fitted on the forecastle - weight 55 tons, generators and magnets, and the buoyancy drums fitted in the wing spaces abreast the main magnet.

The main structural conversion work consisted of:

(i) Fitting a new flat in forward part of the ship about 9ft above the tank-top.

(ii) Filling in of upper deck plating in way of hatches (original hatch coamings removed).

(iii) Erection of new forecastle deck and extension of ship's side plating to forecastle deck level.

(iv) Fitting a new flat below upper deck, amidships.

(v) Erecting new top structure for cabin accommodation, amidships.

(vi) Erection of new bridge structure. This was built of protective plating (15-20lb D1HT).

(vii) Fitting internal bulkheads to suit arrangement of compartments.

(viii) Cutting arched openings in existing longitudinal bulkheads in way of main workshop and stores.

The workshops fitted included: main machine and fitting shop; smithery; plate shop; coppersmith's and plumber's shop; foundry, electrical and light workshop; woodworking shop and radar workshop.

Special storerooms were fitted out for 'LL' spare gear and engineer's spare gear, SA spare gear, Oropesa, etc.

Machinery

Single screw reciprocating engine developed

770ihp and gave an endurance of about 7000 miles on 334 tons of oil fuel.

Propeller particulars:

diameter	13ft 6in
pitch	14ft 6in
developed blade area	67.5sq ft

During conversion an extra 100kW steam generator was fitted and two extra 100kW diesel generators.

Armament consisted of seven single hand-worked Oerlikons and two twin Brownings.

Stability
Corbrae was ballasted with 900 tons pig iron and the virtual metacentric height in the deep condition was 1.43ft.

General
Complement was eleven officers and 157 ratings, including two officers and forty-six ratings for maintenance staff. The ship's normal stores, ie cold and cool rooms, paymaster's stores, provision room etc., were all arranged with capacities to allow provisioning the attendant minesweepers. Also included in the ship's layout was a well-equipped sick bay (six cots) with examination room, dispensary, operation space and bathroom, and a recreation space with canteen, soda fountain and SRE compartment. All the above were intended for the use of visiting crews as well as the ship's company.

Space available in this vessel was less than would be supposed from the dimensions owing to the accommodation amidships being built on top of the original hatch coamings, thereby wasting much valuable space. In addition to this, Departmental requirements were pressed to the limit without regard to the vessel's small size. As a result the ship was very cramped throughout.

Maintenance Ships - Victory Ship Conversions

During the course of the Japanese War it was anticipated that, as Japanese-held territory was captured, the enemy would destroy all port facilities as she retreated. It therefore became essential that waterborne facilities be provided to maintain the large numbers of vessels which would be involved and which would in some instances be operating thousands of miles from the nearest Allied naval base. In September 1943 it was decided that the following types and numbers of maintenance ships were required for service in the Far East:

Maintenance ships for landing craft	4
Maintenance ships for HDML, BYMS and MFV	2
Maintenance ships for LST	4
Maintenance ships for escort vessels	11
Maintenance ships for MTB	1
Armament maintenance ships	2
	TOTAL 24

In view of the urgent necessity for these ships and in order to conserve shipyard labour it was decided to appropriate merchant ship hulls which were then in the course of construction and to fit these out as maintenance ships. A number of type 'C' cargo vessels were building in England, but it was found that sufficient numbers of these vessels could not be made available. The suitability of 'B', 'X', 'Y' and Thompson type cargo vessels was then successively investigated, until finally it was decided that all the conversions were to be carried out in Canada.

General arrangement drawings for the conversion of Liberty ships were prepared, followed by similar arrangements for Canadian oil-burning Victory cargo vessels. It was finally decided to use the Victory ships.

Leading particulars of these vessels were:

Length between perpendiculars	416ft 0in
Breadth, extreme	57ft 1in
Depth to upper deck	37ft 4in
Designed load draught as merchant ship	27ft 0in
Corresponding load displacement	13,770 tons
Speed	11kts
Boilers	oil fired
Machinery	single screw triple expansion developing 2500ihp at 76rpm

Propeller particulars:

diameter	18ft 6in
pitch	16ft
developed blade area	117sq ft

The first arrangement drawings were prepared for a maintenance ship for escort vessels, and it was decided that the arrangements of all other types of maintenance ship should deviate as little as practicable from that for escort maintenance ships in order to simplify the work of the conversions. In March 1944 the numbers of ships required were modified and orders placed accordingly in Canada.

Escort maintenance
    ships   reduced from 11 to 8
Landing craft
    maintenance ship   remain at 4
LST maintenance
    ships   increased from 4 to 5
HDML, BYMS, etc   reduced from 2 to 1
MTB maintenance
    ships   remain at 1
Armament maintenance
    ships   remain at 2

Total 21 ships.

Escort Maintenance Ships

These were designed to maintain twenty-five frigates, corvettes, etc. each. They were taken in hand at Vancouver as follows, the work being under the supervision of the British Admiralty Technical Mission:

Name of Ship	Firm	Taken in Hand
Beachy Head	Burrard Dry Dock Co Ltd	8 Jun 1944
Berry Head	Burrard Dry Dock Co Ltd	13 Jun 1944
Flamborough Head	Burrard Dry Dock Co Ltd	5 Jul 1944
Duncansby Head	Burrand Dry Dock Co Ltd	27 Jul 1944
Kinnairds Head	North Van Ship Repair Co	19 Jun 1944
Trevose Head	North Van Ship Repair Co	12 Jul 1944
Rame Head	North Van Ship Repair Co	12 Jul 1944
Rattray Head	North Van Ship Repair Co	27 Jan 1945

Subsequently it was decided that *Kinnairds Head* and *Trevose Head* were to be converted to maintenance ships for motor craft, and of the remaining six vessels *Rattray Head* was cancelled as it was incomplete at the time of the surrender of Japan.

The structural alterations rendered necessary by the conversions were incorporated in the ships as the hulls were built, the main features being:
(i)   Large cargo hatches plated up.
(ii)   New third deck fitted throughout the ship.
(iii) New platform deck fitted in Nos 1, 3, 4 and 5 holds.
(iv) Boat deck extended forward and connected to bridge deck.
(v)   Additional deckhouses built on upper deck; one forward and one aft.

In order to reduce the freeboard and windage to ensure propeller immersion in all conditions of loading, approximately 2800 tons of ballast was fitted. As it was envisaged that these vessels would be at anchor during the major part of their service in the Far East, good anchoring arrangements were considered essential and the ships' existing 75cwt bower anchors were replaced by 100cwt anchors. In addition two 32cwt anchors and a capstan were fitted on the upper deck aft for mooring by the stern. Adequate mooring arrangements were fitted in order that ships being serviced could be moored alongside.

An auxiliary machinery room was constructed abaft the deep tanks on the aft side of the machinery space and four 150kW diesel generators and two 100 tons triple effect evaporating sets were fitted. In addition, a 300kW turbo generator was fitted in the machinery space.

Several workshops were fitted in each vessel, the largest being the machine shop, 4000sq ft in area, 12ft headroom, situated in No 2 hold. The equipment in this shop included 12in, 8½in, 6½in and 4½ in lathes, milling machines, drilling, surfacing and boring machine, grinding machines, tube screwing machine, shaping machine, drills and hacksaws. Immediately below this workshop was a combined smithery, plate, coppersmith's and plumber's shop and foundry, having a total area of 3300sq ft, containing a plate-punching and sharing machine, plate bending rolls, hydraulic pipe bending machine, pipe flange facing and drilling machine, pneumatic hammer, forces and melting furnaces; for moulding a sand pit of 250sq ft in area was fitted.

A woodworking and pattern shop was situated on the upper deck aft, and the machinery fitted comprised a planing and thicknessing machine, 8in woodworking lathe, mortising and boring machine, bandsaw and circular saw, drill etc. Other workshops fitted were electrical and ordnance workshop, instrument repair shop, optical workshop, radar workshop, motor boat engine workshop and welding shop, and an attack teacher room was also provided. An oxygen plant capable of producing 500-600cu ft per hour was installed in the after deckhouse on *Beachy Head* and *Flamborough Head*, and in each of the remaining vessels, viz. *Duncansby Head*, *Rame Head* and *Berry Head* an acetylene producing plant with a capacity of approx 300cu ft per hour was fitted.

The original ship's derricks, comprising ten 5 tons, one 50 tons and one 30 tons derrick, were retained, and two ramped cargo lighters were included in the boat complement for the carriage of spare parts and repair materials for servicing the attached craft.

Accommodation was provided for twenty-six officers, 350 ratings and twenty-five natives, this being sufficient to house the maintenance and repair party in addition to the ship's own crew. In view of the exacting conditions in the tropics and the probably absence of port facilities, special attention was paid to the provision of amenities for the ship's complement, and recreation spaces, large laundry, canteen, soda fountain, barber's shop, cinema equipment and sports gear was provided. A sick bay with a capacity of twelve cots was erected on the upper deck. Ample ventilation arrangements were fitted, having special regard to conditions during blackout.

Three galleys were fitted, for officers, ratings and natives respectively; also a large bakery capable of supplying bread to attached craft as well as to the ship itself. Refrigerated spaces of approximately 11,000cu ft capacity were provided, and two sets of 90,000btu/hour methyl-chloride refrigerating units were installed. The refrigerated space, provision and clothing stores, vegetable and potato locker, were large enough to cater for the ship and to replenish attached craft.

The armament comprised sixteen Oerlikons and a magazine was fitted capable of holding 200 tons of reserve ammunition.

The vessels were completed on the undermentioned dates, but the early end of hostilities precluded the full value of these ships from being made known.

Ship	Completed
Beachy Head	27 Mar 1945
Flamborough Head	2 May 1945
Berry Head	7 Jun 1945
Duncansby Head	8 Sep 1945
Rame Head	18 Aug 1945

LST Maintenance Ships

These vessels were designed to maintain thirty-six LSTs each, and five ships were ordered in March 1944, these being progressed in Vancouver under the supervision of BATM[3]. In September 1944 it was decided to finish two of these ships as landing craft maintenance ships, little structural alteration being required.

The layout of LST maintenance ships was practically identical to that of escort maintenance ships except that as an attack teacher was not a requirement this space was fitted out as a mess for thirty-six POs. When escort maintenance ship *Rattray Head* was cancelled, the acetylene producing plant which was originally to have been fit-

ted in that vessel was installed instead in the LST maintenance ship *Spurn Point*.

The names of these vessels and their building particulars were as follows:

Name of Ship	Firm	Date in Hand	Completed
Hartland Point	Burrard Dry Dock Co Ltd	18 Jul 1944	12 Jul 1945
Dodman Point	Burrard Dry Dock Co Ltd	6 Jan 1945	5 Oct 1945
Spurn Point	Burrard Dry Dock Co Ltd	16 Feb 1945	22 Dec 1945

Landing Craft Maintenance Ships

Four of these ships, each of which was required to maintain fifty-four major landing craft or 162 minor landing craft or proportionate numbers of both, were originally ordered; subsequently this number was increased to six by utilising two of the LST maintenance ships. The design was based on that for escort maintenance ships with certain differences due to the smaller type of craft to be maintained, the main difference being:

(a) The space used for smithery, plate, coppersmith's and plumber's shop and foundry in escort maintenance ships was fitted as a spare engine stowage space for carrying spare landing craft engines and a coppersmith's and blacksmith's shop.

(b) The large variety of machines carried in escort maintenance ships was not necessary for the maintenance of landing craft so the space used as machine shop in those vessels was fitted out as engine stripping and assembly shop, woodworking shop and machine shop.

(c) Certain of the naval store spaces were fitted out as stores for engine component parts and spare gear.

(d) As in LST maintenance ships an additional mess space for thirty-six POs was fitted, and a proportion of the accommodation made available for crews of attached craft.

(e) Both the officers' and crews' galleys were larger than in escort maintenance ships, as with the lack of cooking facilities on certain types of landing craft it was necessary to supply cooked meals to crews of these vessels.

(f) As no acetylene or oxygen producing plant was fitted in these vessels and the woodworking shop was resited in the machine ship, the space becoming vacant on the upper deck aft was used as a garage for the accommodation of

3 British Admiralty Technical Museum

a workshop lorry, 1 ton truck, jeep, trailer pumps and portable electric welding sets.

(g) The motor boat engine workshop was converted into a store room.

Two of these vessels, *Orfordness* and *Tarbatness*, which were incomplete when hostilities ended, were cancelled. The four ships completed were:

Name of Ship	Firm	Date in Hand	Completed
Buchan Ness	West Coast Shipbuilders	21 Oct 1944	26 Jul 1945
Dungeness	West Coast Shipbuilders	1 Dec 1944	2 Oct 1945
Girdleness	Burrard Dry Dock Co Ltd	7 Dec 1944	6 Sep 1945
Fifeness	Burrard Dry Dock Co Ltd	19 Jan 1945	29 Nov 1945

Motor Craft Maintenance Ships

Originally only one ship, *Mull of Kintyre*, was ordered for the maintenance of HDMLs, BYMSs and MFVs, but owing to the large number of small craft operating in eastern waters it was approved in February 1945 for two additional ships to be allocated to maintain MLs. The ships selected were *Trevose Head* and *Kinnairds Head*, which at the time were being built as escort maintenance ships. These vessels were renamed *Mull of Oa* and *Mull of Galloway* respectively and together with *Mull of Kintyre* were designated motor craft maintenance ships.

Here again the layout of escort maintenance ships was closely followed with certain differences, viz:

(a) Part of the smithery and plate shop was appropriated for the stowage of fourteen spare Hall Scott engines.

(b) The motor boat engine workshop was fitted out as a spare gear store.

(c) Radar workshop was enlarged.

(d) The space on upper deck not required for oxygen or acetylene plant was equipped as an ordnance workshop.

(e) An additional mess for ten POs was fitted in the space used as No 5 naval store on escort maintenance ships.

(f) A small engine test shop and carburettor repair shop were built on boat deck.

Mull of Kintyre varied from the other two vessels insofar as stowage was provided for minesweeping gear for attached vessels, the bulk of this being carried in the space not required for Hall Scott engines in this vessel.

Mull of Oa was cancelled in August 1945, after the Japanese surrender.

Name of Ship	Firm	Date in Hand	Completed
Mull of Galloway	North Van Ship Repair Co	10 Jun 1944	15 May 1945
Mull of Kintyre	North Van Ship Repair Co	21 Dec 1944	5 Nov 1945

Coastal Force Maintenance Ship

This vessel, originally known as maintenance ship for MTBs, was designed to provide full mobile repair and maintenance facilities for at least thirty-two MTBs or MLs. The layout of the escort maintenance ships was largely followed with certain major differences, viz:

(a) Workshops 106-135 platform deck were replaced by a torpedo body store, parting space, etc.

(b) Machine shop 106-135 3rd deck was replaced by a smaller machine shop while in addition naval stores and spare gear store were fitted.

Mull of Kintyre, a motor craft maintenance ship, one of many similar 'Victory' ships built and converted in Canada. Seen here on the Clyde in July 1947 whilst supporting the ship target trials programme.

(c) Nos 1, 2 and 3 naval stores platform deck were replaced by a spare engine store.

(d) Stores and workshops 3rd deck were replaced by an engine fitting and ordnance workshops.

(e) The A/S and E/S test shop was replaced by an electrical workshop.

(f) The welder's shop, upper deck, was replaced by a radio workshop.

(g) The oxygen plant compartment on upper deck was replaced by a coppersmith's, welder's and plumber's workshop, and a power mounting workshop.

Name of Ship	Firm	Date in Hand	Completed
Cape Wrath	West Coast Shipbuilders	March 1945	March 1946

Armament Maintenance Ships

These vessels were designed to carry out maintenance repairs and standard modifications to armaments which included changing of gun barrels up to 5.25in, torpedo modifications, and routine inspection.

The layout of the escort maintenance ships was largely followed with certain major exceptions, viz:

(a) Additional cabins were fitted by extending the boat deck, building cabins over the sick bay, and appropriating the sick bay itself for this purpose, the sick bay being resited in the A/S and E/S workshop.

(b) Slight rearrangement of the messes was carried out and additional offices fitted.

(c) The large workshops 106-135 3rd and 4th decks were replaced by a torpedo store, parting space, etc.

(d) Nos 1, 2 and 3 naval stores 4th deck were replaced by a gun store.

(e) The EAs and OAs shop, engineer's and electrical stores and foundry stores on 3rd deck were replaced by a machine shop.

(f) The battery repair room and welder's shop on upper deck were fitted as an ASIS store.

(g) The coppersmith's, welder's and blacksmith's shop were resisted on upper deck in the shipwright's shop.

Name of Ship	Firm	Date in Hand	Completed
Portland Bill	Burrard Dry Dock Co	Feb 1945	Nov 1945

Selsey Bill was started but cancelled in August 1945, after the Japanese surrender.

Amenities Ships

Menestheus and *Agamemnon*

Among the many interesting conversion jobs which the Department of Naval Construction of the Admiralty carried out during the war was the transformation of two Blue Funnel liners as amenities ships for service in the Far East. As the Prime Minister, Mr Winston Churchill, said, the Pacific Fleet Train was planned to give the British Fleet complete mobility and to enable it to operate continuously in distant waters on a scale never before attempted.

The complete Pacific Fleet Train comprised well over a hundred vessels of thirty specialised types sailing under the White, Red and Blue Ensigns, and although the need for these ships was not so great when the war with Japan was over, it was, of course, still necessary not only to maintain an army of occupation in Japan and other lands which were formerly occupied by the enemy, but to retain a substantial fleet in Far Eastern waters. The amenities ships were intended to provide the fighting forces overseas on shore and afloat with those amenities which make the life of those serving far from home a little brighter.

Several conferences were held at the Admiralty to decide the best method of carrying this out, and eventually two Blue Funnel ships were chosen to be specially converted and the work of planning commenced with the enthusiastic co-operation of Messrs Alfred Holt, who were very keen to make the vessels the success they deserved to be in serving the men of the Fleet.

The two amenities ships were the *Agamemnon* and the *Menestheus*, both owned by Messrs Alfred Holt and Co.

These two ships were built in 1929, the former by Workman Clark and Co, Belfast, and the latter by the Caledon Shipbuilding and Engineering Co. The *Agamemnon* had a gross tonnage of 7593, a length overall of 478ft 3in, a moulded breadth of 59ft 4in and a moulded depth of 35ft 3in. She was propelled by twin-screw diesel engines of 8600shp and had a speed of 16kts. *Agamemnon* was taken over by the Admiralty at the end of 1939, and fitted as a minelayer; she commenced fitting as an amenities ship at Vancouver in December 1944, but when nearly completed her conversion was cancelled as the war had ended and it was considered that one amenities ship was sufficient.

The *Menestheus* was a similar ship, fitted with twin-screw diesel engines of 8600shp and had practically the same peace and war service as the *Agamemnon*.

The *Menestheus* was an expression of the British government to provide the fighting forces

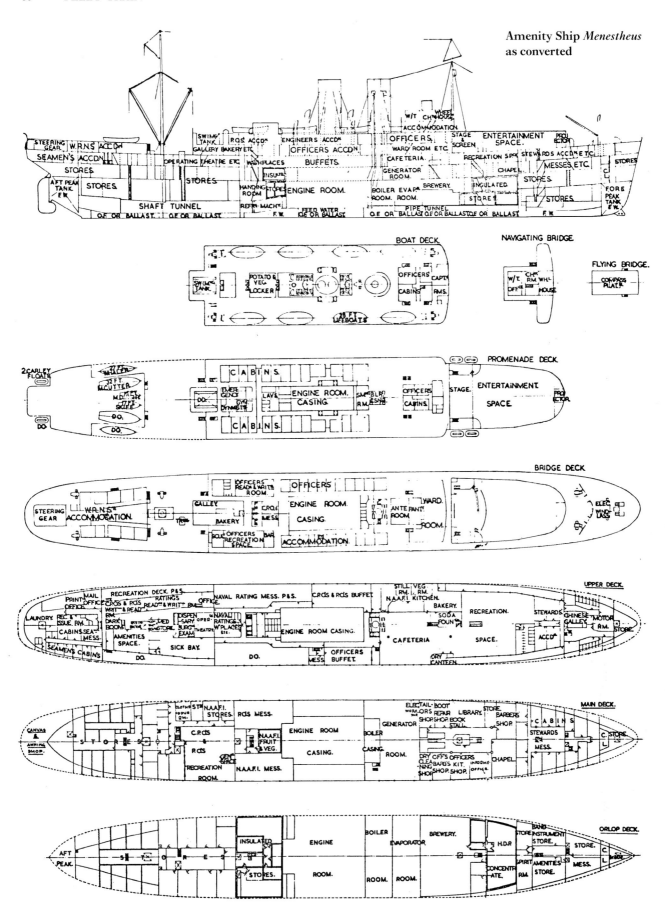

Amenity Ship *Menestheus*
as converted

Menestheus, an amenity
ship. Even the USN, which
was so far ahead of the RN
in most aspects of the Fleet
Train, lacked a mobile
brewery and theatre.

overseas with amenities which could make their lives a little less tedious. Service in the tropics afloat meant, of course, long distances under hot, humid conditions, and, in order to be effective, the opportunities of rest and recreation had to be taken to the men of the Fleet.

A feature of *Menestheus* was the entertainment hall, seating about 350, which could be used as a cinema or theatre. There was a fully equipped stage which was designed in consultation with ENSA in which stage lighting was a special feature; dressing rooms were also provided. A well-fitted cafeteria was provided in which attractive meals could be served, whilst ices and soft drinks could be obtained at a soda fountain nearby.

One of the most important amenities for the ratings in ships in tropical waters is the provision of supplies of beer and, for the first time in the Navy's long history, beer was manufactured in a seagoing ship.

In working out the initial arrangements, it was not long before all concerned had a very healthy respect for beer. It requires pasteurisation in order to preserve its keeping qualities, and if it is not cooled in a certain temperature it gives off large quantities of gas. It was, therefore, necessary to call in brewery experts who had in turn to learn that watertight bulkheads were important and that ships do roll and pitch. But ultimately a suitable compromise was reached and soon a 250-barrel per week brewery took shape on the drawing boards in DNC Department.

The installation of the brewery brought with it a trail of auxiliary problems; for example, large quantities of water were necessary so a distilling plant was required. Again, cooling the beer meant extra refrigerating plant, and storage problems for

unconsumed beer also had to be solved. In fact, the auxiliary requirements of the brewery took up twice as much space as that required for dealing solely with the production of beer. The distribution problem, with a fluctuating demand depending upon the movements of the Fleet, was a somewhat thorny one to solve. *Menestheus* was the only completed floating brewery in the world.

The Brewery consisted of Wort coppers, fermenting vessels with yeast containers on top, refrigerating plant, cold store for stowage of containers after being filled in the filling room, cold store for malt extract and hops and a lift for the transport of stores and containers.

But it is not enough just to provide beer, half the pleasure of drinking it is lost unless it is consumed in the right atmosphere. Great care was taken to provide tastefully laid out recreation spaces complete with efficient bars, and leading firms of ship decorators co-operated so that the best results should be gained. Lighting and ventilation, of course, received much attention in view of the anticipated service of the ship in the tropics. It was also essential that furnishings and floor covering should be bright and cheerful to induce a feeling of relaxation, and the assistance of Messrs Hampton and Sons and Messrs Maples was obtained to ensure that the decorations and furnishings were just quite right. The lighting scheme was designed to suit the general layout of the compartments, and this together with high-class decorations made the various compartments as near like the first-class club as practicable.

The ratings ate in the cafeteria, moved along to the bar in the recreation space for a glass of beer which was piped straight up to the bar from the brewery, and then went to the entertainment hall where they could enjoy a cinema or stage performance.

The cafeteria kitchen equipment included range, griller, bread and pastry oven, mixing machine, steam hot closets, potato peeler, bread slicer and bacon slicer, with the necessary benches for quick service at the cafeteria openings.

Provision for recreation must always include amenities for those who wish to be quiet. This was not overlooked, for reading and writing rooms were available, together with a well-stocked library. A chapel for all denominations was also provided.

After all this there still remained the organisation to replace the lost collar stud or button, and to deal with the small but necessary comforts. Consequently there was a tailor's shop, a kit shop, a bootmaker's shop, a bookstall, a laundry, a barber's shop and an information bureau, a printing office and a dark room. A large, airy sick bay catered for those who found the change from the toil of service too overpowering and for the small accidents which always happen.

One of the most important amenities arranged as the prompt and rapid deliveries of mail. While these ships could not do much to expedite the delivery of mails over long distances, they were fitted with an office for the rapid handling of letters and parcels.

Not only was the *Menestheus* laid out to give the utmost possible scope for recreation, but large outfits of sports gear were supplied so that boxing, football, cricket, water polo etc. could be indulged in when the vessel was anchored in some suitable spot.

The wonderful example of teamwork presented by this whole organisation should be noted. The ship was a product of British yards, sailed under the Red Ensign and manned by a Merchant Navy crew, but the Royal Navy and the NAAFI staff were also on board. The work of planning the conversion to the new role involved calling upon the services of brewery experts, naval engineers, interior decorators, cinema and stage experts, the ship owners and their marine staff, the NAAFI and the Church. The whole of the work was co-ordinated by the Naval Construction Department of the Admiralty.

The *Menestheus* travelled to many parts in the Far East and gave enjoyment to many thousands, proving that in war the use of such a ship is an essential part of the service life of a Fleet.

This vessel arrived home in July 1946 and was dismantled for return to her former service.

Reports from the authorities responsible for the work of amenities in the Fleet were very satisfactory, but it was pointed out that a vessel for such services should sail under the White Ensign and that the crew should be sufficient to give open house from early after lunch until 11pm instead of from 6pm until 11pm.

The brewery was efficient in every way but it was found that supplying beer from 5-gallon containers was more satisfactory than piping direct from the tanks. Another beer bar was also considered necessary.

Seaward Defence Ship

Helvig

In the summer of 1943 a requirement arose for a vessel in the Far East to fulfil the function of a mobile control station, for the underwater defences of an advance anchorage or harbour where the climate was unsuited for European personnel living ashore.

Helvig *was a harbour defence ship, intended to control indicator loops, minefields, Asdics etc.*

The major function of the vessel was the control of such defences as the indicator loop system, the harbour defence asdic system and the controlled minefield, and the carrying of the extended defence officer and the port wireless signal station. The PWSS was to be landed on arrival to provide a link between the shore and the XDO who remained onboard.

The functions of the ship necessitated arrangements being made to moor the vessel by bow and stern using her own resources in such a way that she would not swing with the tide. Further, since it was anticipated that the vessel would be anchored for considerable periods at these advanced bases such amenities as could be readily accommodated were to be fitted.

In April 1944 approval was given to convert *Helvig*, then engaged as a controlled mining base ship, to a seaward defence ship. *Helvig* was an ex-Danish cargo vessel, built in 1937 in Denmark, to British Corporation standards.

Leading particulars of *Helvig* were:

Length overall	346ft
Length between perpendiculars	325ft
Beam	45ft 9in
Depth (moulded)	29ft to shelter deck
Deep displacement	5260 tons
Mean draught (deep)	18ft 2in
Power	3300shp
Cruising speed	12½kts
Endurance	7000 miles at 12kts
Oil fuel	465 tons
Complement	24 officers, 181 men
Main machinery	diesel
Armament	7-single Oerlikons 7-Holman projectors

During operations it was a requirement that *Helvig* should lay in her own minefield and loops. It was therefore necessary to provide some arrangement for leading the tail cables into the control room. To effect this the entire length of the forward well was fitted up with cable troughs which provided a safe anchorage for the thirty-two heavy electric cables coming into the ship over the bulwark. The troughs were themselves wired by means of junction boxes to the control room. Quick release arrangements were provided to enable the cables to be slipped in an emergency.

As the sensitive equipment used in harbour defence had never before been fitted in a vessel, special arrangements were made to provide as steady a platform as possible free from vibration. The mooring arrangements were improved to two head and two stern anchors - additional hawse pipes and capstans being provided aft, special sup-

ports were designed for the equipment, and because the ship was, at that time, rather lively she was ballasted to obtain a condition similar to the one which would be met with in cargo service so far as draught and GM were concerned. The necessary ballasting was achieved by the use of a ballast of high volumetric value, 1200 tons of brick being employed to give a reasonable working condition. This ballast entirely occupied Nos 2 and 3 holds, trunked access being provided to gain entry to the double bottoms.

Owing to the humidity of tropical climates it was necessary to provide air conditioning arrangements to the main instrument room to prevent deterioration in the electrical equipment, and also to provide better working conditions for the personnel engaged on the very exacting and trying duties of harbour defence. The main instrument room, which was 70ft long, 48ft broad, and with 8 to 11ft headroom, was served by a 150,000btu/hr air conditioning plant manufactured by Messrs Hall of Dartford, Kent, situated outside the room to avoid undue vibration in the compartment. To reduce vibration to a minimum it was essential to situate the control room as far from the main machinery compartments as practicable and to keep the vicinity free from mechanical appliances such as winches, pumps, fans, etc.

The extra accommodation and store spaces required in *Helvig* necessitated the construction of a new flat built in Nos 4 and 5 holds. The lower portion of these holds was used to house the additional 50ton/day distilling and evaporating plant. A new boiler for distilling and two 120kW diesel generators were also fitted.

To provide for the wellbeing of the officers and man, such amenities as recreation rooms, canteen, soda fountain and cinema apparatus were provided and provision made for the maximum facilities for washing and sanitation.

Helvig was equipped for tropical service, due regard being given to the ventilation system.

Owing to the cessation of hostilities with Japan, *Helvig*, although completed end of May 1945, was never used on active service but extensive trials carried out to test her function as a seaward defence ship were satisfactory.

Accommodation Ship for Spare Submarine Crew

Aorangi

Amongst the many requirements of the fleet train an accommodation ship for spare submarine crews with facilities for recreation and attendant amenities became one of the first considerations. The ship available for this purpose was the *Aorangi* of the Union Steam Ship Co of New Zealand and was in use as a depot ship during the invasion operations on the French coast having previously been used for trooping.

The leading dimensions of this ship were:

Length overall	600ft
Length between perpendiculars	580ft
Beam moulded	72ft
Depth moulded to shelter deck	46ft 6in
Displacement	21,938 tons
Mean draught	27ft 7in
Machinery	quadruple screwed diesel machinery developing 12,000lhp
Speed (maximum)	15kts

The vessel was fitted to accommodate the following White Ensign crew: seventy-six officers and 750 ratings, these included twelve spare crews for submarines and administrative RN complement for manning, running and minor repairs to boats, issue of naval and victualling stores, manning of gun armament of fourteen Oerlikons and two Bofors, and visual signalling.

The ship sailed under the Red Ensign and was managed by the P&O Co for the Union Steam Line with a crew of 300.

The amenities provided included: entertainment hall with cinema and portable boxing ring; recreation space for officers, POs and ratings; lecture and writing room, also used as a chapel; barber's shop; tailor's shop; boot repair shop; mail office; information office; lending library, canteen and soda fountain; laundry etc. and cinema on the upper deck.

A large sick bay was fitted, and the living spaces were lined for protection in the tropics; awnings were fitted.

The existing auxiliary machinery arrangements were improved by the addition of a boiler and two distillers with a total capacity of 200ton/day, and the replacing of the dynamos, which were twenty years old and rather unreliable, by five 180kW diesel generators. Additional ventilation was also fitted.

Arrangements were made for berthing submarines alongside and the following boats were carried in addition to the twelve Red Ensign lifeboats:

7-32ft motor cutters
1-45ft motor launch
2-16ft motor dinghies
2-14ft sailing dinghies

Stowage for 700 tons of diesel oil for submarines was provided.

Aorangi was converted at Fairfields, being taken in hand on 15 July 1944 and completed on 17 March 1945.

Capt. S/M 2 in May 1945 reported that, although *Aorangi* was only passing through on her way to Capt. S/M 4, he remarked her excellent accommodation and equipment, her sick bay complete with PMO and staff, her fourteen power boats with their own crews and maintenance staff and her theatre all made them envious and that she would undoubtedly be an enormous asset to an advanced base.

CHAPTER 18

Landing Craft

Editorial Note

The vast fleets of British and American landing craft and ships of World War II were, with very few exceptions, designed by three remarkable men. Rowland Baker RCNC was the leading designer and, perhaps, the most unusual. Brought up on a working Thames barge, he retained an unusual command of the English language even when, after the war, he reached high rank.[1] *The US builder, Higgins, was almost as outspoken while to Ken Barnaby of Thornycroft goes the credit of the first successful Allied craft. This chapter is very detailed, requiring few footnotes, but some additional, background reading may be suggested as Ref 2-4.*

Early Developments of Landing Craft

During the Second Wold War the production of a Combined Operations fleet, which included many specialised types of landing ships, craft and amphibians assumed a new importance. The need for special craft to land troops had always been realised, and historical counterparts can be found to many of the types developed during the war, but landing craft have now definitely emerged as important instruments of war.

During the First World War two types of craft, the 'X' craft and the 'Y' craft, were built to DNC's designs. Two other types of craft were improvised – the Bacon pontoon and a number of wood and canvas paddle barges.

In 1924 an inter-departmental committee, consisting of representatives of Admiralty, War Office, Air Ministry and Board of Trade, was formed and charged with the following terms of reference:

(a) To consider the design and numbers of landing craft of all descriptions required for Combined Operations on a hostile coast.
(b) To propose such experiments as are necessary.
(c) To consider and make recommendations as to the best method of transporting tanks overseas, and of disembarking them rapidly in an opposed landing on an open beach, in the first flight of a covering force.

The committee made a number of recommendations, but concentrated their attention upon the provision of a protected, self-propelled craft to land 100 troops. This craft was required to be not more than 40ft x 12ft x 20 tons hoisting weight, and to have silent machinery. A design was produced by DNC and approval was obtained for the construction of the first peace-time landing craft.

This vessel, which became known as MLC No 1, was completed in 1926, and protracted trials indicated that, apart from speed, it met the requirements laid down. The craft was very manoeuvrable and scarcely audible at 100yds, it could carry practically any existing Army gun as well as its designed loads. The speed, due to the low propulsive coefficient associated with jet propulsion, was 4¾kts instead of the 6kts required. It was anticipated that at least 100 of these craft would be required for any amphibious operation and that, with sufficient priority, this number could be produced in two months.

Meanwhile the Landing Craft Committee had been considering the various alternative methods of landing Army tanks in the first assault, and DNC submitted a revised design of a lighter capable of accommodating the standard Army tank of that time, the Vickers Light Tank Mark II weighing 12 tons.

The design was an improved MLC and one vessel – known as MLC10 – was approved for inclusion in the 1927 new construction programme.

Hold dimensions were 29ft 6in x 11ft 0in

Propulsion	Two Gill rotary jets of improved type driven by a 42hp petrol engine.
Endurance	250 miles
Speed (max)	6kts

As a result of exhaustive trials carried out during October 1929, a number of modifications were made. The modified craft underwent further trials in March 1930 and was found to be superior to MLC1 as regards load–carrying capacity, propulsion and retraction from the beach. The lifting weight of the craft was then 20 tons with a mean draught of 2ft 9in. The mean draught when loaded with a 12 tons tank was 3ft 8in.

[1] Brown, D K. 'Sir Rowland Baker, RCNC', WARSHIP 1995 (London 1995).

[2] Maund, L E H. Assault from the Sea (London 1949). A background to the planning of combined operations.

[3] Ladd, J D. Assault from the Sea 1939-1945. Newton Abbott 1976. General history of the operations and the craft.

[4] Allied Landing Craft of World War Two. Originally a wartime recognition book, republished London, 1985. Even lists some craft that DNC - and Baker - never heard of.

During these years various suggestions for tank landing craft had been examined but the War Office was quite satisfied that MLC10 fulfilled all their requirements.

By the end of 1934 MLC10 had been thoroughly tested in Combined Operation exercises both in this country and in the Mediterranean and had proved entirely satisfactory. As a result the 1935 estimates provided £8000 for two further vessels, MLC11 and MLC12.

Landing Craft in the Immediate Pre-War Period

In 1936 the War Office and the Naval Staff pressed for the number of MLCs to be increased to at least ten craft. The naval representatives of the landing craft committee met and generally agreed that, with certain engine modifications to increase power and additional protection for troops, the MLC10 type was still satisfactory. The War Office did raise certain objections to repeat MLC10s but they were not received until June 1937, by which time approval had been sought and given to include provision in the 1937 estimates for six further craft, MLC14 to 19.

The hull particulars of MLCs 14 to 19 were identical with those of MLCs 10 to 12 except that it was now established that craft of this form sailed better ramp-first and the ramped end was accordingly termed the bow. The fitting of two, instead of one, engines and the fitting of improved watertight subdivision forward increased the estimated cost by £2000 to £5000 each.

All these MLC craft were completed early in 1939 and completed trials satisfactorily.

General features of these craft were:

(i)   The ramp door was power-operated off the main engines. The time for lowering the door was 10 seconds, and 12 seconds for raising.

(ii) They could be towed ramp-first satisfactorily at speeds up to 16kts when light, and 14kts with a 10 tons load.

(iii) The metacentric heights were 4.0ft light and 1.5ft in the deep load condition of 34 tons. They were all unstable with the cargo deck flooded.[5]

(iv) Jet propulsion gave excellent manoeuvrability. They could stop and reverse in 14 seconds, turn about their stern and hold themselves square to a beach in cross currents. Retracting from a beach was never impossible for them due to the high static pull of the jets, their scouring action and the longitudinal camber of the bottom of

the craft. These last six craft attained 6kts but jet propulsion was discarded soon after in view of its low propulsive coefficient and the superior efficiency of propellers.

This change was fully justified by later events, particularly in the Narvik assault in May 1940, when both jet-propelled and screw-propelled MLC were used. Due to fouling of the jet inlets with weed, all the MLCs with this type of propulsion were put out of action and were lost.

The Inter Services Training and Development Centre

ISTDC[6] was set up in 1938 at Portsmouth with instructions to consult with the service staff colleges and other authorities, and to enquire into the materials required for Combined Operations, etc. The duties of the Landing Craft Committee were taken over, and the Committee abolished.

The new organisation soon recommended that first importance be given to the development of a ship-borne boat to carry one infantry platoon and land it in not more than 18in of water. The boat was to weigh less than 10 tons so that ordinary lifeboat davits could be used to lift her. This was investigated first by Mr Fleming but his original design was unseaworthy. Fleming then put forward and improved design which, together with a design submitted by Thornycrofts, was accepted as a prototype. Orders for a prototype of the Fleming craft MLC50 and a prototype Thornycroft boat MLC51 were placed in mid-1939; comparative trials were carried out in August.

The Fleming boat was of Birmabright construction and unprotected, while the Thornycroft boat was of wood (double diagonal) and protected by ¼in protective plating. Neither boat was entirely satisfactory, and after the trials it was decided to modify them for use as prototype support craft.

Personnel Carriers

LCA (Landing Craft Assault)

A new design for assault landing craft was produced by DNC in conjunction with Thornycrofts; this was based generally on MLC51 but included the lessons of the trials. A contract for a prototype to this design was placed at the end of September 1939; it was known as ALC2.

This type of craft was from this time on known as ALC until early in 1942, when the names of all types were re-classified. Assault craft were from then onwards landing craft assault (LCA).

[5] See 1.

[6] See 2.

LCA general arrangement

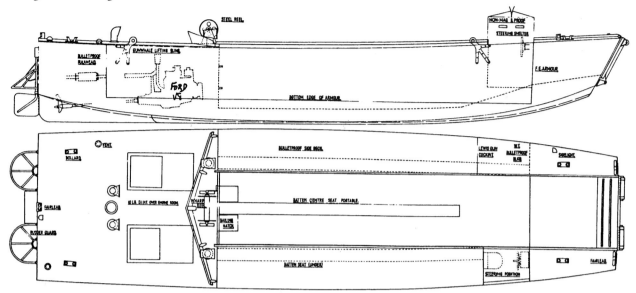

Further orders for seventeen craft were placed in October 1939, and satisfactory trials were carried out with the first of these craft which was completed in April 1940.

ALC2 had a total weight of about 9 tons and was 38ft 9in x 10ft x 4ft 7¾in depth. Extra protection was fitted (2½ tons of protective plating), the corresponding diminished speed – 9¼kts – and increased draught being accepted. Manoeuvrability and retracting power were satisfactory. The turning circle of these craft was 70ft.

The early craft were fitted with Onazote buoyancy material in the bow, stern, at the sides and under the floors to keep the craft afloat even when swamped; this was later omitted as the supply position for Onazote deteriorated. The conning position, originally sited at the after end of the troop space, was moved forward to the starboard side in 1940, and a Bren gun position provided opposite on the port side. Experience with LCA hoisted at carrier davits in 1941 led to the replacement of the original chain slings with bar slings which rendered the hooking on and unhooking a much less hazardous undertaking. About the same time casualties in the engine room during a raid led to a requirement for additional bulletproof protection over the engine room.

The first batch of LCA were engined with two Scripps Ford V8 engines each 60hp, but in May 1940 attention was drawn to the possibility of fitting US Kermath engines in LCA in lieu of the Ford V8 in order to speed production. In June 1940 150 of these Kermath engines were ordered (140 and ten spare) for seventy LCAs – 2:1 reduction gears were ordered from the US with the engines.

In order to improve delivery prospects, Thornycroft sub-let some of the orders to small yacht and boat-building firms. This procedure was followed until 1941 when over 200 boats had been ordered and requirements as regards numbers were very much increased, some alternative capacity had to be found. The Admiralty then placed contracts direct, and widened the field by encouraging mass production and by bringing in public works contractors, joinery firms and furniture makers etc.

Experience led to demand for various modifications; fundamentally, however, the boat was not altered, although the continued addition of requirements added to the weight.

At the end of the war the all-up weight of the boat was about 13½ tons, and the original staff requirement regarding the use of existing davits was, perforce, given up.

Altogether 1929 LCAs were built and during 1944 production averaged sixty boats per month.

LCP(M) (Landing Craft, Personnel – Medium)

In June 1941, in order to meet a Combined Operations requirement for raiding craft suitable for landing on rocky beaches in northern waters, a design was prepared for a vessel similar to, but somewhat smaller than, the Coble used on the Northumberland and Scottish coasts.

No protection was fitted, but great attention was paid to silencing the engine, and in the provision of fine waterline endings forward to eliminate bow-lapping noises when approaching the hostile coast.

The first orders were placed in August 1941; by the time the boats began to come into service conditions had changed again and the type was not much used. A total of sixty were completed.

LCP(M)s were originally known as 'Cobles', then 'Viking Craft' – finally LCPMs.

LCP(L) (Landing Craft, Personnel – Large)

Before Lease-Lend there was a British supply mission in Washington, and the Admiralty naturally tried to meet some of their outstanding demands through this channel. It was not found practicable to get craft to British design, but it was

LCP(M) as designed

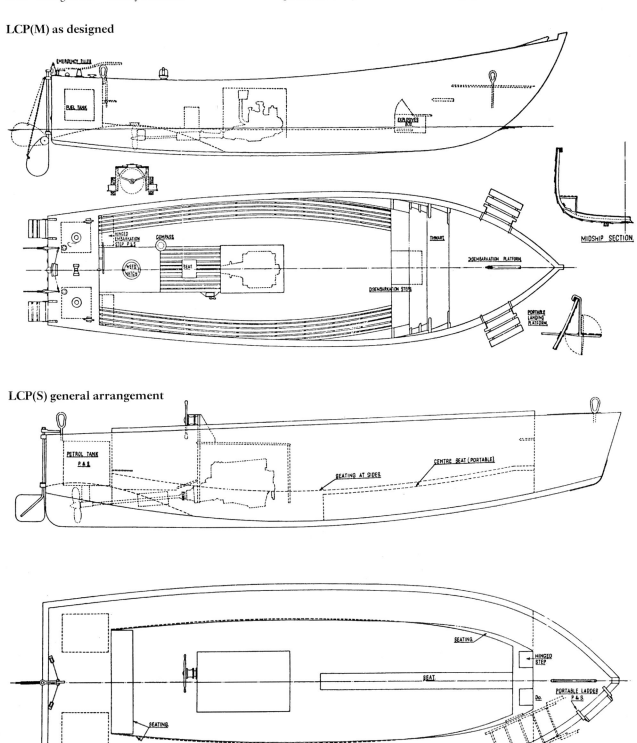

LCP(S) general arrangement

found that Higgins of New Orleans had a standard product which would be useful. This was the Eureka, a hard-chine motor boat about 37ft long fitted with a Kermath engine of 225bhp and capable of a speed of 18kts in the light condition. These boats could carry about thirty men, and, although the speed was very much reduced in the loaded condition, and they had no protection, it was considered that they would be of great use as raiding craft. An initial order was placed for fifty, the first being delivered in October 1940.

Slight modifications were made to the craft to enable them to meet British requirements more fully (eg the slinging arrangements) and the boats were a great success.

Several follow-on orders were placed and when the Lease-Lend Act was passed, very large demands were laid.

When the US entered the war they were very impressed with these assault craft and, after introducing a light personnel ramp in the bow (this idea being borrowed from the LCA), adopted them in service as Landing Craft, Personnel – Ramped – LCP(R).

LCP(S) (Landing Craft, Personnel – Small)

Early in 1942, before LCA production had been organised and before US aid became fully effective, it was decided to augment the assault craft programme by the provision of 'second flight boat', later known as LCP(S). These boats were

such that they could be lifted by LCA davits and stowed on deck and also capable of being lifted by the general run of merchant ship davits, either of the gravity or luffing types. This limited their length to 28ft 6in. They were of simple construction, hard chine, plywood planked, and were propelled by a single 60-90hp LCA engine. The crew was two, and thirty fully equipped troops could be carried.

Most of the boats were built by non-shipyard labour in building contractors' shops and the first deliveries of the 200 ordered were made in August 1942, and production continued until October 1944.

Some of these boats were specially fitted up for ambulance service and were known as water ambulances – WA – but in the main were not used in the manner originally planned. They were, however, widely used as general service harbour craft.

LCI(L) (Landing Craft, Infantry – Large)

In 1942, when the whole of western Europe was occupied, it was decided to carry out some large-scale raids from a home base. Various demands were, therefore, put forward for giant raiding craft, as they were originally called. A firm requirements was produced in April 1942 for a boat to carry 200 fully equipped men, as against the thirty-five of the LCA; to have a speed of 17kts, and draughts not much greater than the LCA.

Landing Craft Infantry (Large) 257. A very successful craft designed and built in large numbers in the USA following a sketch by Barnaby of Thornycroft. This particular craft has had a number of light derricks fitted as a store carrier.

General arrangement of an LCI((L)

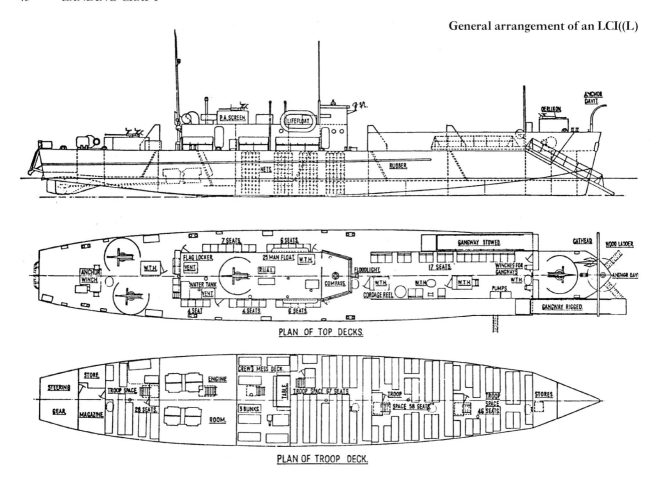

PLAN OF TOP DECKS.

PLAN OF TROOP DECK.

Thornycrofts made some early investigations into wooden craft but it was finally agreed that steel hulls would be necessary if the draught requirement as to be met. This would have meant conflict with destroyer building, so US help was sought and before the end of 1942 they produced the all-welded LCI(L) to a British sketch design.

Principal particulars were:

Length (overall)	158ft 6in
Beam	23ft 8in
Loaded displacement	384 tons
Power	1440bhp
Speed	14kts
Beaching draught F	4ft 9in
A	6ft 6in
No of troops	182 (210 in later vessels)
Crew	3 officers, 21 men

More than 540 of these craft were produced in the USA and though they were never used quite in the manner originally intended, they were used for nearly everything else.

LCI(S) (Landing Craft, Infantry – Small)

Concurrently with the production of LCI(L) the staff requirements were reduced so that it would

be possible to build some wooden craft of this type in the UK.

The help of the Fairmile organisation was sought, and after attempts to modify the Fairmile 'B' craft it was decided to produce a new design.

The principal particulars were:

Length (overall)	105ft 1in
Beam	21ft 5in
Loaded displacement	110 tons
Power	1140bhp (unsupercharged)
Endurance	500 miles at full speed
Speed	14½kts
Beaching draughts F	3ft 3in
A	3ft 10in
Number of troops	6 officers, 96 men
Crew	2 officers, 15 men
Armament	2 Oerlikons amidships

The equipment for these craft included four light gangways over the bow, CSA smoke apparatus, stowage for eighteen bicycles, life-saving apparatus.

In spite of the light scantlings, the craft carried very heavy personnel loads and also a considerable weight of protection in the form of 10lb bullet-proof plating as 'scales'.

The original order for twenty-five of these craft was increased to fifty in July 1942.

Vehicle Carriers

LCM1 (Landing Craft, Mechanised – Mk 1)

This series of craft began with MLC1 and MLC10. Towards the end of August 1938 requirements were put forward by ISTDC for a steel craft to carry a 14 tons tank at about 7kts, and to have a lifting weight of not more than 20 tons. That is, the craft was to have the principal virtues of MLC10 but with higher speed. It was further decided that this new design, originally known as MLC20, should have screw propulsion.

Thornycrofts prepared the detailed design in May 1939, and a prototype craft was ordered. This craft was completed and carried out successful trials in February 1940.

Principal dimensions were:

Length (overall)	44ft 8in
Beam	14ft 0in
Loaded displacement	35 tons
Hoisting weight	21 tons
Power	120bhp

Speed		7½kts
Beaching draughts	F	2ft 6in
	A	3ft 6in
Crew		6 men, 1 officer to 3 craft

During trials a speed of 7½kts was obtained on 33½ tons with 2050rpm.

Circle diameter 30yds in 36 seconds P and S. Metacentric height 2.45ft.

A total of fifty craft were ordered by October 1940 and altogether 536 were built before the end of the war.

It is interesting to note that at the time of Dunkirk this prototype was the only craft we had capable of carrying a tank and beaching, and was the beginning of our invasion fleet proper.

It was found that this type of work was extremely inconvenient for ordinary shipyard facilities which were urgently required for other tasks, and later these boats were built in large numbers by the Great Western Railway Works at Swindon and the Southern Railway Works at Eastleigh. These companies developed a technique quite different from that of the shipbuilders, and from 1942 onwards they were followed by various structural firms.

Average cost was about £5800 per craft.

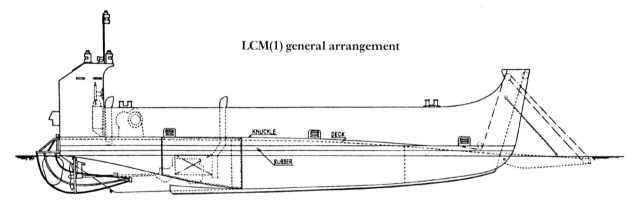

LCM(1) general arrangement

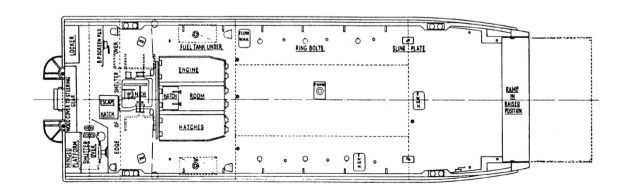

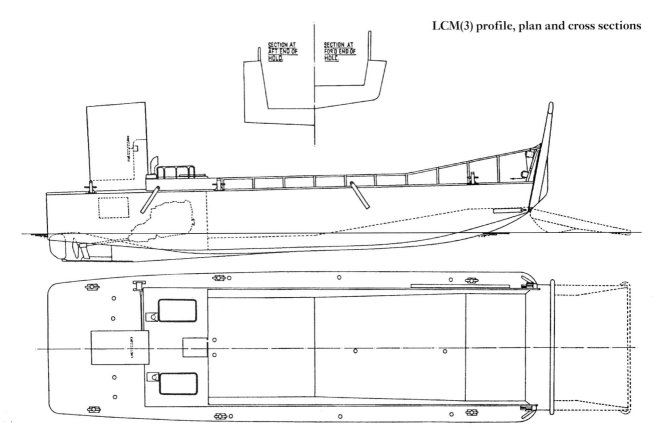

LCM(3) (**Landing Craft, Mechanised – Mk 3**)
This craft was a development of American MLCs which had been converted by Higgins of New Orleans for the US Marine Corps, from a shallow draught tug building for the Peruvian Government.

When a British mission visited the US towards the end of 1941 they realised immediately that with very slight modification these MLCs could be used for 30 tons tanks. Accordingly orders for 150 craft were placed under the Lease-Lend agreement. After trials the US authorities were convinced of the superiority of these craft over their own version of the LCM(1) and, from that date, the LCM(3) became standard, and thousands were built in America for Allied use.

They were all-welded, double-hulled craft capable of carrying a 16 ton tank.

Principal particulars were:

Length (overall)	50ft 0in
Beam	14ft 0in
Loaded displacement	52 tons
Hoisting weight	22 tons
Power	330bhp
Speed	8½kts
Beaching draughts { F	3ft 6in
A	4ft 6in
Crew	3 men, 1 officer to 3 craft

The fundamental difference between the LCM(1) and the LCM(3) was in the fact that the former was really a powered pontoon with bulwarks, with the load carried on the pontoon deck; whilst in the latter the load was carried on the inner bottom resulting in a very low centre of gravity, but corresponding increase in stability.

The LCM(3) carried a load of over twice that carried by LCM(1) on about the same light weight.

LCM(7) (**Landing Craft, Mechanised – Mk 7**)
In November 1943 DNC received draft staff requirements for a new type of landing craft to supplement the existing LCM(1) and LCM(3). As Thornycrofts had designed the LCM(1), they were asked by DNC to prepare the designs for this new craft. The limitations and requirements originally given could not be met and modifications were introduced.

The main requirement was for a craft to carry a 40 ton tank or bulldozer at about 10kts.

The principal dimensions of the design eventually developed known as LCM(7) were:

Length (overall)	60ft 3in
Beam	16ft 0in
Loaded displacement	63 tons
Hoisting weight	28 tons
Power	290bhp

Profile and plan of an LCM(7)

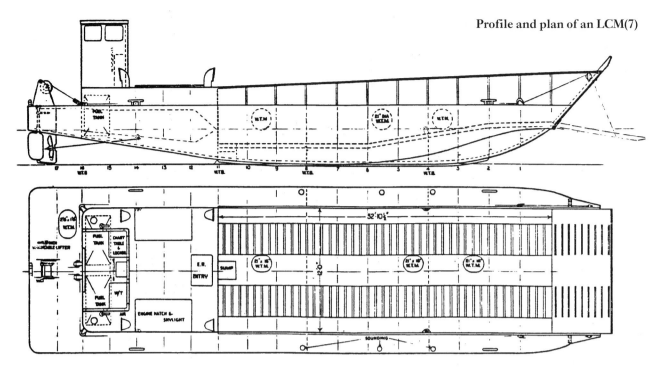

Speed		9.8kts
Beaching draughts	F	3ft 8in
	A	3ft 8in
Crew		3 men, 1 officer to
		3 craft

As originally designed by Thornycroft it was intended to fit two Hudson Invader petrol engines with 2:1 reduction gear; owing to production difficulties, however, direct drive was fitted in some of the craft and the estimated speed thereby reduced a little.

In order to keep the weight to a minimum an all-welded craft was first designed, but it became evident in view of the numbers required that some would have to be built by contractors unable to produce all-welded craft.

Three prototype craft were constructed – all welded, riveted, and a composite craft.

In April 1944 approval was given for the construction of 250 craft, and 140 had been built when construction stopped on the cessation of hostilities.

LCT(1) (Landing Craft, Tank – Mk 1)

Towards the end of June 1940, after the evacuation of Dunkirk, the Prime Minister asked the Admiralty to consider designs for craft for the carriage and landing of tanks (AFVs). This request started an entirely new series of craft and ships for Combined Operations. It was quite evident that modern tanks were too heavy to be carried in 'hoistable' MLCs as the 25 ton 'light' and the 40 ton 'heavy' were to be the basic standard designs. It was decided, therefore, that new craft should be designed capable of carrying three of the heavier tanks at 10kts for landing in 2ft 6in of water on a 1 in 35 beach.

A design was produced by DNC and as the form suggested for this landing craft differed considerably from any previous seagoing craft, four models were tested at AEW Haslar to forms proposed by Fairfields, Stephens, and DNC(2). DNC's second form was found to be the best and the following points were recorded regarding barge forms:
(i)   flow occurs along buttocks rather than level lines.
(ii) cut-ups forward and aft should be as long as possible.
(iii) the prow-bow should be of minimum width and slope.
(iv) an angular curve of areas could not be avoided and eddy motion was found at the stern.
The resistance from all sources was, however, not as great as might have been expected.

Principal particulars were:

Length (overall)		151ft 11in
Beam		29ft 1in
Loaded displacement		372 tons
Power (2 engines)		700bhp total
Speed		10kts
Fuel carried		15 tons giving
		1100 miles
		endurance
Beaching draught	F	3ft 0in
	A	5ft 9in

Tank load	3 Churchills,
	6 Valentines
Crew	2 officers,
	10 men

The side plating of these craft was 15lb DKM plating[7] and the remainder of the hull 15lb MS generally. The equipment fitted included:

- 1-10 ton capstan
- 1-10cwt kedge anchor
- 1-20ton/hr bilge rump (in ER)
- 1-10in searchlight
- 1-15kW generator
- 2-3 ton winches with 2in FSWR to raise bow doors

The craft were propelled by two Hall Scott petrol engines, originally intended for coastal force craft, and twin propellers 3ft 3in diameter at 900rpm.

Trials were run on the first two craft completed and the time to lower the ramp was found to be 8 seconds and 2½ minutes to raise. The first tank was ashore 20 seconds after the craft touched the beach.

The craft were found to be 50 tons heavier than the estimated weight. Owing to the shallow draught the vessels were found to be rather difficult to steer.

After the design had been approved, and while the first twenty craft were being built, it was decided that in the first instance the craft would have to operate from the Eastern Mediterranean; arrangements were made for the raft to be built in four sections. After trials the sections were parted and shipped out as deck cargo.

A total of thirty LCT(1) was constructed.

LCT(2)

These craft were developed on almost the same lines as LCT(1) but with 2ft more beam and provision for three engines instead of two.[8]

The armament remained the same, ie 2-2pdrs.

The carrying capacity was three 49 tons or 6 18 tons tanks or 250 tons miscellaneous cargo.

A total of seventy-three LCT(2) was built, thirty-two with diesel engines.

About this time two new developments were put in hand, one of these was to arrange for the production of suitable diesel engines for future landing craft, and the other came with the realisation that enormous numbers of landing craft would ultimately be required, and that the continued use of existing shipyard facilities was uneconomical.

The Paxman 500bhp was developed and its production expanded, whilst on the other hand the structural engineering industry was co-opted to prefabricate the hulls, and then to arrange for their final erection and completion in disused shipyards especially opened for the purpose. This method, which proved to be extremely successful, was economical not only in shipyard labour and plant but in management as well.

LCT(3)

Early in 1941 Combined Operations asked for landing craft of larger tank carrying capacity; at the same time E in C drew attention to the necessity of keeping the programme inside the Paxman diesel engine capacity. LCT(2) were by this time being constructed in four sections, the midship parallel body section being 32ft long.

[7] Baker realised that bow doors will always leak and introduced measures to limit such flooding. If the vehicle deck was flooded the craft would still float – upright – an example which RO-RO ferry designers might copy.

[8] Buxton, I L. Landing Craft Tanks Marks 1 & 2. Warships 119 et seq. World Ship Society, Kendal 1994.

LCT(3) as designed

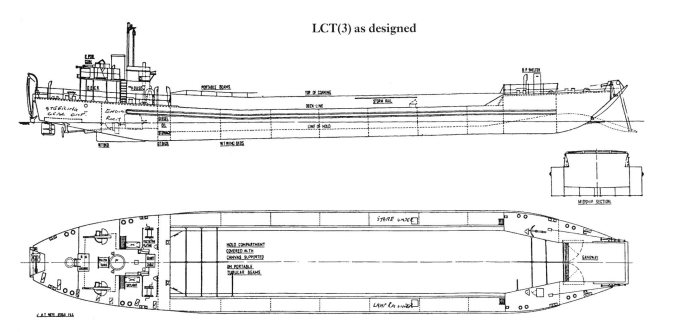

DNC suggested that a craft be built incorporating two midship parallel body sections instead of one as in the LCT(2), and only two engines fitted per craft instead of three.

Actually a LCT(1) being built at Messrs John Brown was lengthened by 32ft and trials carried out in April 1941. A speed of 11¼kts was obtained on a displacement of 480 tons, draughts were 2ft 11in forward and 5ft 5in aft. (Light displacement 280 tons and fuel 20 tons and load 180 tons.)

Speed, manoeuvrability and carrying capacity were found satisfactory and it was decided that future LCTs would be of this lengthened type with two engines. They were known as LCT(3).

DNC prepared the design for these craft which were constructed in five sections.

Principal particulars were:

Length (overall)	191ft 11in
Beam	31ft 1in
Loaded displacement	640 tons
Power	920bhp
Speed	10kts
Beaching draughts ⎰ F	3ft 10in
(with Churchill tanks) ⎱ A	7ft 0in
Tank load	5 Churchills or
	11 Valentines
	or
	11 Shermans
Crew	2 officers, 10
	men
Armament	2-2pdr or
	2 Oerlikons

Although built in sections for the reasons above, LCT(3) were fully assembled as this class was intended for the Cross-Channel Operation.

A total of 235 LCT(3) was completed; this total included seventy-one craft, to slightly modified

plans, which were built by the main shipbuilders during the winter of 1943/4. In this version Sterling Admiral petrol engines were fitted instead of Paxman diesels due to a shortage of the latter. Separate self-sealing petrol tanks were also fitted to give an endurance of 700 miles at 9½kts.

During October 1942 it was decided to fit all new construction LCTs for service in the tropics. The tropical service arrangements included the fitting of single awnings, insulation in accommodation, wheelhouse, etc, improved ventilation, DARs, etc.

The petrol-engined craft, being intended for service in Home waters, were not fitted for tropical service.

LCT(4)

In August 1941 the need for even larger numbers of the bigger craft were again expressed; it was also decided that still shallower draught would be essential. At this time the original idea behind the LCT had been expanded and ships for landing tanks had been proved practicable. For the future, then, there were two possibilities:

(i) to build shallow draught tank landing craft capable of making cross-channel trips;
(ii) to build tank landing ships and use landing craft for use between ship and shore.

Item (i) seemed more promising and to meet such a requirement the LCT(4) was designed. The class was developed to suit the facilities of the structural engineer and their yards as then laid out. No recognised shipbuilder was ever employed on any of these craft or on the drawings.

To help production the armament and protection was omitted, though it was introduced in the later ships.

A Landing Craft Tank (IV) seen after the war as a servicing craft. This photograph has been selected to show the configuration adopted by Baker in all his vehicle carriers. There is a buoyancy space either side abreast the vehicle deck so that, should it be flooded, the craft will still float upright, unlike RO-RO ferries.

Principal particulars:

Length (overall)		187ft 3in
Beam		38ft 8in
Loaded displacement		586 tons
Power		920bhp
Speed		10kts
Tank load		6 Churchills or
		9 Valentines or
		9 Shermans
Beaching draughts	F	3ft 6in
	A	4ft 7in
Crew		2 officers, 10 men

To meet the requirement for a very shallow draught, the LCT(4) was constructed with very light scantlings as compared with earlier types. They were originally required to operate in seas up to force 4 only. When the requirements for armament (two Oerlikons) was re-introduced the craft were strengthened, but much later in the war the need for such LCTs in the Far East led to them being tropicalised and further strengthened. This strengthening was effected by raising the side deck to the height of the old bulwark and fitting heavier plating here and to the bottom.

The various additions made to these craft considerably increased the draught but the ships were still quite light.

787 of these LCTs were built.

LCT(5)

This craft was designed by Bu-ships on the general lines of a proposal by Thornycrofts for a small LCT more or less double ended[9] which could load from an LST and discharge ashore.

Principal particulars were:

Length (overall)		112ft 4in
Beam		32ft 9in
Loaded displacement		311 tons
Power		675bhp
Speed		8kts
Beaching draughts	F	2ft 11in
	A	4ft 7in
Tank load		4 Churchills or
		7 Valentines
Crew		2 officers, 11 men
Armament		2 Oerlikons

These LCTs were designed in conjunction with the parent LST so that the smaller could be carried as deck cargo on the larger.

The LCT(5) were all built in the US mainly by non-shipbuilding firms.

LCT(6)

This was a US version of the LCT(5) incorporating a double-end arrangement, which it was again thought would facilitate working between ship and shore.

LCT(7)

This was another purely American development, and was later known as the LSM. It was 203ft 6in x 34ft 6in x 1095 tons deep displacement, with a ship-shape bow, the main features being similar to early types – but improved as regards speed and seakeeping qualities.

LCT(8)

In October 1943 DNC received draft requirements for an improved type of LCT for use in the Far Eastern theatre; the early types of landing craft, intended for comparatively near-at-hand operations, were not suitable for sustained operations in this new theatre.

An attempt was made in this design to combine the best features of the earlier LCTs and, in addition, to increase speed, endurance, and seakeeping qualities. The best features of the LCT(3) were its relative robustness and depth of girder; the best feature of LCT(4) were its shallow draught, light construction and its suitability for production by the facilities available. To improve speed, the power was doubled and this new craft was propelled by four Paxman 460shp engines geared two per shaft; seakeeping was improved by increase in depth and by the fitting of a ship-shape bow as in the LST and LSM.

DNC prepared the sketch design, sheer drawing and structural sections, etc., Thornycrofts prepared the specification and normal detailed structural fitting-out drawings, while three engineering firms between them prepared the building drawings for both riveted and welded vessels.

Principal particulars were:

Length (overall)		225ft 0in
Beam		39ft 0in
Loaded displacement		895 tons
Power		1840bhp (limited
		to a max 1600)
Speed		12.6kts
Beaching draughts	F	3ft 9in
	A	5ft 0in
Tank load		8 Shermans
Crew		Naval 3 officers,
		19 men
		Military 6 officers,
		36 men
Armament		3 Oerlikons

Protection included 15lb D1 HT around bridge and for the zarebas.

Accommodation was provided on board for the crews of the tanks when embarked, and all accom-

9 Barnaby's original double ended design eventually appeared as the LCT (6)

General arrangement of an LCT(8)

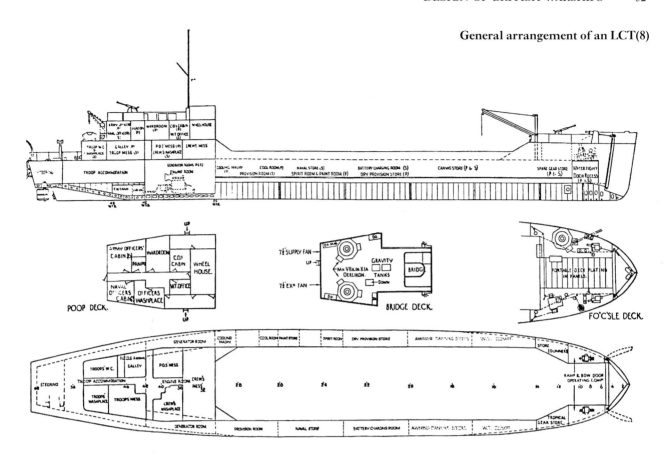

modation spaces were ventilated and insulated in accordance with the latest practices.

In these craft power was provided for operating the bow ramp and bow doors, the machinery being specially designed for the job.

A total of 187 LCT(8) were ordered but on the cessation of hostilities 157 were cancelled. The first LCT(8) was completed in June 1945, trials were held and the craft considered satisfactory.

Support Craft

LCS(M) (Landing Craft, Support – Medium)
The requirement for the first support craft was put forward in 1938, concurrently with the requirement for assault landing craft. The underlying idea was that the support and assault craft would have the same hulls which could be carried at the same davits, but that whilst the assault craft would carry men, the support boats would 'cover' the others on their run in.

Fleming's and Thornycroft's original LCAs were modified to form the prototype support landing craft (originally SLC). They were armed with 2-½in machine guns on tubular mounts, a smoke mortar and two light machine guns. As a result of trials carried out on these craft, a number

of LCAs on order were fitted out for use in this support role. They became known as LCS(M)(1).

In the Autumn of 1941 a requirement that gun crews should be protected led to the substitution of a twin 0.5in power-operated turret for the pedestal mountings and with this change in armament the well of the craft was decked in, except in way of the smoke mortar. Navigational aids and smoke-producing apparatus were later provided and the modified craft became known as LCS(M)(2).

It was gradually realised that too much attention had been given to maintaining LCA features with the result that LCS(M)(2) was not as satisfactory as had been hoped. In 1942 the boat was redesigned, keeping the same armament and power unit.

Principal particulars LCS(M)(3):

Length (overall)	41ft 2in
Beam	10ft 1in
Loaded displacement	13.3 tons
Power	130bhp
Crew	1 officer, 10 men

Production of this type continued until the end of the war.

A total of 196 LCS(M) were built including 166 LCS(M)(3).

LCS(LL)(1) (Landing Craft, Support – Large, Mk 1)

The first shipborne craft was derived from the LCM – the next step, which was first suggested in December 1940, came in the same way from the LCM. The new craft was at first known as the Heavy Support Craft (HSC) and the intention was to provide a boat capable of dealing with a tank, whilst being of a size that could be carried in the ordinary trooper, ie a weight limitation of 20 tons.

A design was produced by Thornycrofts and in all five craft were built.

Trials of the first craft were carried out in April 1943, and showed that the project was really too ambitious.

Principal particulars were:

Length overall	46ft 11in
Beam	12ft 7in
Displacement	24.5 tons

Power	330bhp
Speed	10¾kts
Crew	1 officer, 12 men
Armament	1-2pdr
	1-Besa in Daimler turret
	1-4in smoke mortar
	2-½in Vickers machine guns
Protection	15lb topsides, bulkhead and turret fidley 10lb to deck and top of turret fidley
Steering position	Sides 20lb
	Top 12lb

LCS(L)(2)

In the spring of 1942 it was evident that the proposals for the rearmament of LCS(L)(1) were impracticable, and it was decided to convert the larger LCI(S) into support craft.

Landing Craft Support (Large) MkI. An unsuccessful attempt to mount a tank armament on a light wooden hull for close support of landings.

Landing Craft Support (Large) MkII. A heavier armament on a bigger hull but still with little protection.

Landing Craft Flak Mk II 4. With 8 single pom-poms and 4 Oerlikons it was a powerful deterrent to low level air attack.

Their armament was still of the tank type and their protection was very meagre. It is interesting to note that these craft had wooden hulls.

Principal particulars:

Length overall	105ft 1in
Beam	21ft 5in
Displacement	116 tons
Power	1140bhp
Speed	14kts
Armament	1-QF 6pdr (tank turret)
	1-4in BL smoke mortar
	2-Oerlikons
	2-½in Vickers machine guns
Protection	10lb D1 HT
Crew	2 officers, 23 men

A total of ten landing craft were converted from LCI(S).

LCF(1) was really a small monitor, her armament being equivalent to that of ships three or four times her size.

Principal particulars:

Length (overall)	159ft 11in
Beam	31ft 1in
Displacement	539 tons
Power (diesel)	920bhp
Speed	11kts
Armament	2-4in twin QF mountings
	3-20mm Oerlikons
Protection	Bridge 15lb non-magnetic
	Zarebas 15lb D1 HT
Crew	4 officers, 70 men

These craft were very congested.

Principal particulars of the LCF(2) were:

Length overall	159ft 11in
Beam	31ft 1in
Displacement	470 tons (light)
Power (diesel)	920bhp

[10] A number of designs for small monitors, including one of composite construction, were considered but none found worth the much higher cost compared with LCG.

Speed	11kts
Armament	8-2pdr pom-poms
	4-20mm Oerlikons
Crew	4 officers, 63 men

The LCF(2) conversion was not as spectacular as that of LCF(1) but she proved to be the prototype for a number of subsequent LCF specially provided for A/A defence.

LCF(3) were substantially the same as LCF(2) but being converted from LCT(3) had improved accommodation. The arcs of fire were also improved, and increased protection fitted.

In September 1942 the armament was altered to eight Oerlikons and four 2pdrs and bulk ammunition stowage provided in wing compartments.

Later LCT(4) were used for conversion giving LCF(4).

LCF were not required for the Far Eastern campaign and in consequence none was fitted for tropical service.

In all forty-four craft were converted to LCF.

LCG(L) (Landing Craft, Gun – Large)

In the autumn of 1942 when the Sicilian operations were being planned, a requirement arose for a number of support craft to engage shore batteries and to give supporting fire on beach targets by direct fire. Monitors[10] were unlikely to be available and destroyers and other small warships were too vulnerable, so it was decided to convert LCT(3) for this purpose by fitting them with 4.7in guns ex destroyers.

In view of the limited time available the fittings were the simplest possible; the gun supports were built up from the tank deck level and the guns were mounted at the wing level on islands.

Twenty-three craft were completed.

After conversion these craft had a displacement of 491 tons.

LCG(L)(4) general arrangement

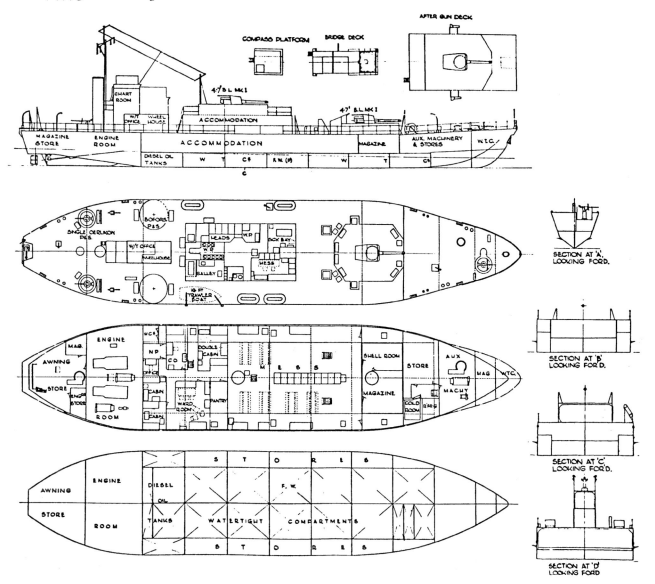

Armament	2-4.7in QF guns
	2-4 single Oerlikons
Protection	25lb DW
Crew	3 officers, 44 men

Subsequently the flimsier LCT(4) was converted to LCG(L)(4) on similar lines; later, for the Far Eastern campaign, a more elaborate conversion was made. In its final form LCG(L)(4) had a ship-shape bow, 2in or 1in armour over vitals and considerably improved accommodation.

A total of ten LCG(L)(4) was built.

LCG(M) (Landing Craft, Gun – Medium)

The invasion of Sicily was only a prelude to the invasion of NW Europe, so at the same time as the LCG(M) was being provided, much thought was being given to the problem of support fire in a full-scale invasion. A joint Naval/Military requirement led to the design produced by DNC for the LCG(M).

The military requirements were that the craft was to meet a tank or pill-box on equal terms, and be able to give artillery cover to troops ashore up to ordinary artillery ranges. The Naval requirement was that the craft was to be capable of making ocean passages. The resulting design was an unusual one. Arrangements were made for the craft, by flooding tanks, to ground itself on a beach, thereby improving its protection and enabling fire to be directed from a fixed platform to a map reference; a special 460ton/hr pump and the gun turrets were designed for this purpose.

Messrs J Brown developed the design, but the whole of the vessels was done by structural engineering firms.

An LCG(M) 1 with armament as designed

Principal particulars were:

Length overall	154ft 6in
Beam	22ft 4½in
Displacement	380 tons
Power (Paxman diesel)	1000bhp
Armament	2-17pdr or 2-25pdr (naval mtgs)
	2-single Oerlikons
Protection	80lb, 40lb, and 15lb
Crew	3 officers, 30 men

The first craft was delivered in June 1944.

The requirement for support craft in the Far East was different and in later LCG(M) the grounding requirement was given up, the protection reduced and additional anti-personnel armament fitted.

Of the seventy-two LCG(M) ordered, fifty-six were completed. The remainder were cancelled on the cessation of hostilities.

LCT(R) (Landing Craft, Tank – Rocket)

To satisfy a requirement for some new form of close support during the initial stages of an opposed landing, it was decided to fit out an LCT(2) with about 800 rocket projectors fixed in bearing and elevation. The rockets to be used were at this time in the development stage, and there was considerable uncertainty about the heat generated on firing and its effect on adjacent massed rockets. DNC was informed that each rocket would develop a momentary deck pressure of 140lb/in² over an area of 40sq in. For 800 rockets fired simultaneously this gave a total thrust of 2000 tons. It was felt that such loading was unlikely to develop in practice and the design proceeded on that assumption, subsequent trials proving the assumption to be correct. LCT125 was selected for conversion as a prototype and was fitted with 792 projectors, a complete reload for all projectors

was stowed in magazines below the upper deck. An insulated cabinet was fitted on the bridge for the fire control operation.

Seven LCT(2) were converted to LCT(R).

Subsequently thirty-six LCT(3) were also converted to LCT(R).

Principal particulars of LCT(R)(3) were:

Length overall	192ft 0in
Beam	31ft 1in
Displacement	560 tons
Power	1000bhp
Armament	1080 Mk I projectors or 936 Mk II projectors
	2-single Oerlikons
Protection	15lb, and 20lb D1 HT
Crew	2 officers, 15 men

LCS(R) (Landing Craft, Support – Rocket)

The success of the LCT(R) led to the suggestion that LCG(M) armed with rockets would be worthwhile, especially as they were such good sea boats. A design was prepared and of the sixty-four craft ordered only two were completed.

LCT(A) (Landing Craft, Tank – Armoured)

In August 1943 trials were carried out with three Sherman tanks mounted in an LCT(5) for the purpose of converting the craft into a shallow draught gunboat. The trial was satisfactory and sixty-nine LCT95) were converted to LCT(A).

The craft were armoured with 2in NC vertically and 1in NC horizontally over the engine room, fuel tanks and wheelhouse. Platforms were fitted to carry two Centaur tanks each mounting a 4in gun. Engines were removed from the tanks to enable additional ammunition to be carried.

These craft were not really a success and after 'Overlord' the armour, tanks and platforms were removed and the craft reverted to their normal function of LCT(5).

Conversions (Other than Support Craft)[11]

LCN (Landing Craft, Navigation)

In November 1943 DNC received requirements for a navigational leader for landing craft. It was also to be capable of carrying out offshore hydrographic reconnaissance off the beaches after the initial assault.

The sketch design was produced by DNC and Thornycrofts prepared detailed drawings and fitted out the prototype which was an LCP(L) modified for this service. In all forty US type LCP(L) were converted.

The navigational equipment included standard and steering compasses; echo sounding; taut wire measuring gear (9 miles); bottom log; trainable A/S oscillator for detection; Loran or Decca receiver; chart work facilities; radar with PPI.

LCH (Landing Craft, Headquarters)

These were LCI(L) fitted out as headquarters ships. This involved fitting a foremast, additional accommodation provided for six officers, eight POs and forty-eight ratings in addition to the crew, offices, sick bay. A total of twenty-one craft were converted for this service.

LCQ (Landing Craft, Administrative)

These were LCI(L) of the 351 or later class converted to accommodate Squadron Commanders and flotilla staffs.

Principal requirements were:- accommodation for fourteen officers, eight POs and forty-eight ratings in addition to the crew, offices, sick bay. A total of twenty-one craft were converted for this service.

LCI (Smoke)

In December 1944 it was decided to fit six LCI(L) of 1-350 class as smoke makers. The apparatus was required to be capable of making smoke continuously for twelve hours; this necessitated provision of CSA and petrol storage tanks. Acid tanks were fitted in the troop spaces and a petrol stowage arranged in the double bottom. Acid pipes were led along the upper deck to nozzles in the stern of the craft and acid discharged by means of compressed air introduced into the fitting of an air compressor, increased accommodation, and store spaces. The craft were concurrently fitted for tropical service.

Of the six craft earmarked for conversion only two were completed.

LCT(E) (Landing Craft, Tank (Emergency Repair))

In January 1944 it was proposed to convert twelve LCTs to repair landing craft on beaches in the Far East. They were required to carry out temporary repairs to hulls of major and minor landing craft and maintenance of landing craft machinery and electrical equipment.

Similar conversions were later made for craft to repair harbour service craft and military craft, and

[11] There were many other conversions, some listed in Ref 4. Others were converted locally for special jobs, eg an LCF converted in Italy to mobile detention quarters.

LCT(E) general arrangement

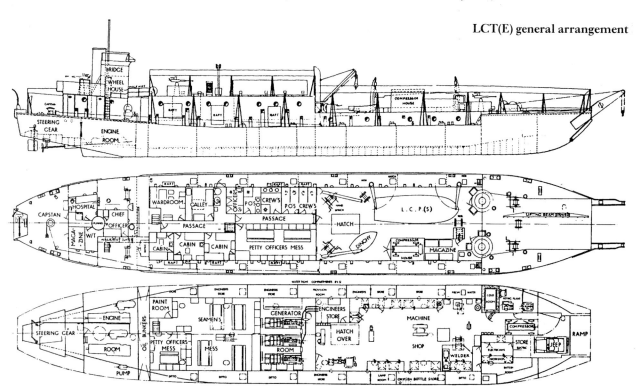

were termed Naval Service Craft, Large – MSC(L) – and Military Floating Workshops – MFW.

The requirements provided special fendering and securing arrangements for craft berthed alongside, and dynamo power to operate the craft's service and repair plant with 50 per cent reserve.

Workshop equipment included 13in and 4½in lathes; carpenter's, engineer's and welder's benches; drilling and valve facing machinery; universal woodworking machine; blacksmith's and coppersmith's slabs; and air compressor.

The other particulars were generally the same as for the LCT(3).

By September 1945 ten LCT(E) and three NSC(L) had been completed; the MFWs were cancelled.

LCT(S/V)

These craft were required to deal with stranded landing craft on the beaches in the Far East and also to be suitable for normal duty as an LCT.

A design was prepared by DNC and an LCT(4) was selected for conversion.

D of S/V proposed that two 4 ton bower anchors should be carried. As it was found impracticable to stow these large anchors in an LCT and also retain the bow door, which was essential if the craft was to function as an LCT, the LCT requirement was withdrawn.

The work of conversion included decking in the forecastle and plating up the bow; fitting hawsepipes for the 4 ton anchors; fitting diesel-driven capstans, bollards, eyeplates, snatchblocks, wire reels, etc.; strops for connecting to the stranded craft and stroppers, etc. were also provided.

Only one ship was actually completed.

Barge Conversions

In a communication dated 28 March 1942 the Chief of Combined Operations informed the secretaries of the Admiralty and Ministry of War Transport that the Chiefs of Staffs Committee had given approval for 1000 open swim barges to be requisitioned immediately, converted for Combined Operations use, and concentrated in south coast ports.

Thames dumb swim-ended barges were taken up for conversion to motor transport carriers. These barges were flat-bottomed for full length of hold and the flat was carried up from the fore bulkhead of the hold to the deck at bow, and from the after bulkhead of the hold to the deck at the

stern. Part of the after swim for a width of 9ft 0in from a point just above the waterline was cut away to accommodate a hinged ramp for the embarkation of vehicles. The craft were intended to be towed to the beaches, anchored and left to dry out with the ebb tide, but owing to the difficulty of finding towing vessels whose draught would permit close approach to the beach and the difficulty of drifting the barges in or using sweeps, a certain number were fitted with Ford car engines and later Chrysler Marine engines.

Cementing depots were opened and most of the barges passed through them for the fitting of 4in of cement protection in the hold to 4ft up the sides; after this they were taken into a pool and drawn on as required for conversion.

To speed the conversions approximately sixty main contractors (mostly in the Thames area) were employed.

The barges varied considerably in size but average dimensions were as follows:

Overall length	70ft 0in
Overall breadth	21ft 0in
Depth	8ft 6in
Length of hold	46ft 0in
Breadth of hold	15ft 6in

As time passed additional requirements arose and various 'specialist barges' were developed by conversions of the original MT barges. Details of 'specialist barges', which were all power driven, are given below.

LBW – Military Oil Barge

These barges were designed by DNC and built under Admiralty supervision to be handed over to the War Office on completion. Their function was to lighter petrol or diesel fuel from tankers in comparatively sheltered waters off ports and in river estuaries during the follow-up states of the invasion. Only one type of fuel was required to be carried in each barge, being carried in a cylindrical tank 30ft long x 12ft diameter, and handled by a power pump.

LBK – Landing Barge Kitchen

In December 1943 a most urgent request was received from ANCXF for ten cooking barges to cook for up to 800 men each during the invasion of Europe. In order to accommodate the equipment, store space and living spaces for the crew, it was necessary to deck in the hold and erect a large superstructure. The resulting barge was very similar in appearance to a Noah's Ark. Due to the extremely short amount of time available (three months was allowed for the preparation of the design and the complete conversion of the barges),

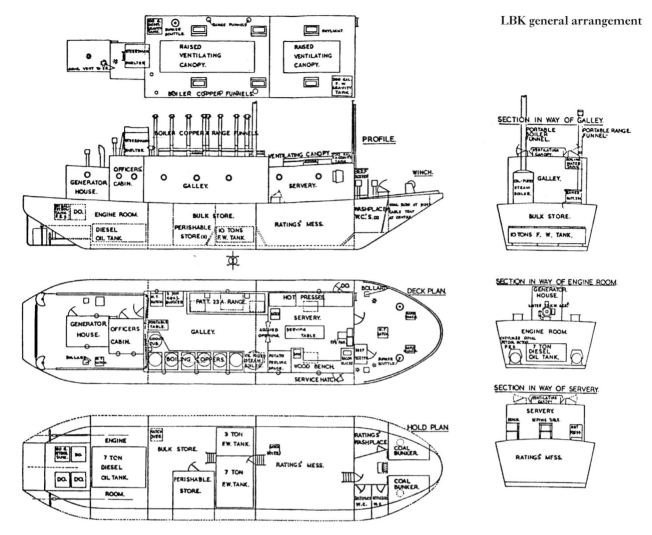

it was impossible to arrange for all the equipment to be suitable for one type of fuel and it was necessary therefore to carry coal, diesel oil, petrol and a Cochrane boiler to supply steam.

The barge was arranged to carry sufficient provisions for one week and one half the hold consisted of a store and the other half contained accommodation for one officer and twenty-two ratings. The galley and servery were contained in the superstructure, the galley being equipped with a pattern 23A range, an oil-fired steam boiler, six 40 gallon boiling coppers with steaming attachments, a set of cook's tubs with steam jets and a boiling water tank. The servery contained all the normal facilities – hot cupboards, dressers, serving tables, sinks, etc.

The craft were highly successful, supplying 1600 men per day at the peak period, the food being issued in hot food containers. They were therefore not only fulfilling their original purpose by supplying cooked meals to the crews of landing craft with no cooking facilities of their own, but were also supplying troops on the beaches.[12]

LBF – Landing Barge Flak

The function of these barges was to provide offshore protection when under way or anchored in the vicinity of the beaches during an assault on an enemy-occupied coast. As a secondary role they were capable of beaching and landing their two 40mm Army Bofors guns by way of the stern ramp so that they could be mounted for use ashore. In addition to the Bofors, six PAC projectiles were mounted. The hold was decked in, a magazine was fitted, a helmsman's shelter aft, and the accommodation allowed for one naval officer, the barge crew of five, guns crews and supply numbers.

LBV(M) – Landing Barge Vehicle (Mechanised)

These barges were simply a mechanised version of the original MT barges. Accommodation was provided in the forward swim for a barge crew of five. Portable hatches were provided at a later date so that the holds could be covered in and the barges used for store carrying.

12 LBK 6 was still in service in 1994. See: Sowden, D A. Warships 119. World Ship Society, Kendal 1994.

LBV(M) profile and plan

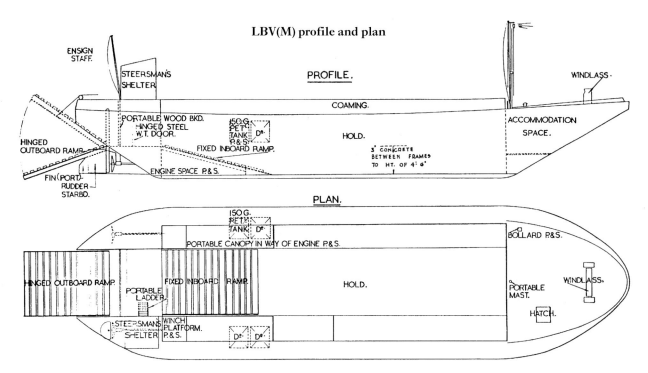

LBE – Landing Barge Emergency (Repair)

These barges were employed to provide emergency repair facilities to damaged landing craft. They were fitted with equipment benches, welding and cutting plant, a mobile workshop lorry, which could be driven out over the ramp if required, and an accommodation for repair staff and crew.

LBO – Landing Barge Oiler

The function of these barges was to provide diesel oil or petrol to landing craft during an assault operation. The fuel was carried in a cylindrical tank 30ft x 9ft diameter fitted in the hold. Originally semi-rotary pumps were fitted but these were later replaced by hand-operated Airpel pumps. The fuelling system was arranged to handle either diesel oil or petrol, four supply points being provided, two each side of the barge. The tanks were protected with 2½in plastic armour.

When Holland was liberated they were engaged in supplying food to the population via the canals. The numbers of craft of different categories which were converted were as follows:

LBV(M)	240
LBW	20
MOB	50
LBE	60
LBF	15
LBO	100
LBK	10

The chief criticisms received were concerning the poor steering qualities of the barges and their inadequate anchor winches. Both of these criticisms are attributable to the shortage of time for conversion. The barges were never intended to be self-propelled and the steering arrangements consisting of a rudder offset to starboard and a fin or budget plate offset to port – had to be considered for each barge separately. The LBKs were fitted with twin rudders and no difficulties were experienced. It was found to be impossible to provide sturdy anchor winches for such a large number of craft without diverting productive capacity from more important work. However, winches surplus to Foxer Gear requirements were fitted, and although not strong enough to haul the craft away from a beach, they were an improvement on the slow barge windlass originally fitted.

While barge conversions of this nature cannot be recommended as assault craft, they certainly provided a means of obtaining support craft of varied types in a very short time.

NL Pontoon Equipment

This equipment was designed and used by the US authorities to provide barges, wharves, causeways, etc., all of which could be built from small standard unit pieces, in the forward areas of an assault operation.

For this purpose, the principal unit consisted of a rectangular all-welded steel tank or pontoon measuring 5ft long x 7ft wide x 5ft deep. A number of these pontoons – 7, 12, 24, 30 being typical numbers – were placed end-to-end to form a string connected together longitudinally by four heavy continuous angle bars, with bolts and interlocking devices, one at each edge of the assembly. The longitudinal angles were provided in standard convenient lengths which could be joined by a 'breech-plug' arrangement. As many such 7ft wide strings as desired could be placed side by side and joined together by a 'link pin' arrangement to form a wide causeway or barge.

Alternative designs of pontoons were provided for inclusion at the ends of a string, viz. scow-ended to facilitate propulsion, or ramp-ended to enable a vehicular load to be discharged from the assembly barge. In the latter case a hinged ramp could be attached to the end of the ramped pontoon formed of small ramps, each capable of being manhandled.

Bollards, fairleads, etc. were attached to the deck of the barge after assembly and formed part of the standard equipment.

In addition to the uses already referred to, the equipment was used by the US authorities to build small floating docks, crane lighters and self-propelled craft; the last-mentioned item involved the use of a specially designed propulsion unit not unlike an outboard motor. British use was mainly confined to causeways and barges and, in a lesser degree, to docks.

Production was begun in the UK by Messrs Williams & Williams of Chester, contact with the Admiralty being made through DNC and a storage and assembly depot was set up in the neighbourhood. At first US plans were followed but, in the course of time, various alterations were made to the design including the simplification of the original rounded scow-end pontoons to one of straight line design and the development of a five-part ramp to supersede the cumbersome wooden design used by the USN.

Ancillary equipment – launching equipment, lifting slings, momentum beaching equipment, anchoring equipment, etc. – was designed and ordered by DNC. To enable the gear to be used in conjunction with British landing ships it was designed quite distinct from the US gear, although on the same general lines.

It became quite clear in the design of LSTs that these vessels would beach on flat beaches with the fore end in water too deep for the vessels to be unloaded. For this reason NL causeways were utilised to bridge the gap between the ship and the shore.

The earliest practice was to carry on the upper deck of certain LSTs two 3 x 24 (3 cells wide and 24 cells long) causeways lashed on specially erected inclined launchways. On approaching the assault area, the lashings were to be removed and the two pontoons launched simultaneously by means of a trigger arrangement.

This method, however, was not used operationally and was superseded by the side-carry method which used a portion of the upper deck for securings leaving a certain amount of deck space for vehicles.

Ships equipped for the side carriage of NL pontoon causeways had a continuous channel bar shelf fitted at each side about 11ft below the upper deck and parallel to it. They carried one 2 x 24 causeway each side. Each causeway had a hinge-bar attached to one of its upper edges which engaged with the ship's side channel. This method was also used in a modified form to transport causeways on the sides of merchant ships.

To launch the causeways into the water from a side-carrying LST, the lashings were removed and the causeways launched simultaneously from both sides by chopping retaining wires. From then onwards they were towed abreast the ship. On arriving off a beach, the momentum of the ship was used to propel one causeway to ground on the beach carrying with it a slack wire which, after the beached causeway had been anchored, was used to haul out the second causeway until it could be secured to the first to complete the causeway from the bows of the ship to the shore.

With the cessation of hostilities the equipment was retained for development purposes.

CHAPTER 19

Landing Ships

[1] Brown, D K . Sir Rowland Baker, RCNC. *Warship* 1995, London 1995

[2] Maund, L E H. Assault from the Sea. London, 1949. A background to the planning of combined operations.

[3] Ladd, J D. Assault from the Sea 1939-1945. Newton Abbott 1976. General history of the operations and the craft.

[4] Allied Landing Craft of World War Two. Originally a wartime recognition book, republished London, 1985. Even lists some craft that DNC - and Baker - never heard of.

[5] Macdermott, B. Ships Without Names. London, 1992.

[6] The Glens had already been converted to heavily armed and armoured store ships for Operation Catherine. See: Brown, D K. Operation Catherine. *Warship* 40

Editorial Note

Most of the ships in this chapter, too, were the creation of Rowland Baker[1] with Ken Barnaby contributing the Landing Ship Stern Chute. The LST (2) which made such a contribution to victory in both the Pacific and European theatres was based on Baker's sketch design backed by US production skill. References 2-4 again provide a valuable background. Some account of their service is given in Ref 5.

Before the Second World War landing ships did not exist. Combined operations had, of course, been considered by the naval staffs before the war began, but the actual developments far exceeded anything envisaged at that time.

After France fell in 1940 it became apparent that at some future date it would be necessary to launch an assault on Europe in order to come to grips once more with the enemy. Several types of landing craft were being designed but as it was realised that the minor types of these would be unable to attempt an open sea voyage under their own power for other than a short duration, it was decided that ships would have to be provided capable of transporting these craft to the scene of operation; ships would also be required to carry the troops etc. to make the assault.

The actual development of landing ships fell into five main groups.

Ships for Carrying the Infantry with their Assault Craft

LSI(L) (Landing Ship, Infantry – Large)

Early in 1940 it was desired to have a special carrier for LCAs (later known as Landing Ship Infantry, Large) and, since time and expense precluded the building of a suitable vessel, the possibility of converting fast merchant ships capable of carrying twelve LCA and approximately 1000 men was investigated.

Three *Glen* ships were selected for conversion to MSI(L), *Glenroy*, *Glenearn* and *Glengyle*.[6] They were taken in hand in June 1940 and completed within six months. Twelve sets of LCA Welin Maclachlan gravity davits were fitted, and the carriage of two MCM was also arranged for. Accommodation was provided for a naval complement of forty-three officers and 280 ratings, twenty military officers and 670 men, and additional washplaces and WCs fitted. The existing ship's galley was used for officers and a second galley constructed for crew and troops. The after holds were subdivided into victualling stores and stores for military equipment, etc. and some of the cargo oil tanks forward were utilised for the stowage of approximately 1000 tons of rock ballast required for stability reasons. 2000 gallons of petrol for use in the landing craft was carried in a cylindrical tank in one of the forward holds. The armament was modified to comprise three 12pdr and four 2pdr guns. In order to increase the domestic water capacity the deep tanks abaft the engine rooms,

Ulster Monarch on 15 Sept 1942. A simple conversion of a cross channel ship to carry troops and LCA.

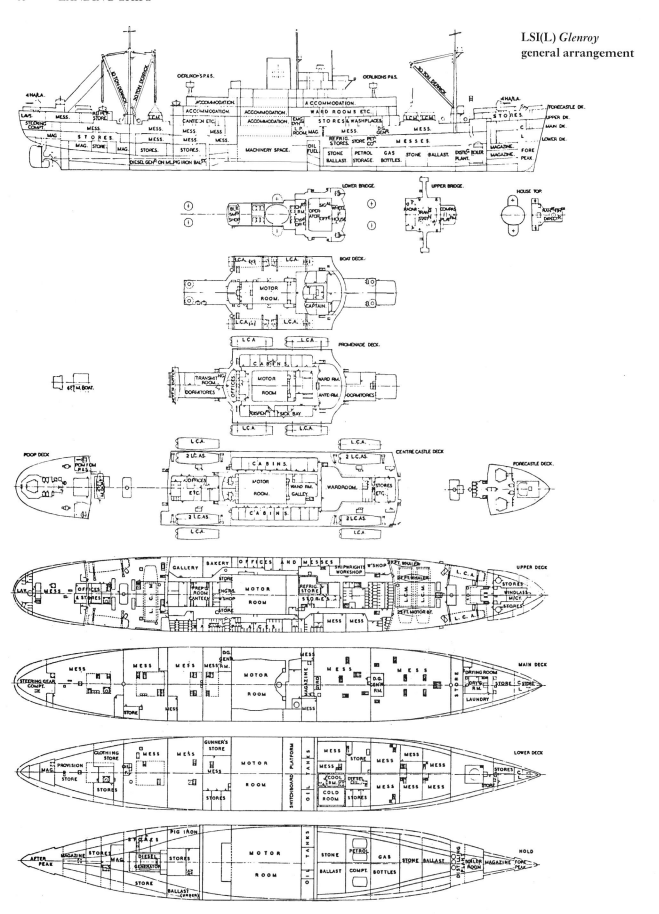

LSI(L) *Glenroy*
general arrangement

which had been used for oil fuel, were cleaned and used for the stowage of fresh water for washing purposes only.

After two years' service as LSI(L) *Glenearn* returned to England for repairs, and it was decided to carry out the fitting of additional LCA davits, special operations rooms, and rearming concurrently. In order to improve seaworthiness, the watertight doors between the machinery spaces were plated over, the sally ports on the main deck plated up and the lower row of side scuttles blanked.

It was found possible to arrange stowage for twenty-four LCAs and this was achieved by carrying twelve in four sets of luffing davits, four in four pairs of gallows davits and the remaining eight in gravity davits. The luffing davits were designed by Messrs Welin Maclachlan Davits Ltd, and each pair consisted of two luffing arms connected at the top by a boom from which the falls were suspended. An LCA was stowed on the deck between the luffing areas, a second LCA above this on a cradle which could be readily dismantled, and a third LCA was carried in the outboard position. In operation, the outboard LCA was lowered into the sea, the davits turned inboard to lift the LCA on the cradle and the davits then luffed outboard to lower this craft. Meanwhile the cradle was dismantled and the third LCA on the deck lowered in a similar manner to the second craft.

LCAs in gallows davits had to be carried in the outboard position but these were fitted high enough in the ship to bring them well above the waterline. 25hp motors were provided for all davit winches. The 12½hp motors already fitted for gravity davits being replaced, and in addition these davits were strengthened to enable the increased weight of LCA (now nearly 14 tons loaded) to be carried. Stowage was arranged for three LCMs and since the weight of an LCM loaded was now 30 tons the after derrick was strengthened from 25 tons to deal with this weight. A minimum of one ton of petrol per landing craft was a requirement and this was achieved by fitting two additional 4000 gallon tanks in the petrol compartment, making a total of 10,000 gallons. Stowage was also arranged for sixty 4 gallon tins of petrol for military use in a protected compartment on the upper deck. A 2200 gallon tank for diesel oil was fitted for the use of landing craft.

Additional accommodation was provided, extra cabins, generally of the dormitory type each suitable for several junior officers, being built as extensions to the superstructure; the wardroom, washplaces and WCs were increased proportionately. Additional mess spaces for crew and troops were fitted by building flats in the forward oil fuel cargo tanks. The total accommodation provided was for 140 naval and military officers, eighty CPOs and POs, 600 other ratings and 1000 troops, the galley and bakery equipment being creased to cope with these numbers. Arrangements were made for stowing dry provisions, flour, and canteen stores for the full complements required for four months, and an additional 5,000cu ft of refrigerated stowage fitted to meet requirements for 45-60 days. The ventilation was improved having regard to the ships future service in tropical climates.

An operations room, combined receiving room and coding office, transmitted room and radar offices were built in the superstructure and protected by 'D' or DIHT plating. The armament was revised and three twin 4in, four single 2pdr pom-poms and eight Oerlikons fitted, together with a fire control installation which included a transmitting station and a rangefinder director. A workshop for the maintenance of landing craft was equipped with pillar drill, lathe, grinder, valve grinding machine, bandsaw, woodworking machine, etc. The boat complement comprised one 32ft motor cutter, a 27ft whaler and a 16ft motor boat.

The final inclining experiment was carried out on completion in November 1943 and it was found necessary to add 400 tons of ballast, making a total of 1720 tons, in order to ensure sufficient stability to give a small positive GM with any two adjacent compartments flooded and to reduce the angle of heel when lowering landing craft.

The generator capacity was four at 300kW each.

On the return of *Glenearn* from the Far East in July 1946 she was returned to trade.

Glenroy was taken in hand in February 1943 and converted similarly to *Glenearn*. *Glenroy* was returned to trade in June 1946.

Glengyle was the third vessel approved to be converted as *Glenearn* and *Glenroy* and was taken in hand in June 1944. She was returned to trade in July 1946.

The principal original particulars of this class were:

Length overall	511ft 0in
Beam extreme	66ft 6in
Gross registered tonnage	9880 tons
HP	12,000
Machinery	Twin screw diesel
Deep displacement as LSI(L)	15,500 tons
Speed (max)18kts	
Propellers – 4 bladed	Diam. 17ft 0in

Racehorse Class

In 1943 twelve CIB type cargo vessels building in America were acquired by the Ministry of War Transport under Lease-Lend and completed as Red Ensign landing ships, infantry (Large). The vessels were driven by steam turbines, single screw, 4000hp with a maximum speed of 14kts and dimensions of 395ft length between perps, 60ft breadth mld and 37ft 6in depth mld. 2300 tons of concrete ballast was fitted for stability reasons. Stowage was provided for 18 LCSAs, four in tripod davits and fourteen in gallows-type davits, and in all these davits the craft were carried in an outboard position. In addition two steel motorboats were carried in Welin gravity davits and two steel lifeboats under derricks, the derricks comprising eight of 5 tons and one of 30 tons, an LCM being stowed under the latter.

Other features of the conversion to LSI(L) were the building of a deckhouse forward of the superstructure for wardroom, troops' recreation space, etc., fitting of troop accommodation in 'tween decks, sick bay, bakery, canteens, increased refrigerator space, landing craft workshop, and petrol stowage in a protected compartment on the upper deck. The ship's original galley was used as an officers' galley and a new galley with cafeteria built for 1300 troops, meals being given in five sittings. The troops were berthed in standees, a form of bunk fitted three or four high and capable of being hinged up when not in use. The armament comprised one 4in, one 12pdr, two single Bofors, and ten Oerlikon guns, with two magazines, one forward and the other aft.

The ships began to arrive in the United Kingdom in early 1944.

Empire Halberd (renamed *Silvio*) was taken in hand in August 1944 for damage repairs and it was decided that she should be converted from Red to White Ensign LSI(L) and for service in the tropics. The large cargo hatches in the lower deck were plated over, those on the weather deck provided with weathertight covers and all openings in the weather deck leading to large spaces below made weathertight. Orlop decks were fitted in two of the holds and these were subdivided for store rooms, including victualling stores, clothing stores, blanket store, naval stores, medical store, Army baggage store, landing craft stores, gunner's store, etc. One of the troop spaces was converted into a mess space for naval ratings and another was utilised as their sleeping space, the standees being retained for this purpose. Certain of the cabins were converted into offices and a dispensary and surgeon's examination room built in the sick bay. The water ballast tanks in the double bottom were incorporated in the freshwater system and a 20 ton pump supplied to deal with the increased stowage. A 50ton/day evaporator and distiller was fitted in addition to the 10ton/day evaporator already onboard, and the existing two 300kW generators augmented by an additional 100kW diesel generator.

The armament was retained and splinter protection was fitted to the bridge, Oerlikons, signal offices, operations room and W/T office. Stowage was arranged for one LCM, two LCA or two LCN under the 30 ton derrick. Spreaders were provided in order that LCV(P), in which the slinging positions were 20ft 6in apart compared with 27ft 3in in LCA, could be carried in the LCA davits. The equipment in the landing craft workshop, which comprised a lathe, drilling machine, grinding machine, valve refacing machine, etc., was augmented by the addition of a woodworking machine.

The accommodation provided was for a crew and flotilla complement of forty officers and 320 ratings, a troop lift of 106 officers (mainly in dormitory-type cabins) and 980 troops in standees, although 1200 could be carried in an emergency.

The remaining nine vessels of the class were taken in hand for conversion to White Ensign LSI(L) and fitting-out for service in the tropics.

Owing to the shortage of hospital ships in the Far East it was approved in January 1945 for eight of the *Racehorse* class LSI(L)s to be fitted out for the carriage of casualties from the assault area to base, but only *Sansovino* was completed as a casualty evacuation ship owing to the early surrender of Japan. An operating theatre, preparation room, plaster room, resuscitation ward and medical store were provided, with a sick bay containing eighteen cots on the deck below, a cot lift being fitted between the two decks. Eight nursing sisters were accommodated in double-berth cabins with a lounge, nine medical officers in two cabins, and fifty RAMC ratings in a mess space, the standee accommodation being reduced thereby by 100 men.

Sansovino, *Rocksand*, *Sainfoin* and *Sefton* were retained as White Ensign vessels, mainly for trooping purposes, until mid-1946, when they were handed back to Ministry of War Transport.

Pampas

Another vessel, *Pampas* (later renamed *Persimmon*), which had been built for Royal Mail Lines Ltd. by Messrs Harland & Wolff Ltd, was converted by the same firm to a Red Ensign LSI(L) in 1943. Her dimensions were 433ft length between perps, 61ft 3in beam and 38ft depth moulded, being driven by diesel engines, 7000ihp, speed 15½kts, and fitted with four 175kW generators. Eighteen LCAs were carried in gallows-type davits, an LCM under a 50 ton derrick (the remaining derricks comprising four at 5 tons and two at 3 tons) and six lifeboats, of which four were motor driven, in Welin quadrant davits. Accommodation was provided for approximately 100 military officers and 1200 troops in addition to the crew and flotilla staff. The armament fitted consisted of one 4in, one 12pdr, two single Bofors and nine Oerlikon guns, supplied from three magazines. 1400 tons of permanent ballast was fitted.

Persimmon was taken in hand in October 1944 for conversion from Red to White Ensign and for service in the tropics. The storerooms were reallocated and refitted, and several new stores added. A new sick bay was fitted out with fourteen cots, the galley equipment augmented and additional WCs built for the troops. The accommodation was modified to that required for a complement of forty-six naval officers and 400 men (including flotilla staff) and 123 military officers and 1030 other ranks. It was decided that the vessel should be brought up to LSH(S) standard and this entailed the enlarging of signal office and transmitter room, fitting of a cypher office and stronger signal mast, and provision of additional communications equipment and aerials.

LSI(S) (Landing Ship, Infantry – Small)

Investigation with regard to the type of vessel suitable for conversion to raiding craft carrier,

later known as landing ship infantry (small) led to the selection of Belgian cross-channel steamers. The vessels finally chosen, and which were loaned by the Belgian authorities for return after the cessation of hostilities, were the 15,000hp diesel-driven ships *Prins Albert* and *Prince Philippe* and the 13,000hp oil-fired steam turbine ships *Prince Charles*, *Prince Leopold*, *Prinses Josephine Charlotte* and *Prinses Astrid*. The approximate dimensions of all these vessels were 360ft length and 46ft beam, with a speed of 22kts.

They were taken in hand in October 1940.

The primary requirement was that they should each be capable of carrying eight landing craft with means of raising and lowering them. The weight of these craft was originally expected to be 6 tons but as the design developed the weight increased until eventually the davits were designed to carry 10½ ton craft. The davits, which were gravity-type operated by 25hp electric winches, were fitted on the upper deck, four port and starboard; this entailed some cutting away of the boat deck.

An endurance of 1300 miles at 17kts was required and this was achieved by fitting additional oil and freshwater tanks in each vessel and in addition a distiller of 30ton/day capacity was installed in each of the steam turbine vessels. Accommodation, washplaces and WCs were arranged for a crew of approximately 200 and 300 troops by the conversion of passengers' quarters

LSI(S) *Prinses Astrid* as converted

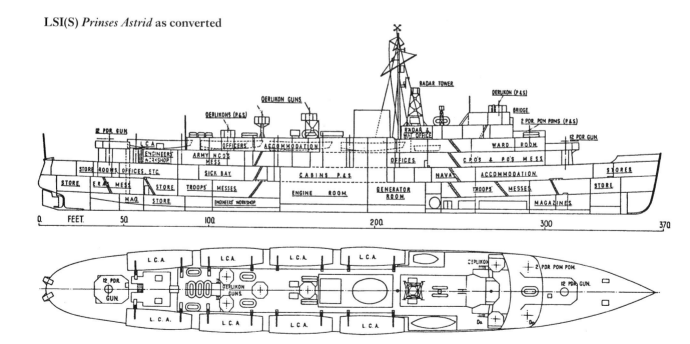

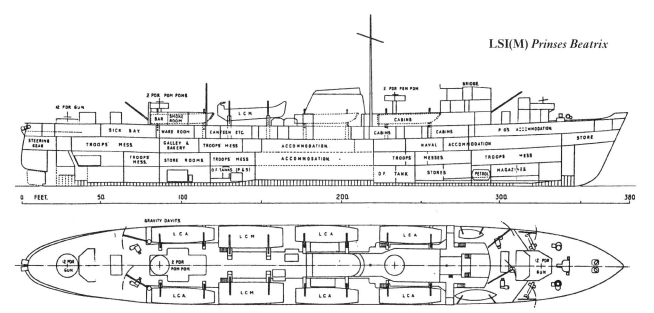

LSI(M) *Prinses Beatrix*

and dining spaces, and in some instances passengers' bunks were retained in order to save time and labour. Several of the existing WCs were below the waterline, drained into sewage tanks, and the contents subsequently pumped overboard, but these were removed and replaced by WCs fitted above the waterline and which could be discharged directly overboard. The galley spaces were enlarged and additional equipment fitted and a refrigerated space of 700cu ft capacity provided. A sick bay, canteen, offices, provision and naval stores were other features incorporated in the conversion.

The armament fitted comprised two 12pdr HA/LA and two 2pdr, with the ammunition stowed in two magazines, one forward and one aft; later six Oerlikons were added. Petrol was required to be carried for fuelling the landing craft and a cylindrical tank, capacity 1200-15,000 gallons, was fitted in a compartment below the waterline. Other equipment fitted included six depth charges in stern chutes, CSA apparatus and taut wire measuring gear. A workshop for servicing landing craft engines was also fitted, containing an engine testing stand, lathe, drill, grinder, etc.

The vessels were completed in approximately six months; *Prince Phillipe* was sunk in collision shortly afterwards, and *Prince Baudouin*, a sister vessel, was converted to LSI(S) in her place. The inclining experiments carried out on these vessels on completion of conversion revealed that their displacements had increased appreciably due to conversion and this increase continued during their service as LSI(S) due to alterations and additions. Despite efforts to reduce weight, the ships eventually attained a draught nearly 2ft in excess of their original plimsoll draughts.[7]

In 1945 *Prins Albert* and *Prince Baudouin*, which had a greater endurance than the remaining vessels, were taken in hand for tropicalisation for service in the Far East, but the cessation of hostilities occurred before this work was complete, and all the ships, with the exception of *Prince Leopold*, which was sunk during war service, were returned to their owners. Operationally, the steam turbine vessels were not found so useful as the diesel vessels *Prins Albert* and *Prince Baudouin* as they were older vessels and required a great deal more maintenance.

LSI(M) (Landing Ship, Infantry – Medium)

Two ships were taken in hand for conversion to landing ship, infantry (medium), (LSI(M)), and these on completion of conversion differed only from the LSI(S) insofar as their endurance was greater and the landing craft carried comprised six LCA and two LCM instead of the eight LCA carried by the Belgian vessels. The Dutch diesel-driven ships *Queen Emma* and *Prinses Beatrix* owned by the Zeeland Steamship Co., Flushing, and which had engaged on the passenger and main service between Harwich and Flushing, were the vessels selected in August 1940 and completed in January 1941.

The conversion followed closely on that described for LSI(S), and as for those vessels, the undesirability of increasing topweight was a major consideration when considering alterations and additions during service. As a result of the inclining experiment carried out on completion, each vessel was ballasted with 130 tons of permanent ballast in order to give sufficient stability for handling MLCs and LCAs.

[7] Note the problems of stability with these small cross channel steamers. Some accounts criticise the work needed in conversion but there is little doubt that it was justified.

In March 1945 the ships were taken in hand for refitting for service in the Far East, where they served until they were returned to their owners a year later.

Principal particulars of these ships were:

Length overall	380ft 0in
Length between perps	350ft 0in
Beam	47ft 2½in
GRT	4135
HP	13,000
Machinery	twin screw diesel
Deep displacement as LSI(M)	4000 tons
Speed	22kts
Complement	
Ship	20 officers, 147 men
Landing Craft	5 officers, 55 men
Army personnel	22 officers, 35 men
Armament fitted	2-12pdr HA guns
	2-2pdrs
	8-single Oerlikons

Six depth charges were also carried.

Ships for Carrying Assault Craft in Bulk

For a comparatively small operation the LSI with its troops, a certain amount of transport, the LCA and the LCM represented a self-contained unit. It was clear that for anything other than a short raid the build-up on shore provided by one or two LCM would be very slow, which resulted in a demand for each LSI to be provided with more LCM than she could carry.

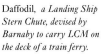

Daffodil, a Landing Ship Stern Chute, devised by Barnaby to carry LCM on the deck of a train ferry.

The real need was for landing craft transports, and a number of schemes were considered by the Admiralty, but little progress was made as it was felt that time would not permit building a special vessel. Other methods had to be adopted: these resulted in the LSS, LSG and LSD.

LSS (Landing Ship, Sternchute)

Three train ferries belonging to the LNER were considered for use as landing craft carriers in the event of a landing operation being undertaken. It was decided that owing to their large deck space the ferries would be well suited to carry LCMs and two of the vessels were converted for this purpose.

The train ferries selected were No 1 and No 3 and their principal dimensions were as follows:

Length overall	363ft 6in
Length between perps	350ft 0in
Beam moulded	58ft 6in
Beam over fenders	61ft 6in
Depth moulded to car deck	17ft 6in
Gross registered tonnage	25,000
HP (reciprocating, twin screws)	3000ihp

The vessels were converted in 1940 and were renamed *Iris* (later *Princess Iris*) and *Daffodil*.

Thirteen LCMs were carried stowed on trolleys running on three liens of fore and aft rails on the car deck and transferred from the port or starboard stowages to the centre line or vice versa by means of a power-driven traversing trolley situated at the fore end of the car deck. All launching or recovery was carried out from the centre line by means of the slipway built into the stern. LCMs could be handled with loads up to 16 tons.

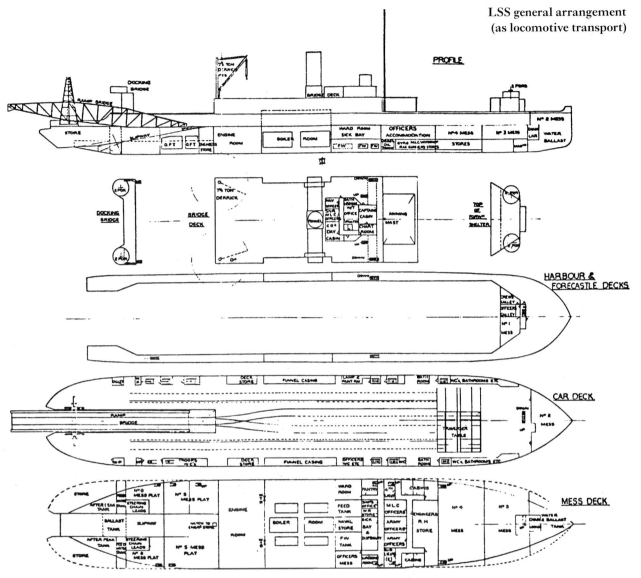

LSS general arrangement
(as locomotive transport)

Complement (13 LCM)

Army personnel	5 officers, 100 men
Landing craft crews	5 officers, 70 men
Ship	15 officers, 110 men

The ships were not used operationally due to their low endurance (1200 miles) but they performed useful service ferrying landing craft from Combined Operations bases and were particularly valuable in collecting craft in preparation for 'Overlord'.

In late 1943 it was approved to carry out the reconversion of the two vessels to carry locomotives and rolling stock so that they could be used for this purpose after a landing had been made on the continent. The time for conversion was not to exceed six weeks and the normal handling of landing craft was not to be impaired. The reconversion arrangements were worked out by the Admiralty and War Office and consisted of a new layout of rails, modifications to the traversing trolley, raising of the docking bridge and the fitting of a gantry and winches to handle a 90 ton stern brow which could be embarked or landed by the ship. The new equipment was prefabricated without direct reference to the ship.

The arrangement proved successful and many locomotives were transported. *Daffodil* was mined in French waters while employed on this duty.

LSG (Landing Ship, Gantry)

Another of the methods of transporting LCMs was by landing ship gantry. Approval was given to take up and convert three 12,000 tons 12kts vessels for this purpose.

The vessels selected were tankers building as RFAs, viz *Derwentdale*, *Dewdale* and *Ennerdale*.

The principal dimensions of these ships were as follows:

The Landing Ship Gantry, converted from an RFA tanker to carry LCM.

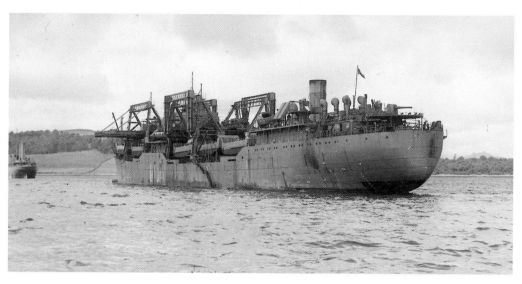

Length overall	483ft 3in
Breadth extreme	59ft 3in
Depth moulded	34ft
Gross registered tonnage	8218 tons
HP	3500bhp
Machinery	Diesel single screw
Speed	12½kts
Complement	
Landing Craft / Army Personnel	16 officers, 250 men
Ship	15 officers, 77 men

Arrangements were made to carry fifteen LCM on board each ship stowed on the upper deck, nine in the after well and six in the forward well. (*Ennerdale* carried only fourteen LCMs due to oiling-at-sea gear in the after well.) The LCMs were unloaded by means of special gantry traversers designed and constructed by Messrs Stothert & Pitt in conjunction with DNC. Due to the presence of the bridge structure amidships it was necessary to build a gantry in each well, just forward and just aft of the bridge. The use of two gantries shortened the time required for loading and unloading. The LCMs were stowed on rollers so that they could be hauled fore and aft by means of winches. Some modifications to the run of pipes on the upper deck were necessary, but arrangements were made to maintain the function of the vessels as RFA tankers.

The load draught as oil tanker was 27ft 6in with a displacement of 16,780 tons. The draught as an LCM carrier was limited to 23ft to provide a reasonable freeboard for the deck cargo. The load carried at this draught was fifteen LCMs each loaded with 9 tons of stores etc. and, in addition, 6955 tons of oil in the cargo tanks. During the original conversion only a small additional complement was catered for, but in 1943 extra accom-

modation was built into certain cargo tanks for the LCM crews and maintenance staff.

Although arrangements were made for these ships to maintain their function as oil tankers, it was found on service that they were employed almost exclusively for ferrying LCMs. However, as the war in the Far East developed, it was considered that they could perform invaluable duties by carrying fresh water as well as oil fuel to the forward areas in addition to the LCMs on the deck, and certain tanks with a capacity for about 3000 tons of fresh water were arranged for this purpose in *Derwentdale*.

Consideration was given to converting the vessels to carry additional LCMs in the cargo tanks but in view of the amount of labour and time involved for the gain in carrying capacity (five additional LCM) this alteration was not proceeded with.

These ships performed a very useful wartime service in ferrying LCMs for landing operations, particularly in the Mediterranean and the Far East, but this type of ship did not constitute a very economical conversion since the craft carrying capacity was low. It was recommended that in any future conversions of this type consideration should be given to the selection of vessels capable of carrying LCMs in the hold as well as on the deck.

These LSGs reverted to ordinary tanker duties as RFAs.

LSD (Landing Ship, Dock)

These ships represented the most ambitious attempt at landing craft carriers.

The object of having LSDs was to carry the large tank landing craft fully loaded and float them off near the enemy coast so that a raid or assault using tanks and heavy vehicles might be possible.

LSD *Highway* profile, plan and cross-sections

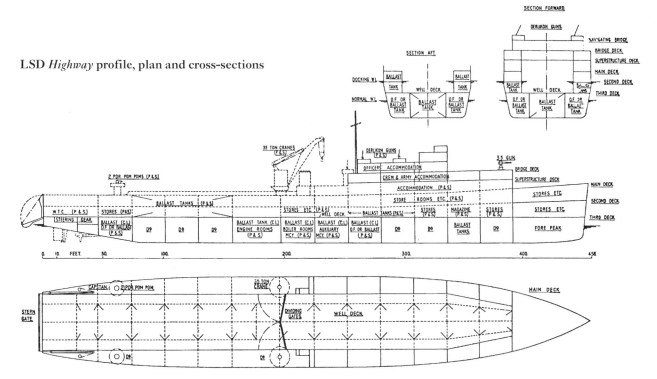

As indicated by the name the ships were in fact large self-propelling ship-shape floating docks. A speed of 15kts was asked for.

These LSD were designed in the US and developed by Messrs Gibbs and Cox of New York.

The whole idea was viewed with scepticism by both builders of floating docks and also by naval personnel, but the design was completed and the ships were built, and they were used most satisfactorily by both the UK and the US.

One of the first difficulties arose from the fact that the ship might be lost through over-flooding; full investigation, however, showed that this fear was groundless and the great difficulty was finding means of sinking her to the desired waterline for floating the craft in an out. An interesting stability problem also arose, for the beam of the vessel on the pontoon deck was fixed by the size of the largest craft expected to be embarked and by the width of the dock walls necessary to give stability with the water just over the deck. Had the vessel been built wall-sided from this deck downwards, stability in the seagoing condition would have been excessive with a consequential difficulty

The Landing Ship Dock,
Highway *on 19 Nov 1943, designed and built in the USA from a sketch by Baker. A most successful design which would form the basis for post war LPD such as* Fearless *and* Intrepid.

in docking the craft down. For these reasons the ship was built with a very pronounced flare below the pontoon deck.

The actual metacentric heights were:

Deep sea-going condition	7.7ft
Light sea-going condition	8.7ft
Worst condition (deck awash)	8.0ft

The principal dimensions were:

Length (overall)	457ft 9in
Beam	72ft 2in
Moulded depth	37ft
Dock size	Approx. 398ft x 44ft x 9ft water over the sill
Displacement (fully loaded with LCT and tracks)	7500
Deep draught	15ft 6in
Displacement (fully loaded) ballast to 9ft water in dock	18,000 tons
Power	7000shp
Speed	16–17kts
Fuel	1500 tons
Range	8000 miles at 15kts

The capacity of these craft is illustrated by the following alternative loads:

(i)   2 LCT (3)
(ii)   23 LCM (1)
(iii)   38 LCA
(iv)   46 Valentines

As finally arranged pumping and flooding were effected through a common main system, with branches forward and aft. The total pumping power was 18,400 gallons per minute and the dock could be sunk in 1½ hours or pumped up in 2½ hours. The intakes and exhausts from the machinery spaces were led to positions well above the submerged waterline and the machinery could be run with the dock flooded. If necessary the dock could be operated with way still on the shop.

Machinery consisted of two Parsons steam turbines 3500shp each set, and two oil-fired boilers in closed stokeholds.

Two 3-bladed propellers were fitted 11ft 3in diameter and 9ft 9in pitch. Generators included two 150kW turbo generator and 1075kW diesel generator.

Armament   1-3in/50 QF (American type)
16-20mm Oerlikons
4-2pdr
or   4-40mm Bofors

Accommodation was located in the superstructure built over the forward third of the well. All amenities, in particular the laundry and sick bay, were to a high standard. Accommodation was arranged:

Ship	15 officers, 126 men
Landing craft	(according to loading)
Military	23 officers, 240 men

General

Four ships were allocated to the Royal Navy – *Eastway*, *Highway*, *Northway* and *Oceanway*. None of these ships was ever used for the role originally intended because, before they were completed, the principle of the LST had been generally accepted. LSD were, however, invaluable as carriers of minor landing craft, major landing craft and amphibians.

Incidentally, these ships could be used as mobile floating docks and repair bases for all types of small craft.

LST Carrier (Landing Ship Tank – Carrier)

At the time when LST were first ordered in America the British authorities also ordered a large number of 112ft LCT. The intention was that these craft should be shipped to this country as deck cargo, either in three units in the ordinary merchant ship or as a complete unit on the deck of LST. The latter case would require a 150 ton crane lift for disembarkation.

This method of transportation, however, was of little use for delivery of craft to ports where heavy cranes were not available, so it was suggested that once the craft had been stowed on the deck of the LST it might be delivered by launching from broadside launching ways. The practicability of this suggestion was thoroughly investigated by means of tank trials which proved it practicable and it was finally adopted with success.

To carry out the launch it was necessary to heel the LST to about 11° by flooding tanks; the launching arrangements were generally similar to those usual in broadside launches, but the ways were greased and grease irons put in when the craft was placed on board. During passage the craft was carried on wedge-shaped support blocks, which at the time of launch were slackened and the craft 'set down'. The height of drop over the ship side was about 10ft.

Subsequently a similar scheme was used for the delivery of LCT(5) to the Far East.

Even at the end of the war there was still a demand for more ships capable of carrying minor landing craft and some of the LST(3) then completed in this country were specially fitted out for the transport of seven LCM(7). The landing craft

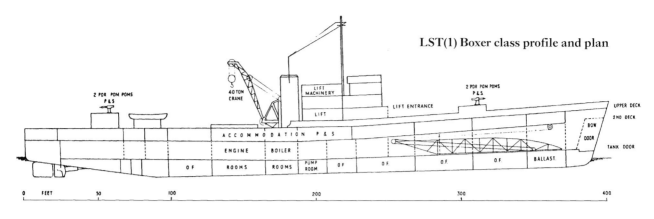

LST(1) Boxer class profile and plan

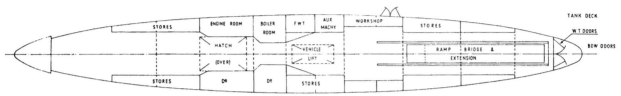

were hoisted in by means of a derrick and landed on to a trolley or pair of trolleys fitted with hydraulic jacks. The trolleys ran in rails at each side of the deck and were hauled to and fro by means of whips.

Six LST(3) were to be converted to LST(C) but four were eventually cancelled.

Ships for Carriage of Tanks and Motor Transport

LST(1) (Landing Ship, Tank – Mk 1)

Maracaibo Class

In November 1940 DNC was asked to investigate the question of the transport of tanks and motor transport, and the landing of them in shallow water on selected beaches, anywhere in the world.

In view of the time required to build new ships new construction was out of the question as regards immediate delivery but, in order to pro-

vide something quickly *Maracaibo* oilers, because of their shallow draught, were selected as suitable ships for conversion.[8]

Three of this class were accordingly taken over and fitted up to carry 20-25 ton tanks and to launch them over the bow.

The bow disembarking gear consisted of a very ingenious double ramp arrangement suggested by DNC Department and developed by Messrs Clarke Chapman. The tanks were carried abreast the original turret deck of the ships and were enclosed by a new deck and extension of the ship's side. Considerable attention was given to the ventilation of the tank deck, particularly when vessels were warming up, as there was a very high CO concentration in the exhaust gases. In these ships the problem was tackled by fitting exhaust trunks which had flexible asbestos hoods with adaptors at the ends which could be secured to the vehicle exhausts.

The trials with these ships proved that such comparatively large ships could be grounded for-

Empire Charmian, a heavy lift merchant ship, also known as a Landing Ship Carrier which could carry LCM to a landing area.

[8] These ships were built as shallow draught oil tankers for service on Lake Maracaibo from which their class name is derived.

ward and aft after disembarkation and kedge themselves off the beach without outside assistance.

There were the first tank landing ships in the world.

Principal particulars:

Length overall	383ft 0in
Beam	64ft 0in
Gross tonnage	6455
Horsepower	3000
Displacement as LST	5710 tons
Beaching draughts ⎰ F	4ft 2in
⎱ A	15ft
Speed (max)	10kts
Endurance	7200 miles at 8kts

They were fitted to carry

LCM	-	2
Tanks	-	20 (25 tonners – later Churchills)
or MT	-	33

Complement

Army Personnel ⎱ landing craft crews ⎰	12 officers, 195 men
Ship's complement	14 officers, 84 men

Armament

3–2pdr pom-poms
2–single Oerlikons
4–3in smoke mortars

LST(1) Maracaibo class profile and plan

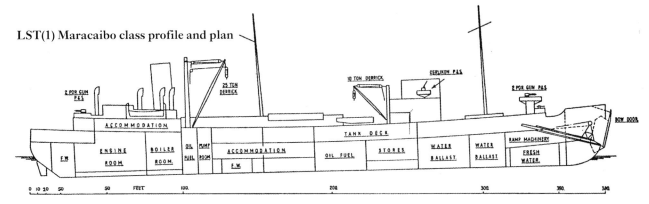

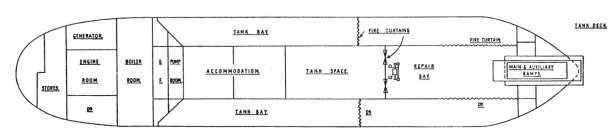

An early Landing Ship Tank conversion from a Lake Maracaibo tanker. (Possibly Misoa*)*

These conversions, which took about 4-5 months, were not ideal but they contributed very largely to the solution of many problems in the design of tank carriers and much useful information was gained from them.

Boxer Class

Concurrently with the conversion of the *Maracaibo*s the design of special ships for landing tanks direct on to beaches was progressed. The design was undertaken without any real back history which could be used for guidance and actually before the *Maracaibo*s were tried. Many of the requirements were fixed somewhat arbitrarily, and on the whole the ships were more elaborate than was later shown to be necessary.

The first sketch design was for a vessel to carry sixty 25 ton tanks unofficially named *Winston*. DNC, however, proposed that the Prime Minister's requirements be met by three smaller ships; the design was approved in December 1940.[9]

The speed requirement was 17kts and it was clear that if this was to be achieved the blunt-ended layout of the LCT and of the *Maracaibo* class would not be good enough. It was intended originally to fit a false bow, horizontally hinged at the upper deck level, outside the watertight door forming the end of the ship; at the suggestion of Harland & Wolff this was discarded in favour of vertically hinged doors meeting on the centre line of the stem. Such doors became standard in all LST and also in the larger types of tank landing craft.

These vertically hinged doors, which were non-watertight, were operated by screws actuated by electric motors; watertightness was maintained by a hinged WT door 19ft x 19ft fitted immedi-ately abaft the bow doors. This door was hinged to the underside of the deck over and operated electrically. Large screw clips were fitted to clamp the door to the frame and make it watertight.

Tanks were landed over a bridge or brow 119ft x 17ft 6in overall; a causeway or beach roadway 85ft long, could be extended beyond this bridge if so desired. The bridge and causeway were stowed at the fore end of the tank storage space. The bridge was articulated for landing on uneven beaches and designed for loads up to 40 tons.

A 10 ton electric lift was fitted to take vehicles to and from the upper and tank decks. A 40 ton electric crane was also fitted.

Principal particulars of the three ships built, viz *Thruster*, *Bruiser*, *Boxer*, were:

Length overall	400ft 0in
Beam	49ft 0in
Depth moulded	31ft 7in
Deep displacement	6007 tons
Horsepower	7000
Machinery	Geared turbines
Speed (deep)	16¼kts
Beaching draught F	5ft 6in
A	14ft 10in

They were fitted to carry:
13 Churchill tanks
27 3 ton lorries

Army personnel	13 officers, ... men
Ship's complement	26 officers, 143 men
Armament	12- single Oerlikons
	2-4in smoke mortars
	2-FAM

These ships originally intended for use in the initial assault were not entirely suitable for this purpose on account of the deep beaching draughts.

[9] The original proposal by Churchill was for a very large ship, known informally as the 'Winston'. This was seen as impractical and the smaller *Boxer* designed; known as the 'Winette'.

Bruiser, a purpose built Landing Ship Tank Mk I, originally known as the 'Winette'. They were far too elaborate for building in the numbers required.

LST(2)

The type of landing operation envisaged when LST(1) were designed was one involving large-scale raids on distant enemy-held territory. In 1941, however, it became clear that final victory could only be preceded by a large-scale re-invasion of the continent. The first estimate of the craft needed gave astronomical figures, and two possible solutions offered themselves; the first was to build far bigger landing craft and the second was to obtain American assistance under the recently approved Lease-Lend Act.

A small mission was eventually sent to Washington to explain our requirements carefully to the Americans and as a result Messrs Gibbs & Cox were invited to build large landing craft capable of crossing the Atlantic Ocean. The conception of the craft and outline requirements were provided by the Admiralty; it was for a craft about 300ft long to carry about twenty tanks. It was originally called the Atlantic TLC but was later renamed LST(2).

The first ships were ordered in February 1942 and delivered in November of that year.

The tanks were carried on a deck near the waterline and a simple lift was fitted between the tank deck and the upper deck; this enables the lighter vehicles to be carried on the upper deck and transferred to the tank deck for disembarkation as in LST(1). The bow ramp arrangements consisted of the LCT type but with the additional vertically hinged doors of the LST(1).

The wing compartments at the sides of the main tank deck were used for the accommodation of the Army personnel. Gravity davits were fitted suitable for carrying the standard American assault boat.

The ships were all welded and the scantlings were reduced to a minimum.

Principal particulars:

Length overall	327ft 9in
Beam	50ft 1½in
Deep displacement	3710 tons
Horsepower	1800
Type of machinery	Twin screw diesel (locomotive type)
Speed	10kts
Beaching draughts F	3ft 0in
A	9ft 6in

The ships were fitted to carry:

13 Churchill tanks
27 3 ton lorries and 8 jeeps
or one LCT(5)

Army personnel	12 officers, 165 men
Ship's complement	13 officers, 73 men
Armament	2-40mm Bofors
	6-Oerlikons

In all over 1000 LST(2) were constructed in the US – 115 ships were allocated to and operated by British forces.

LST(3)

With the success of the LST(2) design it seemed that further LST development would not be necessary. However, towards the end of 1943 there was some difficulty over the allocation of American-built ships for purely British operations, and it was decided to undertake a programme of LST(2) type ships in this country and Canada.

As we could not obtain the locomotive type diesels used in LST(2) for main propelling

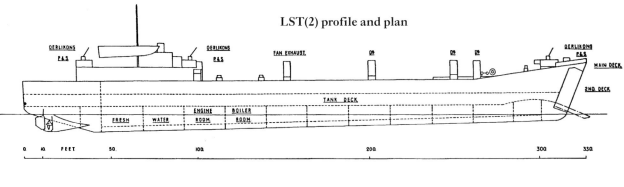

LST(2) profile and plan

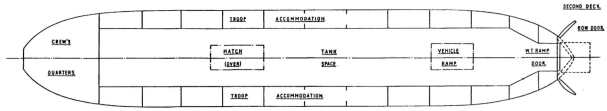

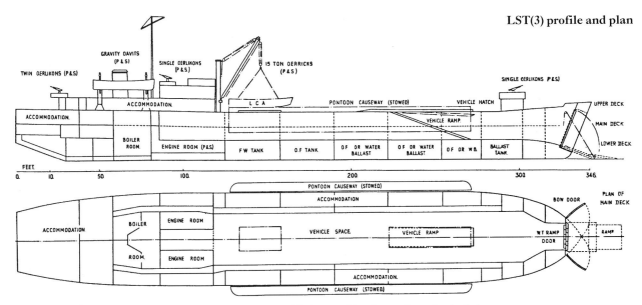

machinery, and also with our comparative lack of welding facilities, we could not build repeat LST(2); investigations were made into a new design of LST. A preliminary design was prepared and approval given to proceed with the design on 9 December 1943. The design submitted to the Board quoted speeds of 13kts in the deep condition and 13½kts in the beaching condition using the frigate-type machinery.

The design was prepared and drawings were supplied to all firms two and a half months after the first request for a sketch design.

Approval was given to order eighty ships to this design to complete by 1 April 1945; orders were placed for forty-five ships in the UK and thirty-five in Canada. Further orders were placed in Canada for thirty-six ships.

Thirty-one ships were completed as LST(3), two as LST(C) and two as LST(Q) in the UK and twenty-six as LST(3) in Canada, the remainder being cancelled in August 1945.

The main characteristics as laid down in the staff requirements were:

To embark and disembark tanks, motor transport, etc on beaches of varying slopes, and amphibians and DD Shermans into deep water.

To carry five LCAs or similar craft and one LCT(5) or LCT(6) on the upper deck at the expense of motor transport and, as an alternative to LCT(5) two NL causeway to be carried; the LCT(5) and NL causeways to be capable of launching direct from the deck.

To carry 500 tons of military load and to beach with military load and sufficient fuel and stores for 1000 miles return journey at 10kts, on draughts 4ft 6in forward and 11ft 6in aft.

To be fitted for operations in the tropics and in cold climates.

To be capable of carrying a load of sixty tons over the main ramp and ten tons over the vehicle ramp.

The principal dimensions and particulars of LST(3) were as follows:

Overall length	347ft 6in
Breadth extreme	55ft 2¾in
Depth moulded	27ft 0in
Propeller diameter	10ft 0in
Deep displacement	4980 tons
Beaching draughts F	4ft 7in
A	11ft 6in
Horsepower	5500
Type of machinery	Twin screw steam reciprocating
Speed	13kts
Propellers (3-bladed) diam.	10ft 0in
pitch	10ft 2in

The ships were fitted to carry equipment on the lines of LST(2).

Complement		
Army	13 officers,	150 men
Ships	14 officers,	90 men

Lloyds Register of Shipping and British Corporation were responsible for the approval of all drawings connected with hull work below the upper deck, and for the supervision of the building of the hull with the exception of the bow ramp arrangements.

A feature of the design was the bow door and ramp arrangements, a special feature being the provision of an auxiliary ramp considered necessary in the first instance because of the draughts of LST(3) compared with LST(2). Another feature was the vehicle ramp approximately 50ft in length by which vehicles could be stowed on the upper

Attacker, *a Landing Ship Tank Mk III, seen soon after the war. Ships of this class were to form the backbone of the post war amphibious force and, on commercial charter, were to pioneer RO-RO operation.*

deck and brought by means of the ramp to the bow opening. It was considered that this ramp was an improvement and a time saver when compared with the lift method used in LST(2).

To simplify construction a straight line form was adopted throughout.

The method of securing vehicles and tanks during passage was generally similar to that fitted in LST(2), modified in the light of experience.

As was to be expected in a design of this nature, where the time factor was limited in the early design stages and where every day brought fresh ideas gained in actual operation of LST(2), the number of modifications during the building stage was considerable.

As a result of the various trials and the loading and unloading of vehicles whilst the vessels had been in service, it was decided to dispense with the auxiliary ramp which proved to be of little value under most beaching conditions. The removal of this auxiliary ramp considerably reduced the time of operation in getting the vessel ready for unloading.

The habitability of LST(3) compared favourably with that of LST(2) and the other HM ships.

LSH(L) (Landing Ship, Headquarters – Large)

One of the new types of ship introduced into the Navy during the war was the Landing Ship Headquarters (Large).

The function of these vessels was to accommodate the force commanders and staff of the three services and to provide them with headquarters facilities suitable for command and control of the forces involved in a landing up to a divisional scale.

The requirements for a separate ship for this purpose was put forward on 14 January 1942.

The requirements were passed to DNC in

March 1942 and it was stated that the first vessel was required by 13 June. In view of the short time available, it was decided to convert *Bulolo*, an armed merchant cruiser which had just arrived in this country for refit and the work was taken in hand in that April.

The principal items of work included:
(i) the stripping of the existing ward room to make the lower flat of the citadel containing control receiving room, cypher office, signal control office and L/T room.
(ii) Stripping out the original music room and converting it into the middle flat of the citadel containing support control room, Army operations room, Naval operations room, signal distributing office and intelligence office.
(iii) Building of the war command room and two senior officers' cabins as the upper flat of the citadel.
(iv) Building two new transmitting rooms, one at the after end of the bridge deck and one at the after end of the boat deck and protecting these spaces with 30lb and 40lb 'D' quality steel plating.
(v) Large alterations to the messing and sleeping arrangements in order to accommodate nine senior officers, seventy-one officers and 399 other ranks.
(vi) Removing all 6in guns except the stern gun and fitting two 2pdr guns and eight Oerlikons, magazines being altered as necessary.
(vii) Fitting type 273 and 286 PQ radar.
(viii) Installing three 35kW diesel generators, for W/T and R/T requirements.
(ix) Fitting quick-flooding valves to the after tanks for beaching.
(x) Stowing 550 tons of extra ballast.

Staff requirements stated that an endurance of 9000 miles was required but this was later reduced to 3000 miles at 15kts and 8000 miles at 12kts.

Bulolo completed on 14 June and undertook command and control of the forces involved in the landing operations at Algiers in October 1942 carrying a British staff of the three services.

From the Command point of view the vessel was a success except that, although she was fitted out to staff requirements, the RAF complained that she fell far short of what was required for the control and direction of aircraft. This criticism by the RAF was the origin of the Fighter Direction Tenders which were later converted for the specific purpose of being attached to the LSH for aircraft control.

Bulolo acted as headquarters ship for Force 'G' in the Normandy landings. During this operation she was hit by a bomb in the vicinity of the operations room and during the necessary repairs which followed she was completely modernised and brought up-to-date ready for service in the Far East.

This modernisation of *Bulolo* amounted to practically another conversion in view of the greatly increased W/T and radar requirements. The fitting of sufficient radar for complete fighter direction duties was impracticable but sufficient was fitted to provide for the control and briefing of carrier-borne aircraft. The refit took eight months to complete although the time was extended due to the decision made, late in the refit, to air condition the operations spaces.

Principal particulars:

Length overall	412ft 6in
Length between perps	390ft 0in
Beam extreme	58ft 2in
Displacement (loaded)	9330 tons
Mean draught (loaded)	22ft 0in
Machinery	diesel 6150hp
Speed max.	15kts
Armament	2-2pdr
	5-40mm Bofors
	14-single Oerlikons

Other ships converted to LSH(L) were:

Largs	vessels operating as ocean boarding vessels
Hilary	
Lothian	cargo vessel
and *Keren*	an LSI(L)

The conversions carried out on these vessels were generally similar to that for *Bulolo* except in the case of *Keren* where many items were incorporated in this vessel which had not previously been fitted in other LSH(L)s; in fact all the known requirements for the vessel if required to act as an LSH (Command).

The principal additions were as follows:

(1) A joint operations room two decks high to increase display area and enable more persons to view it. (This had been recommended in August 1943 but previous LSH(L)s had not been large enough.)

(2) A separate bombardment control room.

(3) Increased Army accommodation.

(4) Offices for planning staffs to enable the ship to be used as a planning centre not only before but during an operation.

The Landing Ship Headquarters Bulolo. Fitted with a command centre and communications for tri service control of the early phases of a landing.

[10] Adams, T A. Operation Neptune; Fighter Direction Tenders, *Warships* 119. World Ship Society, Kendal 1994.

(5) Two high-power transmitters for long distance.

(6) Generally increased operations, signal and living accommodation.

(7) An extra mast to simplify aerial rig.

(8) Visual teleprinter system (US equipment).

(9) Increased radar equipment.

(10) Improved photographic and printing arrangements.

Work on this vessel was suspended after the end of the war.

FDT (Fighter Direction, Tender)

As a result of experience during the North African landings it became apparent that:

Command control and direction of aircraft should be combined in a ship specially designed for the purpose.

Or, alternatively, the HQ ship should be provided with all requisite radar information from a tender so linked by R/T communication that the efficiency of radar reporting would be equivalent to what it would have been had the radar equipment been installed in the HQ ship. A ship if the size required for the former was not available and in December 1943 approval was given to convert three Lease-Lend LST(2) for use as fighter direction tenders radar and VH/FD/F & R/T requirements were given precedence over other items.[10]

Armament   1-12pdr
6-Mk IX twin Oerlikons
4-FAM

Protection

60lb NC armour (about 70ft x 30ft in extent) on the main deck over the operations room which was sited on the 3rd deck. GC1 beacon and fighter direction officers position were built of 30lb DIHT steel.

Complement

In addition to the normal LST(2) complement temporary accommodation was required for five RN ratings and an RAF complement of eighteen officers and about 150 other ranks.

Stability

In order to decrease the excessive GM and increase the period of roll, 720 tons of pig iron ballast were stowed on the weather deck. Also, the two longitudinal bulkheads between the wing water ballast tanks and the dry compartments in the centre were pierced and all water ballast, oil fuel, lubricating oil and FW tanks kept slack so as to maintain maximum free surface. In order to meet an RAF requirement that the GCI aerial should not be more than 35ft above the waterline it was necessary to keep the forward WB tanks flooded. Resultant stability was as follows:

Deep condition	GM 4.05ft
Half oil condition	GM 4.23ft
Spend condition	GM 3.16ft

The ballasting was arranged so that with three compartments bilged the vessels would have a small positive GM. Radar etc. fitted included:

GCI set with facilities for interrogating MK III IFF

Type II set with facilities for interrogating MLIII IFF

Mk IV A1 beacon

Mk VIII A1 beacon

V.H/F R/T, H/F.R/T., H/F. W/T, V.H/F.D/F.

The fitting of the above sets necessitated the fitting of four additional masts, two 92ft, one 72 ft and one 54ft high. On the 3rd (tank) deck the following were constructed: a large operations flat 118ft x 60ft containing aircraft direction room with skiatron, filter room with ARL plot radar display room, general communication office, W/T and R/T receiving room, Y office, cypher office and small workshop.

VH/F D/F office (FV3)

VH/F D/F office (FV4)

Transmitting room

RCM office and store room and three generator rooms

On the main deck (weather) – GCI office

On the navigating bridge – beacon office

On the conning bridge – bridge plotting room

The three vessels were converted by Messrs J Brown Clydebank, the first in ten weeks and the other two within three months.

CHAPTER 20

Trawlers & Drifters

Editorial Note

This chapter will be particularly welcome as little has been published on the design, construction and conversion of trawlers and similar vessels. The breakdown of the vast numbers involved – about 1700 in all – can be found at the end of the chapter. The vast majority of these were requisitioned ships whose stability and condition had to be checked individually and necessary treatment applied.

The quality of Admiralty planning is worthy of emphasis; there was a prototype conversion in 1933, then came two experimental new construction ships, Basset *and* Mastiff *in 1934 and 1936 which formed the basis for the purpose built naval trawlers. In 1937, Smiths Dock and Isherwoods were drawn into a planning organisation to supervise the conversion of fishing trawlers. Refs 1 and 2 give some idea of life on these ships as does the fictional ref 3.*

A/S – M/S Trawlers

In the First World War out of 1800 trawlers available from the fishing fleet 1300 were requisitioned, and in order to reinforce the trawler patrol it was decided to build additional trawlers, the design being such that they would have good commercial value on the cessation of hostilities.

Three types were selected:

Strath - dimensions 115ft BP x 22ft mld x 13ft moulded

Castle - dimensions 125ft BP x 23ft 4in mld x 13ft 6in mld

Mersey - dimensions 138ft 4in BP x 23ft 7½in mld x 13ft 6in mld

Details of these designs can be found in *Records of Warship Construction During the War (1914-1918)*.

A total of 285 trawlers were built up to the Armistice and of these fourteen *Mersey* class, two *Castle* class and one *Strath* class were subsequently retained in service. Four *Axe* class, requisitioned during the war, were also retained.

In 1933, when the requirements for fitting out A/S and M/S auxiliaries in emergency had been formulated, it was decided to equip the *James Ludford*, a *Mersey* class trawler, for A/S experimental work. Information was required regarding the operation of asdics in trawlers, a trawler type set being in the course of development. It was also desired to find the easiest and most economical way of fitting out commercial trawlers in emergency and the suitability of a 4in gun in the forward position under seagoing conditions. The following arrangements were fitted:

1-4in Mk VII gun

25-depth charges, 2 rails and 2 throwers

Asdic set, comprising dome, training unit, with operator's shelter fitted above the wheelhouse

Admiralty-Designed Trawlers

Basset

Provision was made in the 1934 estimates for the design of *Basset* for A/S service. The requirements for a vessel to be equipped similarly to *James Ludford*, to be of medium trawler size with scantlings in accordance with the requirements of the classification societies so that the normal trawler builder could proceed with production with the minimum delay. The underwater portion was of warship form and Admiralty requirements only were catered for, no provision being made for subsequent commercial employment. Comparative tank trials *Mersey* v *Basset* were carried out during preparation of the design.

The vessel was built by Messrs Henry Robb of Leith, being laid down on 6 March 1935 and completed on 29 November 1935.

Particulars were:

Length between perps		150ft 0in
Breadth (mld)		27ft 6in
Depth (mld)		14ft 6in
Displacement	(deep)	775 tons
	(light)	551 tons
Draughts (deep)	F	8ft 9½in
	A	13ft 7in
Speed		13kts
Endurance		3000 miles at 9kts

Armament, etc.	1-4in QF gun
	1-.303in Lewis gun
	Type 123 Asdic

Machinery	1-850ihp triple expansion, 150rpm
	Boiler, coal-fired, 15in drum x 11ft 6in 200lb/sq in

[1] Lund, P & Ludlam, H. Trawlers go to War. London, 1971.

[2] Lambert, J. Requisitioned trawlers of WW II. Warship World, Vol 5, Liskeard, 1995.

[3] Brookes, E. Proud Waters. London 1949. Clearly based on personal experiences.

Propeller   one 3-bladed, cast iron
- diameter   8ft 6in
- pitch   10ft 8in
- area   22.5ft²

Two 15kW 100 volts DC generators

Stability Particulars

	Light Condition	Deep Condition
GM	2.18ft	2.17ft (fl)
Maximum GZ	0.85ft	0.93ft
Angle of max GZ	34°	33°
Range	59°	64°
Displacement	551 tons	775 tons

Complement   3 officers, 21 ratings

Mastiff

It was decided in 1936 to replace one of the *Mersey* class fishery protection trawlers and provision was made for the building of *Mastiff*. The design was developed from *Basset*, the main departures being in the reduced beam, increased moulded depth and reduced sheer aft. The design provided for ready conversion to A/S and M/S service, an M/S winch being fitted at the after end of the superstructure to admit of sweeping through fairleads over the stern. On service *Mastiff* was considered a very good seaboat, and a great improvement on the converted trawler for fishery protection work in that she had a small turning circle and a comparatively light draught. The speed of 12½kts was considered to be on the slow side, 15kts being considered desirable.

The vessel was built by Messrs Henry Robb of Leith and was laid down on 30 June 1937 and completed on 16 May 1938. The particulars were:

Length between perps		150ft 0in
Breadth (mld)		27ft 0in
Depth (mld)		15ft 0in
Displacement	(deep)	690 tons
	(light)	508 tons
Draughts (deep)	F	8ft 9½in
	A	12ft 3½in
Speed		12.7kts
Endurance		3300 miles at 9kts

Armament, etc   1-4in LA gun
- 2-.303in Lewis guns
- 4-depth charges

Machinery   1-950ihp triple expansion at 150rpm
- Boiler-1 cylindrical oil-fired 200lb/sq in

Propeller   one 4-bladed, cast iron
- diameter   8ft 6in
- pitch   10ft 8in
- area   20sq ft

Two 15kW 110 volt DC generators

Stability Particulars

	Light Condition	Deep Condition
GM	1.26ft	1.35ft (fl)
Maximum GZ	0.72ft	0.94ft
Angle of max GZ	36°	33°
Range	57½°	61½°
Displacement	508 tons	690 tons

Complement   3 officers, 22 ratings

Purchased Trawlers (1935 – 1939)

Approval was given in 1935 to purchase twenty trawlers for service in the Mediterranean, ten for A/S and ten for M/S duties. The ships, subject to an hour's steaming trial, were selected from ACR's Requisitioning List and were placed with local firms for conversion. The main items of work involved in the conversion scheme were stripping of the fish hold and fishing gear (except in the M/S trawlers where the trawl winch gallows and fairleads were retained for minesweeping) and fitting the necessary items for Admiralty service, such as armament, asdics, W/T, additional accommodation and ballast. The conversions took approximately ten weeks from date of acceptance to completion of final sea trials.

In 1939 approval was given for the purchase of a further fifteen trawlers, ten for M/S and five for A/S service. It was a requirement that these trawlers were to be capable of at least 8kts under favourable weather conditions. These conversions were on the lines of those for the 1935 programme and they were completed prior to the outbreak of hostilities. Some delays in completion were caused by plans and data not being available and, in order to assess the amount of ballast to be fitted, the vessels had to be inclined. Further time could have been saved by selecting firms acquainted with trawler construction and Admiralty procedure, situated in less widely dispersed areas, and by putting sister vessels at the same firms.

Particulars of the typical M/S trawler (*Oropesa*) were:

Length between perps		140ft 0in
Beam (ext)		24ft 6in
Depth (mld)		14ft 0in
Displacement	(deep)	732 tons
	(light)	557 tons
Speed		11kts
Fuel		165 tons coal (135 tons to burn)
GM	(deep)	1.77ft
	(light)	1.2ft

Armament, etc
1-4in QF gun and 12pdr HA/LA
1-0.5in twin or Oerlikon aft
2-twin Browning, Lewis and Hotchkiss
4-depth charges, 2 chutes

Machinery   1-steam, triple expansion
reciprocating engine 600ihp

M/S Gear   Oropesa Mk II* sweep, winch,
gallows, fairleads, etc. as used for
fishing. Capable of sweeping in pairs
and one leg of sweep when singly.

Complement   3 officers, 20 ratings

Particulars of the typical A/S trawler were:
Length between perps	151ft 8in	
Beam (ext)	25ft 6in	
Depth (mld)	14ft 6in	
Displacement	(deep)	850 tons
	(light)	633 tons
Speed		11.3kts
Fuel		154 tons coal
		(134 tons to burn)
GM	(deep)	1.74ft
	(light)	1.3ft

Armament, etc
1-4in QF and BL gun
1-0.5in twin and Oerlikon aft
2-sided Oerlikons
2-twin Browning, Lewis and Hotchkiss
25-depth charges, 2 rails, 2 throwers
Asdic type 123A

Machinery   1-steam, triple expansion
reciprocating engine 635ihp

Complement   3 officers, 26 ratings

Emergency New Construction A/S and M/S Trawlers

Tree, Dance, Shakespeare and *Isles* Class Design

In order to meet possible deficiencies in the 703 Auxiliary A/S and M/S vessels required in Stage 1 of an emergency, it was decided in the event of outbreak of hostilities to build 100 trawlers, the type, ie A/S or M/S, being dependent on the deployment of enemy minelaying and submarine units.

The general requirements formulated in 1933 for A/S and M/S trawlers were:

A/S Trawlers
Function: to attack and destroy enemy submarines. Vessel to be designed for war purposes and if possible for fishing.
Armament: required for self-defence and to have good ahead fire. A 4in gun was the largest a trawler could carry, a QF being preferred to a BL. One Lewis gun and three rifles required for the destruction of floating mines, and the vessel to carry twenty-five depth charges with two throwers and three double chutes.
General: to be able to put to sea in all weathers. A comparatively deep draught was required for the satisfactory operation of the Asdic set provided. Minimum speed required was 10kts, and new construction vessels were to have as high a speed as practicable; endurance 3000 miles. Accommodation was required for two officers and eighteen ratings, and W/T sets with a range of 100 miles were required in a few vessels.

M/S Trawlers
M/S Equipment: floats, otters, etc., winch fairleads and davits aft; sweeps to be streamed out over the stern.

Unst, *an Isles class trawler in mid war configuration.*

Crowlin, in a later configuration (4 Feb 1944) with tripod mast and more oerlikons.

Armament: to combat raiding submarines a 4in gun or 12pdr required; a Lewis gun was considered sufficient A/A armament. Four depth charges carried.

General: to be able to put to sea in all weathers. Compared with the normal fishing trawler, draught to be shallow to lessen risk of damage from mines. Speed of 12kts desirable and an endurance of 3000 miles required to allow vessels to proceed to foreign stations. Provisions for one officer and sixteen ratings to be on the basis of fourteen-day supply. W/T sets with a range of 100 miles were required in a few vessels.

The need for rapid production pointed to building vessels of the medium trawler size with scantlings in accordance with the requirements of the Classification Societies; this arrangement would enable trawler builders to proceed with construction without delay. A special contract was placed with Messrs Smith's Dock Co Ltd in 1938 for the preparation of design information, hull specification, complete set of working drawings and detail demands for hull material and fittings. This information prepared in advance enabled prompt starts to be made by the shipbuilders when the time arose for ordering. The design based on the foregoing requirements was approved in 1938; the layout was arranged to suit either A/S or M/S to admit a rapid changeover from one to other.

The particulars of the design of the *Tree, Dance, Shakespeare* and *Isle* class were as follows:

Length between perps	150ft 0in
Breadth (mld)	27ft 6in
Depth (mld)	15ft 0in
Displacement (deep)	760 tons
(light)	527 tons

Draughts	F	8ft 6in
	A	13ft 7in
Speed		12.5kts
Endurance		183 tons coal, 4000 miles at 9kts

Armament 1-12pdr HA/LA or 4in BL
3- Oerlikon single mountings
2-twin Lewis or Brownings
30-depth charges, 2 throwers
Type 123 Asdic

Machinery 1-850ihp triple expansion, 150rpm coal-fired boiler working at 200lb/sq in
Propeller 3-bladed cast iron

diameter	8ft 9in
pitch	11ft 0in
area	30sq ft

Dance class (only)

diameter	8ft 6in
pitch	11ft 0in
area	24sq ft

1-15kW and 1-7½kW 110 volt generators

Minesweeping Equipment Mark II* Oropesa sweep

Stability Particulars

	Light Condition	Deep Condition
GM	1.38ft	1.71ft
Maximum GZ	0.72ft	0.98ft
Angle of max GZ	33°	30°
Range	55°	59°
Displacement	527 tons	760 tons

Complement 3 officers, 28 ratings

A total of 211 vessels were built, of which 177 were constructed in the UK, sixteen in Canada and eighteen in India to Indian account.

As a result of war service a number of modifications were made in A/S and M/S trawlers. The armament was improved by the fitting of additional Oerlikons and Lewis guns, while the ammunition allowance for each gun was increased; radar types 286PU and 253 were also fitted.

It was decided in 1940 that all future vessels should be equipped to carry both A/S and M/S outfits at the same time, and arrangements were made accordingly.

Additions to complement were necessary to man the increased armament, radar, etc. This involved extra stowage for fresh water and provisions and increased WCs and washing facilities, etc. Some complements were increased to thirty-eight ratings, and slinging berths were arranged for the additions.

Protection from machine-gun fire from aircraft and surface craft was provided by fitting protective plating and mattresses round bridges and in way of gun platforms, etc.

Commercial Trawlers Built During the War for A/S and M/S Duties

Approval was given in 1940 for a proportion of the trawlers to be built to be of commercial design in order to replace the losses of fishing trawlers.

It was decided to build both large and small vessels and, as far as possible, improvements suggested by trawler owners were incorporated. Included were raked stem, cruiser stern and steam hydraulic steering gear.

The vessels were built under Lloyds survey and to the Society's requirements for classification 100 A1 for fishing trawlers. The main features of the fishing design were adhered to for rapid conver-

sion for fishing at the conclusion of hostilities. Steel upper decks, wood covered in way of accommodation were fitted.

The following is a brief description of each class:

Military Class

The prototype *Lady Madeleine* was designed by Messrs Cook, Welton and Gemmell, who built nine of this class during the war.

Length overall		190ft 3in
Length between perps		175ft 0in
Breadth (mld)		30ft 0in
Depth (mld)		16ft 0in
Displacement	(deep)	1192 tons
	(light)	816 tons
Draughts (deep)	F	10ft 9in
	A	18ft 10in
GM	(deep)	2.5ft (fl)
	(light)	1.34ft
Speed		12kts
Fuel		280 tons coal
Ballast		72.5 tons

Armament   1–4in HA/LA gun
4–Oerlikons
2–twin Brownings
65–depth charges, 2 rails, 4 throwers
Asdic type 123D

Machinery   1–triple expansion steam
reciprocating, 1000ihp at 123rpm

Propeller particulars:
one 4–bladed cast iron
diameter   10ft 9in
pitch   10ft 11¼in
area   42.5sq ft
1–20kW DC generator

Complement   4 officers, 54 ratings

Lancer, *a wartime Admiralty order to a commercial design. (28 Feb 1943)*

Hill Class

The prototype *Barnett* was designed by Messrs Cook, Welton and Gemmell also and eight of this class were built by the firm during the war.

Length overall		182ft 4in
Length between perps		155ft 0in
Breadth (mld)		28ft 0in
Depth (mld)		15ft 0in
Displacement	(deep)	1007 tons
	(light)	733 tons
Draughts (deep)	F	9ft 7in
	A	17ft 5in
GM	(deep)	2.04ft (fl)
	(light)	1.10ft
Speed		12kts
Fuel		212 tons coal
Ballast		70 tons

Armament 1-12pdr HA/LA
3-Oerlikons
2-twin Lewis guns
55-depth charges, 2 rails, 4 throwers
Asdic type 123A

Machinery 1-triple expansion steam
reciprocating, 970ihp at 120rpm

Propeller: one 4-bladed cast iron
diameter   10ft 9in
pitch   11ft 7½in
area   43sq ft

1-15kW DC generator

Complement   4 officers, 35 ratings

Hill class general arrangement

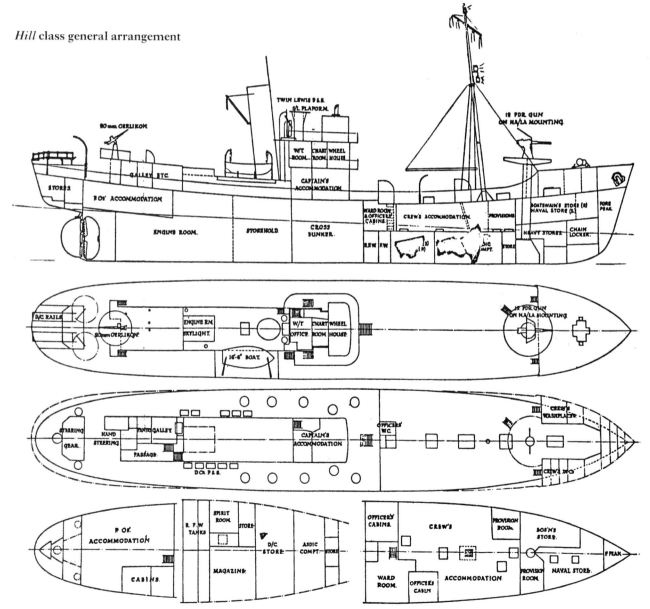

Fish Class

The prototype *Gullfoss* was designed by Messrs
Cochrane & Sons and eight of the class were built
and equipped by this firm during the war.

Length overall		162ft 6in
Length between perps		146ft 6in
Breadth (mld)		25ft 0in
Depth (mld)		14ft 0in
Displacement	(deep)	829 tons
	(light)	583 tons
Draughts (deep)	F	10ft 2in
	A	16ft 4in
GM	(deep)	2.06ft (fl)
	(light)	1.10ft
Speed		11kts
Fuel		200 tons coal
Ballast		50 tons

Armament   1-12pdr HA/LA
3-Oerlikons
2-twin Lewis guns
40-depth charges, 2 rails, 2 throwers
Asdic type 123A

Machinery   1-triple expansion steam
reciprocating, 700ihp at 115rpm

Propeller: one 4-bladed cast iron
diameter   10ft 3in
pitch   10ft 9in
area   39.5sq ft

1-15kW DC generator

Complement   3 officers, 30 ratings

Redoubtable Class

The prototype *Star of Orkney* was designed by
Messrs Hall Russell of Aberdeen, who also built
four of the class. Two vessels were fitted out for
M/S (Oropesa), the rest M/S (LL/SA).

Length overall		137ft 8in
Length between perps		125ft 0in
Breadth (mld)		23ft 6in
Depth (mld)		13ft 9in
Displacement	(deep)	560 tons
	(light)	430 tons
Draughts (deep)	F	9ft 9in
	A	14ft 9in
GM	(deep)	2.0ft (fl)
	(light)	1.1ft
Speed		10kts
Fuel		100 tons coal
Ballast		22 tons for M/S duties
		15 tons for LL/SA service

Armament   1-12pdr HA/LA
1-Oerlikon
2-twin Lewis guns

Machinery   1-triple expansion steam
reciprocating, 600ihp at 125rpm

Propeller: one 4-bladed cast iron
diameter   9ft 3in
pitch   11ft 3in
area   35sq ft

1-15kW DC generator in all vessels
2-54kW in LL/SA sweepers

Complement   2 officers, 21 ratings

Trawlers Built in Foreign Countries

Portugal – Professor Class

Approval was given in 1940 for the construction of
eight steel and six wooden trawlers in Portugal,
the Loch Fishing Co of Hull being the nominal
owners. The design was based on the diesel
trawler *Fishes*, which was constructed by Smith's
Dock Co, who provided design data, etc. of *Fishes*
for guidance. The vessels were built under the
survey of Lloyds Register, the steel vessels being
classified as 100 A1 motor trawlers; the wooden
vessels were not classified. Important items such
as structural steel, main and auxiliary engines,
piping, steering gears, etc. were supplied from the
UK.

Two of the steel vessels were eventually
exchanged for four existing Portuguese wooden
vessels.

On service the wooden vessels gave a lot of
trouble; outer bottom planking was very poor and
there were several instances of dry rot.

The vessels were employed on coastal duties as
LL/SA sweeps.

General Particulars

Length overall		154ft 0in
Length between perps		133ft 9in
Breadth (mld)		27ft 9in
Depth (mld)		16ft 7in
Displacement	(deep)	654 tons
	(light)	578 tons

Brazil

A contract was placed in July 1940 for building six
steel trawlers in Brazil. These vessels were laid
down in 1941 but progress during building was
very unsatisfactory and they were eventually taken
over by the Brazilian government.

Danlayers

To meet mine clearance commitments, both during the war and in the post-war period, it was approved in 1943 to convert forty A/S-M/S trawlers for Danlaying, two danlayers to work with each flotilla of fleet minesweepers.

The method of laying 'dans' was developed on the *Sylvana* and is known as the *Sylvana* method; the dans, sinkers and floats are streamed from the stern and recovered abreast the bridge by means of a Samson post and winch.

The main modifications involved in these conversions were:

Removal of 12pdr gun, depth charges, asdic and minesweeping gear.

Addition of boat deck extension for the stowage of fifty-four dans, stowage for sinkers, etc. on the upper deck, and winches for recovery of dans.
Special battery-charging arrangements for lights and taut wire measuring gear was also fitted.

Thirty-four vessels were actually converted and fitted as described. Twelve were converted from A/S-M/S and twenty-two were switched over during the building stage.

Conversion of Trawlers, Whalers, Drifters and Yachts

Before the war it was envisaged, as a result of the experience of the 1914-18 War and the taking up of fishing trawlers at short notice in connection with the Italian-Abyssinian War in 1937, that a conversion of several hundred small craft for duties in Home waters was to be expected within a period of a month from the commencement of any new war; a hundred or more of these vessels would be required at forty-eight hours' notice for minesweeping.

Investigations were therefore made into the stability and seaworthiness of numerous trawlers, whalers, drifters and yachts, based on essential armament and accommodation requirements, and emergency outline plans and specifications were prepared for as many types as possible on the assumption that only essential conversion work would be undertaken. For a large number of vessels it was found that no drawings or hydrostatic particulars were available, and in such cases assistance was rendered by Messrs Smiths Dock in providing full information for typical vessels and by Messrs Isherwoods in taking off the lines of a required ship when in dock, and preparing from them hydrostatic particulars and stability curves.

[4] Note the more technical discussion of trawler stability given in: Spanner, W F. Some notes on the Design of Trawlers and Drifters with particular reference to Seaworthiness and Stability. Trans INA, London, 1947.

The work of conversion was given to a number of small firms, in order to minimise interference with other naval work, and was supervised by an emergency conversion organisation under the Warship Production Superintendents, who were responsible for the adjustment of the outline arrangements supplied by the Admiralty to suit the individual ships as they came in hand. A similar procedure was followed for conversions abroad, and a large number of vessels were converted at ports in South Africa, the Mediterranean, Near East and India. It was found practicable to incline only a proportion of the vessels before completion; but as many were undertaken as time and labour permitted; final ballasting instructions were then issued to the WPS, who was responsible for its installation. As the war progressed, inclining experiments were made on as many ships as possible to discover the accretion of weight and so maintain stability and trim.

Due to limitations of stability and freeboard, it was necessary on conversion to land all non-essential stores and spare gear, and the fitting of armament and other naval equipment necessitated the addition of ballast, usually in a forward position to reduce the stern trim. In some of the earlier conversions, due to lack of time, labour, etc. a stated quantity of coal was retained as ballast, instructions being issued that it was only to be burnt in an emergency. In order to preserve seaworthiness, careful attention was paid to the condition of shifting boards in cross bunkers and the watertightness of openings in the upper deck. A serious menace in Arctic waters was the accumulation of ice on deck which, if unchecked, could quickly reduce stability to a dangerous extent; pickaxes and similar equipment were issued for keeping the decks clear, and the possibility of covering the deck with a de-icing material was investigated, but without yielding a satisfactory solution.

To ensure reasonable stability and seaworthiness, a minimum standard of 12in metacentric height was worked to, and the minimum freeboard in the deep condition was taken at 24in in the small craft to 30in in the larger vessels. These standards could only be maintained during service by the imposition of restrictions on the amount of fuel, etc. which could be carried but, even so, it was not generally possible to incorporate alterations and additions that were made to Admiralty-designed trawlers.[4]

All these craft were vulnerable to underwater damage, especially aft, due to lack of watertight subdivision, and in the connection an extra WT bulkhead between the engine and boiler rooms would have effected a considerable improvement.

Stella Carina, a typical requisitioned trawler with a 4 inch LA gun forward.

Trawlers

In general, the larger trawlers of 140ft length and over were used for anti-submarine duties, the smaller vessels being allocated to minesweeping.

The deck over the fish-hold (used on naval service for accommodation), was usually in a very bad condition in the older trawlers, and in some of the worst cases the fitting of a steel deck was necessary. In principle, however, this was generally unacceptable due to the additional weight involved and the limited supply of suitable labour in the small shipyards concerned.

Improvements were made to the natural ventilation and in the larger vessels awnings, domestic automatic refrigerators and forced ventilation were fitted to make them suitable for operations under tropical conditions.

Whalers

These vessels were able to operate at higher speeds than trawlers and, with their powerful rudders, possessed exceptional manoeuvring qualities. The larger of them, of 130ft length or more, were converted for anti-submarine duties, and the smaller were used as LL minesweepers.

Whaling gear was landed and additional accommodation and natural ventilation fitted. In vessels required to operate in tropical waters artificial ventilation was provided.

The helmsman's position on the bridge, which was open and in most cases sufficiently large to enable a standard compass to be fitted in addition to the steering compass, was fitted with steel or plastic armour protection.

Windermere, a wartime built whaler.

Drifters

In drifters taken up for wartime service, additional accommodation was fitted in the fish-hold, and WCs and washplaces were provided on the upper deck adjacent to the companion ways. Hatches and doors were made reasonably watertight with adequate securing arrangements and alternative emergency escape arrangements were provided for officers and crew.

In a number of vessels the mizzen mast was removed to allow a 0.5in machine gun or an Oerlikon to be fitted over the galley aft, but it was generally considered that the lack of the mizzen sail appreciably increased the difficulty of handling the vessel, particularly at slow speeds and in wind.

In most drifters it was found that the freeboard was insufficient for adequate dryness, reserve of buoyancy and range of stability, and this necessitated the limitation of the amounts of coal and water carried on board.

The standard compass was fitted over the wheelhouse, and was surrounded with stanchions and canvas weather protection 4ft 3in high, the wheelhouse being too small to accommodate both the compass and binnacle. A helmsman's shelter, constructed of non-magnetic steel plates, was provided in the wheelhouse, although in some cases, due to lack of space, the steel plating was bolted over the outside.

Most drifters were fitted with acetylene lighting only, and in many of these steam-driven electric generators were installed later in the war, together with electric lighting.

Yachts

Many yachts of from 100ft to 220ft length were taken up for wartime service as anti-submarine training vessels, dan-laying, escort and armed boarding vessels, etc.

In most cases the accommodation was found to be adequate with only minor alterations and the addition of extra natural ventilation. For vessels required to serve in the tropics, awnings, artificial ventilation and domestic refrigerators were added.

These vessels were of light scantlings and built for fair-weather conditions, and it was found necessary to make a number of alterations to improve seaworthiness. These included the blanking over of all side-lights within 6ft of the waterline, the raising of sills on hatches and doors on the upper deck to 2ft 6in in height, the overhaul of all doors and hatches on the weather deck to ensure reasonable watertightness, wherever practicable, and the fitting of suitable covers and protection to exposed light scantling glass skylights. In some cases it was necessary, due to the greatly increased displacement, to plate up the ship's side to the level of the boat deck and also to fill in the well deck forward to improve the seaworthiness and reserve of buoyancy. Wherever possible WCs and bathrooms, etc., which were originally positioned below the water line, were raised one deck higher in order to discharge above the waterline.

Emergency escape hatches had to be fitted to give extra access from below deck, the original access being insufficient for the vessel's wartime duties, and the large amount of interior woodwork making the risk of fire a serious menace. Lack of time and labour precluded the possibility of the removal of inflammable material, and the fire risk was minimised by an increased allowance of fire-fighting appliances.

Depending on the type of bridge layout, suitable protection was provided in each vessel for the helmsman.

Details of representative groups of conversions for anti-submarine or minesweeping duties are given in the appendices, but, in addition to these principal conversions for minesweeping and anti-submarine duties, smaller numbers of trawlers, whalers, drifters and yachts were fitted out during the war as follows:

Torpedo recovery drifters; D/F calibration drifters and yachts; A/P and E/A trawlers, drifters and yachts; A/S instructional yachts; danlaying trawlers, drifters and whalers; flare-burning drifters; balloon barrage drifters and trawlers; harbour defence drifters and trawlers; target towing trawlers, whalers and drifters; drifters for de-perming and wiping units.

Conqueror, *an armed yacht. She carried some unusual rocket weapons -* Pillar Box *on the quarter deck and* Strength Through Joy *further forward. (See* Rocket propelled AA Weapons used by the RN during the Second World War. Warships Supplement 102, *Kendal, 1990.)*

In addition, a large number of drifters were used as passenger and store-carrying tenders in the various drifter pools which were set up for servicing the fleet, at Scapa, Kirkwall, etc.

General

Approximately 1700 trawlers, whalers, drifters and yachts were requisitioned for wartime service as Auxiliary White Ensign Vessels.

Minesweepers

Trawlers LL M/S	220
Trawlers 'O' M/S	290
Whalers LL M/S	100
Drifters LL M/S	70
Drifters 'O' M/S and Skid Towing	10
Yachts for M/S Attendant Duties	5

A/S Vessels

Trawlers Ocean Escort	109
Trawlers Coastal and Local Escort	100
Whalers	50
Drifters	17
Yachts	52

Esso Smoke-Producing Trawlers	50

Auxiliary Patrol Vessels – Harbour Defence Patrol Vessels, etc.

Trawlers	120
Drifters	130
Yachts	50

Balloon Barrage

Trawlers	69
Drifters	64
Yachts	25

Examination Service and Contraband Control

Trawlers	20
Drifters	36
Yachts	25

Mobile Wiping Units

Drifters	27
Yachts	2

Torpedo Recovery Vessels

Drifters	19

D/F Calibration Yachts	15

Accommodation Vessels and Base Ships

Yachts	12

Target Towing Vessels

Yachts	10

Submarine Escort and Target Towing	7
Radar Training Ships	2

Total 1706

M/S Whalers

Full Speed 11-12kts
Towing speed 7-9kts
(approx 100 in number)

Size:	116ft x 24ft x 13ft 6in
Gear fitted:	LL M/S Mk II* (total weight 29 tons including structure) SA Gear Mk II with 'A' frame (weight 3 tons) In some cases LL M/S Mk III was fitted in lieu of Mk II* (weight 32 tons) at the cost of one day's reduction in steaming A few larger vessels of 130ft x 26ft x 14ft were also fitted out with LL Mk III. These vessels were equipped with a 12pdr gun in addition to the armament stated In a few cases radar type 286 PQ was fitted at the cost of ½ day's reduction in steaming NB: Whaling winch and whaling equipment weighing approx 25 tons was landed
Armament:	One 0.5in twin Vickers Mk IV or one Oerlikon Mk VIIA forward plus three .303in twin Browning machine guns In some cases one additional Oerlikon was fitted aft at the cost of one day's reduction in steaming
Ballast:	Approx 20 tons in accumulator space
Fuel & Water:	65 tons* oil fuel (7 days' steaming plus 2 days' reserve at economical speed) In a number of cases, due to increases of weight, the oil fuel was restricted to 40 tons 6 tons domestic fresh water 16 tons reserve feed water, reduced in a number of cases to 10 tons *out of a total oil fuel tank capacity of 90 tons
Complement:	2 officers, 21 ratings

Drifters

Max Speed 8-9kts
Towing Speed (LL Mk V 5-6kts
('O' Mk III 4-5kts
(approx 80 in number)

Size: LL Vessels 87ft x 19ft x 10ft 6in

Gear fitted: LL Mk V Total weight 18 tons
Approx 8-10 tons of fishing gear was landed

Armament: Three .303in machine guns
One Oerlikon Mk VIIA
In a few vessels a second Oerlikon Mk VIIA was fitted aft on the galley in lieu of a .303in machine gun at the cost of one day's steaming

Ballast: 5 tons forward for trim

Fuel & Water: 12 to 15 tons of coal (approx 3 days' steaming plus one day reserve)
1 ton reserve feed water
1 ton domestic water

Complement: 2 officers, 9 ratings

Size: 'O' M/S Vessels 87ft x 19ft x 10ft 6in

Gear fitted: 'O' M/S Mk III (weighing 5 tons)

Armament: As for LL drifters

Ballast: As for LL drifters

Fuel & Water: 15-18 tons of coal
1 ton reserve feed water
1 ton domestic water

Complement: As for LL drifters

M/S Trawlers

Full speed 8½-10kts
Towing speed {LL M/S 5½-7½kts
{'O' M/S 4-6kts
(approx 510 in number)

Size: LL M/S vessels 115ft x 22ft x 12ft 5in to 125ft x 23ft 6in x 13ft 6in

Gear fitted: As for whalers
NB: trawl winch and trawling equipment (weight approx 20 tons) were landed

Armament: As for whalers except in larger vessels, where 12pdr was fitted forward

Ballast: 25-35 tons at after end of fish hold

Fuel & Water: 70-80 tons of coal* (7 days' steaming plus 2 days' reserve at econom-

ical speed – consumption 8-10 tons per day)
In a number of cases due to increases of weight only 40 tons of coal was carried
Domestic water 5 tons
Reserve feed water 10 tons
*full bunker capacity 110-150 tons

Complement: 2 officers, 21 ratings

Size: 'O' M/S vessels 125ft x 23ft 6in x 13ft 6in to 140ft x 24ft x 14ft

Gear fitted: 'O' Mk II (total weight 7 tons)
Trawl winch, fairleads and gallows were retained
5-10 tons of fishing gear was landed
Later in the war radar type 286PQ was fitted at the cost of ½ a day's reduction in steaming

Armament: One 12pdr on HA Mk IX mounting forward
Two .303in twin Brownings on lower bridge wings P & S
One Oerlikon Mk VIIA aft on galley-
In some of the larger vessels one additional Oerlikon gun was fitted aft at the cost of one day's reduction in steaming
2 double depth charge chutes

Ballast: 30-40 tons at fore end of fish hold

Fuel & Water: 70-100 tons of coal
Domestic water 10 tons
Reserve feed water 10 tons

Complement: 3 officers, 25 ratings

A/S Whalers

Full seagoing speed 12-13kts
(approx 50 in number)

Size: 130ft x 26ft x 14ft 6in. A few larger vessels were also fitted out, viz 148ft x 27ft 6in x 15ft 0in

Gear fitted: A/S gear type 123A – later converted to type 123D in some of the larger vessels
Whaling winch and whaling equipment (approx 30 tons) was landed
Later in the war radar type 286PQ was fitted in a number of vessels at the cost of ½ a day's reduction in steaming

Armament: 4in QF Mk IV with P Mk IX mounting forward
One 0.5in twin Vickers Mk IV or one Oerlikon Mk VIIA aft
Two .303in Browning machine guns fitted, one port and one starboard on bridge wings
In some of the larger vessels a second Oerlikon Mk VIIA was fitted aft at the cost of one day's reduction in steaming
25 depth charges carried – 15 in rails over stern
2 depth charge throwers

Ballast: 30-40 tons in accumulator space

Fuel & Water: 90 tons* oil fuel (7 days' steaming at economical speed, consumption 9 tons per day plus 2 days' reserve)
Due to the fitting of radar type 286PQ and an additional Oerlikon Mk VIIA, the fuel oil was reduced to 72 tons
Domestic water 10 tons
Reserve feed water 20 tons
*out of a total oil fuel capacity of about 140 tons

Complement: 2 officers, 30 ratings

Ocean Escort Trawlers

Full seagoing speed 11-12kts
(approx 100 in number)

Size: 160ft x 28ft x 15ft 6in and larger

Gear fitted: A/S gear type 123A. Later converted to type 123D 27ft whaler and 14ft 6in drifter dinghy
Winch gallows, fishing gear (approx 30 tons) landed later in the war radar type 286PQ and unifoxer gear was fitted. This involved ½ to 1 day's reduction of steaming endurance

Armament: 4in QF Mk IV with P Mk IX mounting forward
One 0.5in Vickers twin Mk IV or one Oerlikon Mk VIIA aft
Two 0.303in Brownings on bridge wings
55 depth charges (25 heavy and 30 light) 16-18 on rails over stern
4 Mk IV depth charge throwers
2 additional Oerlikons – one port and one starboard on lower bridge

wings were subsequently fitted at the cost of 2 days' reduction in steaming

Ballast: 60-80 tons ballast under fish hold and coal in bunkers as required

Fuel & Water: 200 tons of coal (14 days steaming at economical speed consumption 11 tons per day plus 3 days' reserve)
Domestic water 20 tons
Reserve feed water 20 tons

Complement: 4 officers, 46 ratings

A/S Coastal and Local Escort Trawlers

Full seagoing speed 10½-11½kts
(approx 100 in number)

Size: Coastal escort trawlers: 150ft x 25ft 6in x 14ft 6in and a few larger vessels 155ft x 25ft 6in x 14ft 9in
Local escort trawlers: 126ft x 24ft x 13ft 9in and a few larger

Gear fitted: A/S gear type 123A
Winch, gallows and fishing gear (approx 25 tons) landed
Later in the war radar type 286PQ was fitted

Armament: 4in QF Mk IV with P Mk IX mounting forward
1-0.5in Vickers twin or 1-Oerlikon Mk IIIA aft
2-.303in Brownings on bridge wings
2-depth charge throwers & 25 depth charges
2-additional Oerlikons, one port and one starboard on lower bridge wings were subsequently fitted at the cost of 2 days' reduction in steaming

Ballast: 40-60 tons of ballast under fish hold and coal in wing bunkers as required

Fuel & Water: 140-150 tons of coal (11 days steaming at economical speed consumption approx 10 tons per day plus 2 days' reserve)
Domestic water 10 tons
Reserve feed water 15 tons

Complement: 3 officers, 35 ratings

CHAPTER 21

Boom Defence Vessels

Editorial Note

As in the case of trawlers, one may note the careful pre war planning with a small number of vessels being built from 1930 onwards leading to a satisfactory design by 1935 which was built in large numbers during the war.

In order to carry out the functions of boom defence to harbours, fleet anchorages, etc. it was necessary to have vessels to lay the moorings, to tow and rig the boom to act as gate vessels for opening and closing the section for vessels passing through, and to give constant attention to repairing the boom to maintain the utmost efficiency.

The general requirements for gate vessels for anti-submarine booms were:

(a) Strong construction and good weatherly qualities to withstand the stresses set up by the net sections supported on either side and those experienced when the vessels were moored bow and stern in exposed positions.

(b) Medium size of about 100ft long.

(c) Good standard of accommodation.

(d) Heavy bollards for moorings.

(e) Double-barrelled winch (to take duplicate wires) fitted with warp-ends capable of exerting pull of 10 tons.

(f) Turtle deck aft with special fairlead for allowing boom connecting wires to slide off the vessel when net is attacked.

(g) Signalling searchlight and in some cases W/T.

(h) Mast and yards for gate signals.

(i) Anti-submarine gun.

The above requirements could, of course, be met by the conversion of trawlers but, owing to the many other requirements for these vessels in an emergency, it was considered other arrangements should be made.

Provision was made in the 1930 programme for the construction of a *Standard Gate Vessel*.

General particulars of the design were:

Length overall	98ft 8in
Length between perpendiculars	93ft 0in
Breadth moulded	25ft 0in (later 26ft 0in)
Depth (moulded)	13ft 6in
Displacement (deep)	371 tons
Mean draught (deep)	9ft 8in
Complement	5 officers, 35 men

The vessel was dumb but fitted with auxiliary boilers to provide steam for working the winches, viz. two vertical oil-fired boilers, and stowage for 21 tons of oil fuel.

In view of the possibility of deterioration of hull due to the vessel being laid up for considerable

Barhill: taken on 3 Dec 1952, this photo shows her very much in wartime state except for the removal of the 3 inch from behind the funnel.

periods, extra thickness of hull structure was provided to meet this contingency.

Gate equipment fitted consisted of 1-10 ton double-barrelled winch with warp ends, fairleads, etc.

Armament fitted was 1-3in gun and two Lewis guns.

Stability particulars:

	Deep Condition
Metacentric height	1.7ft
Max GZ	0.65ft
Angle of max GZ	27°
Range	46°
Displacement	371 tons

Due to extra weights being added when the first vessel was building, 25 tons of ballast was added to improve stability.

The first vessel, *Moorgate*, was laid down in May 1931 and completed in December of the same year. Further vessels were included in the 1931, 1932, 1933 and 1934 programmes.

These later vessels were of similar size and construction but with the beam increased by 1ft to 26ft and, in the case of one vessel, a third boiler was fitted to provide additional steam power.

The gate equipment on these ships was originally designed for the working of a single gate, but in those vessels used for the working of a double gate it was necessary to convert the double barrelled winch into a four-barrelled winch and provide additional fairleads, etc. Girdling was fitted to improve stability consequent on fitting additional items for the second gate.

A total of six boom defence vessels was built to this design: *Moorgate*, *Bishopsgate*, *Aldgate*, *Watergate*, *Ludgate* and *Dowgate*.

Boom Working Vessels

The laying of moorings for booms was originally carried out by means of a mooring vessel and maintenance of booms by a small converted trawler known as a boom working vessel. Such boom working vessels required good seagoing qualities in view of booms having to be laid in exposed positions, a speed of about 10kts, and the equipment etc. for remaining at sea for periods of a week or more.

In 1935 a *Mersey* class trawler, the *Barnet*, was re-purchased from trade and adapted for boom work.

The modifications necessary to be carried out included the removal of the forecastle and the fitting of bow troughs, one each side, for handling moorings and weights of the order of 8 tons; fitting of derricks on the foremast and mainmast, gallows, fairleads and bollards, etc. A small set of taut wire measuring gear was provided for fixing the position of moorings. The fish hold was gutted and a platform deck arranged in the hold to provide for crew's accommodation and store rooms. Armament was also fitted for defence against submarine attack; W/T and signalling arrangements were also provided.

The general particulars of the trawler as converted were as follows:

Length overall	13ft 4in
Breadth (moulded)	23ft 9in
Depth (moulded)	12ft 8in
Displacement (deep)	596 tons
Mean draught (deep)	10ft 0in
Speed	10kts
Complement	25 officers and crew

Boom Working Equipment consisted of a trawl winch, bow troughs to handle 8 tons, 5 ton derrick on the foremast, 3 ton derrick on main-mast, 3 ton gallows forward, 2 ton gallows aft and a tow hook.

Machinery consisted of one cylindrical coal-fired boiler with one triple expansion main engine giving 600ihp to give the ship a speed of 10kts.

150 tons of coal were carried as fuel; endurance was approx 2000 miles at 9kts.

Armament fitted was 1-12pdr gun and two Lewis guns.

Stability was maintained by the fitting of 40 tons of permanent ballast to give the following figures:

	Deep Condition	Light Condition
Metacentric height	1.43ft (fl)	1.03ft
Displacement	596 tons	413 tons

In the 1934 programme approval was given to build to Admiralty design a boom working vessel; this vessel was eventually named *Dunnet* and was laid down in November 1935.

She was fitted out similarly to *Barnet* except that twin horns were fitted, in lieu of bow troughs, to lift 10 tons. In addition to the 10 ton double-barrelled winch forward, two 5 ton winches were fitted aft. The after gallows were arranged over the stern instead of port and starboard.

The general particulars of the design were:

Length overall	138ft 2in
Length between perps	125ft 0in
Breadth (moulded)	26ft 6in
Depth (moulded)	14ft 0in
Deep displacement	440 tons
Mean draught, deep	9ft 10in
Speed	10½kts
Complement	4 officers, 17 men

Boom working equipment consisted of two bow horns tested to 20 tons, one double-barrelled 10 ton winch forward, two single-barrelled 5 ton winches aft and one derrick to lift 10 tons at 16ft radius.

Machinery: one coal-fired cylindrical boiler and a steam reciprocating main engine giving 350ihp and a maximum speed of 10½kts. The 80 tons of coal carried gave an endurance of 3000 miles at 8kts.

Armament as in other boom working vessels consisted of 1-12pdr gun and two Lewis guns.

Stability in the light condition – 324 tons displacement – gave a metacentric height of 1.44ft.

In order to improve pulling power and to gain experience, approval was given after completion of vessel to fit a Kort nozzle. This nozzle was fitted in position by welding to hull and satisfactory trials were carried out at Sheerness in 1939. During these trials the *Dunnet* exerted a static pull of 6.8 tons compared with the previous maximum of 3.5 tons, but the improvement was considered to be partially due to improvements in the machinery.

Barricade **Class**

In the 1935 programme approval was given to design a vessel embodying all experience gained in the operation of boom defence vessels. These vessels, *Barricade* Class, were designed to carry out the duties of operating gates, laying booms, handling heavy moorings and for transporting moorings and boom working gear.

The design was worked out in conjunction with the Department of Boom Defence and the general particulars were as follows:

Length overall	173ft 9in
Length between perps	150ft 0in
Breadth (moulded)	32ft 0in
Depth (moulded)	17ft 0in
Displacement (deep)	959 tons
Mean draught (deep)	11ft 5½in
Trim by stern	7ft 5in
Speed	11kts
Endurance	3100 miles at 10kts
Complement	44 officers and men (maximum)

The construction of the hull and machinery was to Classification Society Rules except for certain parts of the hull, viz: turtle stern and bow ramp which required special consideration in design.

The vessels were fitted with twin bow horns, two winches and a derrick. A large hold was provided forward for the carrying of four 8 ton stretcher weights and power worked drums to take winch wires. A rigger's workshop was fitted on

deck over hold. Special roller fairleads and fittings were arranged on the upper deck for numerous gate and boom working leads. Provision was made for working of double gate.

A navigating bridge was fitted at the forward end of the boiler casing.

Boom Working Equipment etc consisted of:
  2-bow horns tested to 20 tons in early vessels and 27 tons in later vessels
  2-double-barrelled, 10 ton winches, with warp ends
  1-derrick to lift 8 tons at 28ft
  4-15in bollards, roller fairleads etc.
  1-17ft 3in boom boat

Armament consisted of:
  1-3in HA/LA or 12pdr
  2-single Lewis or Brownings
  2-PAC projectors

Machinery

Two cylindrical boilers working at 200lb/sq in, and one triple expansion steam reciprocating engine developing 850ihp at 175rpm to give a max speed of 11kts.

The boilers were coal-fired and 175 tons were carried in the main bunkers and 39 tons in the reserve bunkers. Endurance was 3100 miles at 10kts.

Propeller particulars were:
  one 4-bladed cast iron propeller
  diameter   9ft 1in
  pitch   7ft 5in
  developed blade area   30sq ft

Propeller shrouds were fitted to prevent wires fouling. Steering gear was steam and hand-controlled, and in the earlier vessels was of the chain and quadrant type while in ships of the 1939 programme and later it was of screw type.

Electric power was provided by two 20kW steam generators.

Stability Particulars

	Light Displacement	Deep Displacement
Metacentric height	2.0ft	2.7ft (fl)
Max GZ	1.43ft	1.49ft
Angle of max GZ	30°	33°
Range	65°	70°
Displacement	682 tons	959 tons

Accommodation

Two double cabins were fitted on the after steering flat and messes were provided on the lower deck forward for twenty-nine men.

After the order of the first seven ships of the class, all vessels were fitted out for laying first-

Barricade class general arrangement

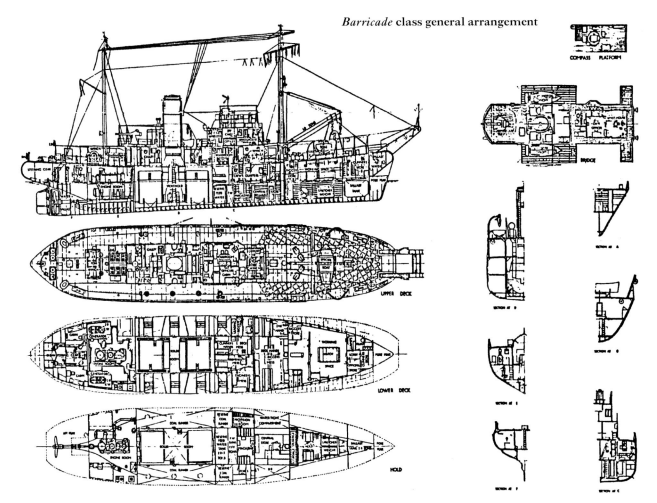

class moorings, the horns being lengthened and redesigned to lift 27 tons, and heavy bollards and clench plates were fitted. Except for the provision of canopies, breakwater and additional items required for proceeding to tropics and for long sea voyages few modifications were found necessary on service.

In addition to the duties for which these vessels were designed they did very useful work in the clearing of harbours during the many operations which were undertaken during and after the war.

The particulars of this design were supplied to other Allies for information and formed the basis for boom defence vessels built in the USA.

In all, seventy-two vessels of this class were laid down and the first and last completed in April 1938 and November 1945 respectively. The length of time for building varied between ten months and one and a half years.

Bayonet Class

In 1937 approval was given for a design for six boom working vessels – *Bayonet* class. The vessels were required for the purpose of laying booms in waters too shallow for the larger *Barricade* class.

In addition to laying booms requirements were for gate opening, transport and handling booms, laying moorings. Derricks and steam winches were provided. The general layout of the design was similar to that approve for the *Barricade* class.

General particulars for the class were:

Length overall	159ft 8in
Length between perps	135ft 0in
Breadth (moulded)	30ft 6in
Depth (moulded)	16ft 0in
Displacement (deep)	780 tons
Mean draught (deep)	11ft 5½in
Trim by stern	3ft 1in
Speed	11kts
Endurance	1900 miles at 10kts
Complement	44 officers and men

Boom Working Equipment included:
2-bow horns tested to 20 tons (six vessels were fitted to lay first-class moorings and the horns were tested to 27 tons)
2-double-barrelled 10 ton winches with warp ends
1-derrick to lift 10 tons at 23ft radius
4-15in bollards, roller fairleads etc.

1-17ft 3in boom boat

Armament consisted of:
   1-3in HA/LA gun
   2-single Lewis guns
   2-PAC projectors

Machinery
One cylindrical coal-fired boiler, working at 200lb/sq in and a triple expansion steam engine developing 850ihp and a maximum speed of 11kts at 175rpm (free).

Coal capacity was 134 tons (plus 18 tons in the reserve bunkers), giving an endurance of 1900 miles at 10kts.

Propeller particulars:
   one 4-bladed propeller
   diameter   9ft 4in
   pitch   7ft 2in
   developed blade area 32sq ft
Propeller shrouds similar to those in *Barricade* class were fitted to prevent wires fouling.

Steering gear in this class was of the screw steam and hand type.

Electrical power was provided by 1-25kW steam generator.

Stability Particulars	Light Displacement	Deep Displacement
Metacentric height	2.55ft	2.65ft
Max GZ	1.3ft	1.3ft
Angle of max GZ	35°	30°
Range	62°	62°
Displacement	540 tons	780 tons

Accommodation was typical for the type of ship and consisted of COs cabin aft of the navigating bridge; wardroom and cabins for the officers on the lower deck aft. Crew space was arranged forward of the boiler room, and provision was made for naval, civilian or native ratings as appropriate.

A total of eleven vessels of this class were ordered and were completed on the outbreak of

Bayonet **class general arrangement**

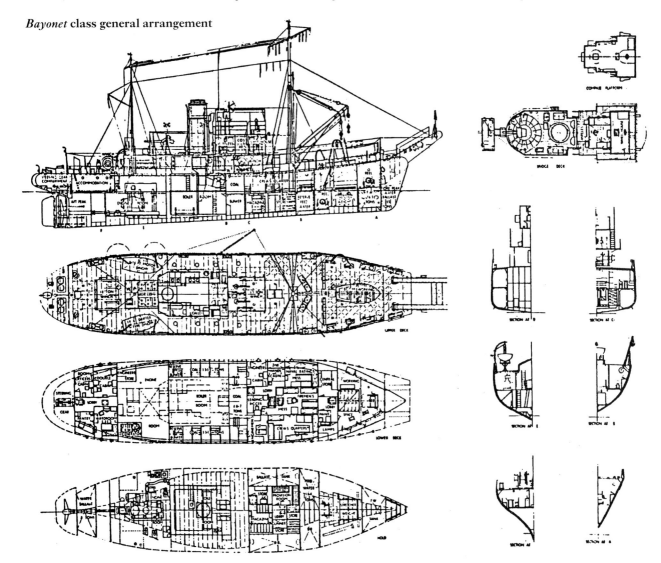

war. The last six completed were equipped for laying first-class moorings, decks being strengthened as necessary and heavy bollards and clench plates fitted; the horns were also modified to lift 27 tons.

The length of time for building varied between nine and fifteen months.

As compared with the *Barricade* class these vessels were not so suitable for acting as gate vessels as they had only one boiler, which necessitated their withdrawal from the gate for boiler cleaning.

Trawler Conversions

In addition to the *Barricade* and *Bayonet* classes, it became apparent that other vessels would be necessary for carrying out boom working and gate duties in conjunction with the larger boom defence vessels. Orders were placed in January 1939 for four trawlers to be taken up and converted for this purpose. The modifications were generally as for *Barnet*, with the addition of 10 ton winch, necessary fairleads, etc. and ramp deck aft to enable vessels to carry out gate duties. Two types of trawlers were taken up, large and small, generally of the dimensions of the *Mersey* class and *Castle* class respectively. Large vessels were capable of working a double gate, small vessels a single gate. At the close of war about ninety trawlers had been converted for this purpose. In addition to the boom working trawlers it became necessary to fit out other small trawlers as single gate vessels. In addition to providing for the complement by gutting the fishhold and fitting a flat it was necessary to fit additional roller fairleads and bollards; about twenty trawlers were so converted.

(i) Particulars of small type boom and gate working trawlers were:

Length between perps	121 0in to 135ft 8in
Breadth (moulded)	22ft 1in to 24ft 0in
Depth (moulded)	13ft 0in to 14ft 0in
Deep displacement	about 575 tons
Complement	2 officers, 23 men

Machinery usually of the steam reciprocating type, with a coal-fired boiler; coal capacity between 100 and 120 tons, giving endurances of about 10 tons coal per day at 10kts. Speeds of the ships were between 8 and 10kts.

Each trawler was armed with two Lewis guns and protection from machine-gun fire was fitted around the bridge.

The boom equipment fitted included two bow troughs to lift 10 tons each; one double-barrelled trawl winch with warp ends forward; a single-barrelled 10 ton winch aft, and one derrick to lift 2 tons. Each trawler carried a 17ft 3in boom boat and was capable of boom working or working a single gate.

Typical stability particulars for a trawler of the *Castle* class were as follows:

	Light Condition	Deep Condition
Metacentric height	1.3ft	1.81ft (fl)
Max GZ	0.84ft	0.63ft
Angle of max GZ	35°	33°
Range	66°	64°
Displacement	437 tons	576 tons

To maintain reasonable stability it was necessary to fit permanent ballast in all these small trawlers – about 30 tons. Further, it was necessary to restrict the use of coal for light condition with deck load.

(ii) Particulars of large type boom and gate working trawlers:

Length between perps	138ft 4in to 161ft 0in
Breadth (moulded)	23ft 3in to 28ft 6in
Depth (moulded)	13ft 6in to 15ft 0in
Deep displacement	about 685 tons
Complement	3 officers, 26 men

Machinery was dependent upon the individual vessel but, for the majority of the class, consisted of a steam reciprocating engine with a cylindrical coal-fired boiler. Coal capacity was 120-150 tons and endurances were based on 10 tons coal per day at 10kts.

Speeds of ships were 9-11kts.

Armament and protection were as for smaller trawler type boom and gate working vessels.

Boom equipment was also as for the smaller trawlers.

Stability particulars for a typical ship, *Mersey* class, were:

	Light Condition	Deep Condition
Metacentric height	1.12ft	1.49ft
Max GZ	0.68ft	0.54ft
Angle of max GZ	37°	35°
Range	63°	62°
Displacement	534 tons	684 tons

Permanent ballast fitted consisted of 65 tons of rock ballast, and the usual coal restrictions were imposed for the vessels in the light condition with a deck load.

Owing to the age of many of the trawlers it was necessary for the wood decks to be removed and replaced by steel decks. In some cases exhaustive rebuilding of the hull was involved.

The time taken to carry out a conversion of a trawler to a boom working vessel was of the order 4-6 months.

Boom Defence Vessels in the Far East

Requirements in the Far East called for a further number of boom working vessels, but due to large commitments of steel shipbuilders, repeats of vessels of the *Barricade* class could not be undertaken.

It was decided to build vessels of composite construction and to employ firms with wood shipbuilding experience. The design of vessel was approved to be similar to that of *Bayonet* class except that only one bow horn would be fitted and to overcome difficulties in building a turtle back stern to fit steel bolsters. No provision was made for laying first-class moorings. The hull scantlings were generally to conform to Classification Society rules for composite vessels. As some of the shipbuilders had little steel capacity, it was arranged for the steel structural work such as bulkheads, frames, floors, keels, etc. to be supplied from steel shipbuilders.

Separate orders were placed by the Admiralty for all items, such as oil fuel tanks, freshwater tanks, reserve feed tanks and for roller fairleads.

The armament was to be 1-3in HA/LA gun, two Oerlikons, two twin Brownings, two PAC projectors and one depth charge thrower.

Dimensions, estimated weights and capacities were as follows:

Length overall	168ft 0in
Length between perps	140ft 0in
Breadth (moulded)	34ft 1in
Depth (moulded)	17ft 0in
Displacement (deep)	885 tons
Mean draught (deep)	12ft 1in
Trim by stern	7ft 0in
Freeboard	6ft 6in
Metacentric height	2.7ft (fl)
Oil fuel	100 tons

The approved 1943 programme provided for fourteen vessels.

Owing to low priority, progress in building was slow and at the end of hostilities none of these vessels had been completed, and construction was suspended and vessels subsequently cancelled.

Prefect Class Wooden Boom Vessels

Five vessels of this class were built by the US Navy and allocated to the RN under the Lease-Lend agreement.

In order to bring the vessels to our requirements for laying of moorings and boom and gate working, the following modifications were made to the class:

(a) Plating to horns in wake of rollers filled in and fitted with facing pins to prevent shackles fouling when passing over rollers.

(b) Tread strips welded on fore deck and between horns.

(c) WT door fitted to give access from working space to paint store, etc.

(d) Screen fitted over after winch.

(e) Fairleads for stern anchor with pedestal and heel fitting to davit made portable and flush with deck.

(f) Two pedestal fairleads aft on each side of special fairlead.

(g) Berger fairleads on port and starboard quarters removed and one fitted on centre line, second stowed in hold.

(h) Wood coaming round main hatch made solid and sheathed with plate.

(i) Additional bollards, eyeplates and clench plates fitted as necessary.

General particulars of the class:

Length overall	194ft 6in
Length between perps	169ft 2in
Breadth (moulded)	34ft 7in
Depth (moulded)	20ft 0in
Deep displacement	1329 tons
Mean draught (deep)	13ft ½in
Diesel oil	104 tons
Speed	12.3kts
Complement	36 officers and men

Boom Equipment

2 horns tested to 25 tons
2-10 ton electric double-barrelled winches
1 derrick forward to lift 12ton at 25ft radius
1 derrick aft to lift 3½ton at 21ft radius
4-10in bollards, fairleads, etc.

Machinery was diesel electric driving a single shaft at 220rpm – maximum horsepower 1500. Auxiliary power was provided by two generators giving 620kW at 240 volts. Steering gear was of electric type.

Armament

1-single 3in HA/LA gun
2-Oerlikons

Stability Particulars

	Light Displacement	Deep Displacement
Metacentric height	3.48ft	3.52ft
Angle of max GZ	40°	39°
Range	74°	71°
Displacement	1098 tons	1329 tons

The length of time to build a ship to this design was 14 to 16 months.

CHAPTER 22

Salvage and Wreck Dispersal Vessels

Editorial Note
As explained in the text, there was little salvage capability or experience in the UK prior to the war and, in this case, the Admiralty had not made advance plans. A large building programme was needed as was, presumably, a training programme.

Salvage Vessels

The work of the Salvage Department of the Admiralty was severely hampered in the first years of the war by a shortage of suitable salvage ships. In the years preceding the war, marine salvage had been, in this country, a declining industry, with the result that at the beginning of the war there were less than half-a-dozen salvage vessels in commission and only a very few professional salvage men. When war appeared imminent arrangements were made to establish an Admiralty Salvage Department and the resources available were brought under its control without delay; steps were also taken to provide more ships and additional salvage equipment and to establish bases all round the coast.

The requirements for the various salvage craft were formulated by the Salvage Department and DNC prepared the new designs, plans for the conversion of vessels and checked the stability of all craft for which the Salvage Department was responsible.

Ocean-Going Salvage Vessels
The requirements for ocean-going salvage vessels were formulated in Autumn 1940 and a design was produced by the Admiralty for a class of vessels later to be known as the *King Salvor* class.

These vessels were designed for off-shore or shallow water salvage operations, for rendering assistance to ships under adverse weather conditions and for fire-fighting purposes. They were built to Lloyd's 100 A1 class and Ministry of War Transport requirements, but local increases were made in scantlings to suit special Admiralty requirements.

Length overall	216ft 6in
Length between perps	200ft 9in
Beam moulded	37ft 9in
Depth to upper deck	18ft 0in
Deep displacement	1710 tons
Mean draught (deep)	11ft 9½in
Speed (max)	12kts
Oil fuel	310 tons

In the *King Salvor* design provision was made for pinning down above wrecks and taking a 300 tons tidal lift distributed 150 tons at the bow and stern.

Machinery
Main engines consisted of two sets of triple expansion reciprocating type capable of developing a total of 1500ihp at 140rpm.

Propeller particulars:

two 3-bladed propellers at 140rpm	
diameter	9ft 0in
pitch	10ft 0in
developed blade area	22½sq ft

Steam was supplied by two single-ended oil-fired Scotch boilers with a working pressure of 200lb/sq in.

The steering gear was steam-operated type with telemotor control from the navigating bridge.

Three 60kW generators were fitted.

Armament was for anti-aircraft purposes only and consisted of four 20mm single Oerlikons.

The general layout of the vessel varied according to the type of crew with which they were to be operated, ie some had a Chinese crew (total 65) and some Indian (total 72). Those fitted out for a Naval crew accommodated a total of fifty-seven.

Salvage Equipment
The deck machinery consisted of:

    2-8 ton steam capstans on upper deck forward
    2-5 ton Warping capstans on upper deck aft
    3-5 ton steam winches, 2 at foremast and the
    other at the mainmast
Towing hooks were fitted.

The main salvage pump was a 14in Gwynne's centrifugal pump driven by a steam reciprocating engine fitted in the engine room. The pump output was 100ton/hr with suction lift 28ft, for priming six 6in suction hoses fitted on each side of the manifold boxes on the upper deck.

For salvage work two cast steel bolsters were fitted on the forecastle deck at side, and six U-ports in upper deck bulwarks, over which ropes could be led when engaged in lifting a wreck. Two heavy mild steel fabricated bollards were erected on upper deck aft and several heavy clench plates fitted on the upper and forecastle decks to take the necessary blocks for lifting over the bow bolsters and through the U-ports.

One Alley and McLellan's steam-driven air compressor with a 50cu ft reservoir was fitted in the engine room, and two diesel-driven Ingersoll-Rand portable air compressors in the pump room.

The sundry portable equipment carried by each ship included:

2-4in and 2-6in motor-driven centrifugal pumps
6-non-submersible electric pumps, cables and hoses etc.
1-8in steam-driven centrifugal pumps
2-6in Worthington steam pumps
12-2½in Ingersoll-Rand sump pumps and hoses
1-recompression chamber for use of divers
2 sets (4 blocks) 100 tons working load purchase blocks, also various other purchase blocks of smaller size
2 set of diving gear
2-motor-driven cement mixers

Derrick Arrangements
The derrick on the fore side of the foremast was designed to lift 10 tons, or 20 tons at the lower bank; that on the after side of the foremast 5 tons and that on the mainmast 10 tons.

Firefighting Equipment included a foam-making apparatus of Pyrene's manufacture for use in connection with monitors and hose manifolds, including the necessary foam inductors and tank an engine room for storage of 1000 galls of Pyrene Improved Foam Compound with connections to foam inductor.

Carbon dioxide equipment consisting of forty-five 50lb cylinders of liquid gas, together with portable fittings, adaptors and hoses etc. was also fitted.

An engineer's workshop was fitted out on the lower deck aft; included in the equipment were: a motor-driven lathe, milling machine, screw machine, grinding machine, drills, punches and welding plant, etc.

Stability Particulars

	Loaded Condition	Light Condition
Metacentric height	3.95ft	3.06ft
Max GZ	2.3ft	2.0ft
Angle of max GZ	34°	31°
Range	73°	60°
Displacement	1710 tons	1273 tons

A total of twelve vessels was built to this design, viz:

1941 Programme	1942 Programme	1943 Programme
King Salvor	*Salvage Duke*	*Salvigil*
Salvestor	*Ocean Salvor*	*Salviola*
Salventure	*Salvictor*	*Salvalour*
Salvikin		
Prince Salvor		
Sea Salvor		

The average time on the slip for these ships was 10-14 months, a mean cost of about £210,000.

A fourth vessel, *Salverdant*, was included in the 1943 Programme, but this was completed as the deep diving vessel *Reclaim*.

Salveda
The fourth vessel included in the 1942 Programme for ocean-going vessels was *Salveda*, which was built by Cammel Lairds for the Admiralty, but to meet the special requirements of the Liverpool and Glasgow Salvage Associations. She was generally similar to *King Salvor class*.

General particulars were:

Length overall	191ft 0in
Length between perps	184ft 0in
Breadth (moulded)	34ft 6in
Depth (moulded)	17ft 0in
Deep displacement	1360 tons
Speed (max)	12kts
Oil fuel	150 tons
Endurance	4500 miles at 10kts
Complement	62 (European)

Machinery consisted of one set of triple expansion reciprocating engines driving one screw with 1200ihp, and two oil-burning boilers at 200lb/sq in.

Two 40kW generators were fitted.

Armament fitted was:
1-20mm Oerlikon gun on wheelhouse top
2-.5in m/c guns on navigating bridge wings

Salvage Equipment
The deck machinery included one steam windlass and one steam warping capstan forward, and a

Salveda, *seen on the Mersey on 16 Oct 1946.*

steam warping capstan on the upper deck aft. A steam winch with extended warping ends was also fitted on the upper deck aft of the main mast.

U-ports were fitted in the forecastle side plating to take lifts at the bow; heavy forged steel eye plates were fitted on the upper deck to take the standing end of the heavy purchases.

The remainder of the equipment was similar to that in *King Salvor* class.

Salveda was laid down in July 1942, launched in February 1943 and completed in May of that year.

American Salvage Vessels

These four vessels were obtained from the US under the Lease-Lend agreement and were named *American Salvor, Boston Salvor, Lincoln Salvor* and *Southampton Salvor*.

They were wooden vessels built to rules of the American Bureau of Shipping.

Principal dimensions:

Length overall	183ft 0in
Length between perps	169ft 2in
Breadth (moulded)	34ft 7in
Depth (moulded)	20ft 0in
Displacement (deep)	1470 tons
Mean draught (deep)	13ft 8in
Complement	12 officers, 48 crew

Machinery consisted of two sets of Cooper Bessemer diesel electric engines giving 1200hp. Maximum speed attained with these engines was 12kts.

Armament fitted was:
1-3in HA/LA gun
2-Oerlikons

Deck Machinery etc.
Windlass on main deck
1-10 ton cargo winch forward of foremast
1-4 ton cargo winch forward of mainmast
2-10 ton capstans on main deck abaft house

2-U-ports forward on main deck
2-U-ports aft on main deck
2-pole masts of Oregon pine
1-Derrick on foremast capable of hoisting 20,000lb
1-Derrick on mainmast capable of hoisting 8000lb

Stability Particulars, as taken from the results of an inclining experiment at the builder's yard, were:

	Light Condition	Deep Condition
Metacentric height	2.13ft	2.39ft (fl)
Max GZ	1.37ft	1.59ft
Angle of max GZ	38°	37°
Range	62½°	68°
Displacement	1122 tons	1470 tons

Coastal Salvage Vessel

During the Battle of Britain in 1940, there were heavy casualties amongst ships around the coast and in all our great ports, and this new phase of the war brought with it a new danger affecting docks, harbours and rivers. One or two ships sunk in awkward places could easily hold up the shipping of a port for a considerable time, bringing about delays which would have had a widespread effect on the whole industry of the country and the progress of the war. This resulted in an anxious time for the salvage departments for, despite all efforts to keep pace with the ever-increasing demands for salvage ships and equipment, they were still short.

After the Battle of Britain, the British Offensive in North Africa saw the liberation of a large number of African ports – Casablanca, Oran and Algiers, etc.; the salvage departments were thus faced with a new type of operation, the opening up of blocked ports.

The need for more salvage ships had become so great that it was decided about this time that the

Coastal Salvage Vessel general arrangement

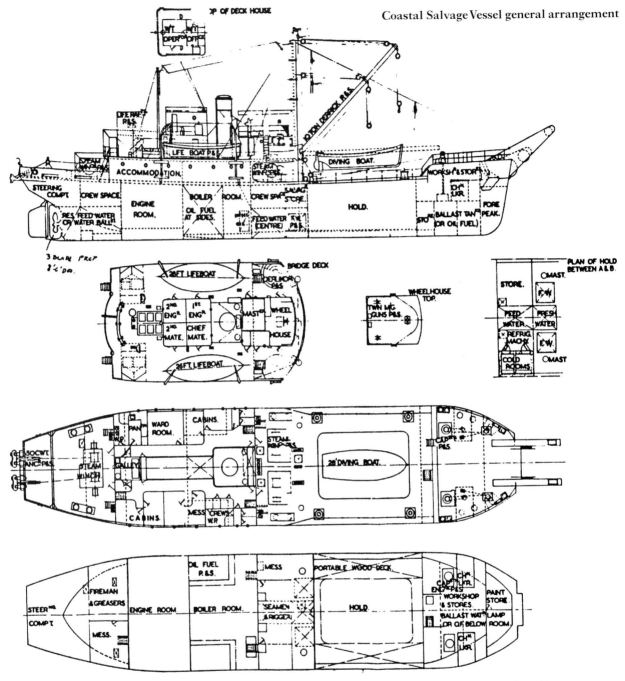

seven vessels being built to joint wreck dispersal and salvage requirements would be taken over entirely for salvage operations, other vessels being modified as necessary for wreck dispersal operations.

In all, nine vessels were built to this design as coastal salvage vessels: *Dispenser*, *Help*, *Lifeline*, *Succour*, *Uplifter*, *Swin*, *Kingarth*, *Kinbrace* and *Kinloss*.

The outline design was prepared by DNC and Messrs Smiths Docks Ltd undertook the build the vessels to a slightly modified design to meet the proposed dual-purpose role of wreck disper-

sal/salvage ship. The last four ships were eventually built and engined by Alexander Hall.

General particulars:

Length overall	179ft 2in
Length between perps	150ft 0in
Breadth extreme	35ft 6in
Depth	16ft 0in
Displacement (deep)	1050 tons
Mean draught (deep)	10ft 4½in
Speed	10kts
Oil fuel	70/124 tons
Complement	3 officers, 31 men

Dispenser, one of a successful class of coastal salvage vessels. (Taken after the war)

Every effort was made to make the construction of these ships as simple and straightforward as possible for quick production, ie good merchant ship practice except for special fittings.

The Deck Machinery consisted of three specially designed steam winches each capable of pulling 14 tons at 25ft/min, and two 5 ton steam capstans. Two of the winches were fitted forward and capable of lifting 100 tons from the sea bed by means of suitable tackles led over the lower bow sheaves, and also arranged to work two large derricks when not engaged in an actual bow lift. The remaining winch was fitted aft for working in connection with two 50cwt salvage anchors.

The capstans were fitted on the forecastle deck primarily for handling the main anchors and cables. In addition to the usual cable whelps the head was arranged for warping while holding the cable.

Bollards were provided and the deck edge well rounded to enable a buoyancy lift to be taken when required.

A complete system for the supply of compressed air was fitted, and hydrants for fire fighting were fitted fore and aft.

Machinery fitted was a triple expansion reciprocating engine etc. giving a maximum speed of 10kts on 600ihp. One 30kW steam generator and two 15kW diesel generators were fitted.

Propeller Particulars:

one 3-bladed propeller	
diameter	8ft 0in
pitch	10ft 3in
developed blade area	22sq ft

Armament fitted was 2-20mm single Oerlikons.

Stability Particulars

	Fully Loaded Condition	Light Condition
Metacentric height	3.8ft	3.18ft
Angle of max GZ	30°	30°
Range	59°	54°
Displacement	1050 tons	815 tons

The first ship, *Dispenser*, was completed by Smiths Dock in October 1943, and the last by Alexander Hall in July 1945. The times for building ships to this design varied considerably but the earlier vessels built in the war period took between 11 and 14 months. Average cost was bout £110,000.

Some of these vessels were employed on harbour clearances in the Mediterranean and in continental harbours and rivers. The reports received spoke highly of their usefulness in this class of clearance work. Those used on foreign service were fitted with refrigerating machinery and cold rooms, etc., and carried an increase in fuel, viz. 124 tons instead of 70 tons.

Requests were received from the American, Russian and French governments for particulars of these vessels.

Lifting Craft

The essential features of this type of craft were:
(i) Provision of ballast tank capacity equal to the lifting capacity required.
(ii) Facilities for flooding the ballast tanks through sea valves and for pumping the tanks.
(iii) Provision of bollards or grippers along the length of the craft to enable the lifting hawsers to be made fast.
(iv) Bow lifting sheaves and deck machinery for working bow lift.

This type of craft are usually operated in pairs, one either side of the wreck to be lifted. The ballast tanks are flooded and lifting hawsers passed beneath the wreck from one side of one craft to the far side of the other craft at each lifting point. The ballast tanks in the craft are pumped and the craft and wreck towed.

There were three general types built during the ear, classified according to their lifting capacities.

1200 ton Lifting Craft

Length overall	180ft 0in
Breadth (moulded)	39ft 0in
Depth (moulded)	17ft 6in

These craft were built to Lloyd's survey and classed 100 A1 Wreck Lifting Lighters; they also conformed to Ministry of War Transport regulations.

Equipment

Two bow sheaves were fitted at the forward end of the upper deck to take a load of 120 tons. Two similar sheaves were fitted at the after end.

Twelve heavy type 36" diameter steel bollards were fitted, six on each side of the upper deck, to take heavy lifts over side and for attachment of heavy wires and tackles when engaged in taking bow or stern lifts in conjunction with the heavy capstans.

The foremast was fitted with one 10 ton steel derrick on the fore side, and a 5 ton steel derrick on the after side; main mast was fitted with two 5 ton derricks.

The deck machinery included a steam-winch windlass on the upper deck, four steam capstans and a further steam winch forward of the main mast.

The main salvage equipment consisted of one reciprocating steam-driven engine centrifugal ballast and salvage pump capable of discharging 1000 tons of water per hour against a head of 40ft, and one steam-driven reciprocating fire pump capable of discharging 150ton/hr at 160lb/sq in, together with a complete fire-fighting equipment including foam apparatus.

Auxiliary machinery was fitted for supplying steam, viz. two coal-fired steam boilers working at 130lb/sq in.

One 5kW steam-driven electric generator was also fitted.

Complement

Six ship's staff and forty-two salvage crew.

A total number of four such craft were built (LCs 8, 9, 10 and 11).

600 ton Lifting Craft

Length overall	126ft 0in
Breadth (moulded)	36ft 0in
Depth (moulded)	15ft 0in

They were built to Ministry of Transport regulations and to Lloyd's survey and were classed as 100 A1 Wreck Lifting Lighters. Salvage deadweight lifting capacity of 600 tons at a mean draught not exceeding 11ft 6in extreme in salt water.

Equipment

Two self-contained steam capstans to exert a pull of 4 tons from barrel to 65ft/min were fitted at fore end; one tandem-barrel steam winch fitted with warping ends was also fitted forward.

Two U-ports were fitted, one on each side of the craft, to take the heavy wire ropes when engaged in salvage work. The steel pole mast fitted at the fore end supported two 5 ton derricks.

Eight main lifting bollards, 36in in diameter, were fitted each side to take heavy tackles and wire ropes used in salvage work.

Main Salvage Arrangements etc.

Exclusive of the forward peak tank, the craft was divided up to the lower deck by longitudinal and athwartship bulkheads from fore peak bulkhead to forward machinery bulkhead into twelve main outer ballast tanks which could be flooded or emptied to assist in lifting operations.

Four heavy blocks – working load 100 tons – were provided, also several other blocks of smaller dimensions.

The main ballast pump was of steam-driven centrifugal type, discharging at 600ton/hr against a total head of 40ft.

An air compressor was fitted in the machinery space for self-salving in the event of damage.

Steam was provided by two auxiliary coal-fired boilers working at 130lb/sq in.

One steam-driven electric generator was also fitted.

Complement

Eight ship's staff and sixteen salvage crew.

A total of eleven 600 ton lifting craft were built (LCs 12 to 22 inclusive).

750 ton Lifting Craft

This was a development of the 600 ton lifting craft, and was built to Ministry of Transport regulations and to Lloyd's survey and classed 100 A1 as a wreck lifting lighter.

Length on waterline	147ft 0in
Breadth (moulded)	36ft 0in
Depth (moulded)	15ft 0in

These craft were subdivided into fifteen independent ballast tanks for lifting purposes and on the upper deck forward were the two heavy bow sheaves, one each side of a semi-circular bull-nose plate.

Nine heavy bollards, 3ft in diameter, were fitted each side of the upper deck while several heavy clench plates to take block shackles and sunk eyeplates were arranged on this deck to take every lead of rope which could be foreseen.

Other equipment included two steam capstans giving 4 ton pulls at 65ft/min, two 10 ton derricks, and steam winch giving 12 ton pulls from both barrels simultaneously at 24ft/min. The salvage gear included four heavy blocks of working load 100 tons, also several other smaller blocks of smaller dimensions.

For self-salving an air compressor was fitted in the machinery space and connected up by steel piping so that in the event of the craft sinking or any ballast tanks being holed, compressed air could be blown into the damaged compartments and the craft floated.

Generally the equipment of these craft was similar to the 600 ton type.

Complement
Eight ship's staff and sixteen salvage crew.

A total of six of the 750 ton lifting craft was built (LCs 23 to 28 inclusive).

Salvage Pontoons
A number of salvage pontoons was designed and built for Admiralty. The essential features of these pontoons were:
(i) Tanks to be of the lifting capacity required and capable of being flooded and blown by compressed air.
(ii) Means to be available for securing the lifting hawsers or cables.

Method of Operation
The lifting wires or cables were secured to, or parbuckled under, the wreck and the ends passed through a chain pipe in the centre of the pontoon by diver. The pontoon was then flooded until it descended into position over the wreck, where the lifting wires or cables were tautened and made fast by divers to the pontoons by special grippers or toggles. The pontoon tanks were then blown.

Towing bridles were supplied with the pontoons.

Miscellaneous Salvage Vessels
Listed below, together with the main items of work carried out, are the miscellaneous craft which were converted for use as Admiralty salvage vessels. Certain of the vessels were employed on salvage operations prior to the war and others were converted for salvage store carries and accommodation vessels as well as for salvage operations proper.

In many cases, protection was fitted to the bridge and Oerlikons and Lewis guns fitted for anti-aircraft purposes.

Ships	Type	Remarks
Abigail	Steam salvage vessel	Bridge protection fitted. 2 Oerlikons and four Lewis guns fitted.
Alita, Carmenita, Dorita and Polita	Motor salvage tenders	Mast and 30cwt derrick fitted. Accommodation altered. Bridge protection fitted. Two light machine guns fitted.
Akershus	Steam salvage depot ship	Requisitioned Norwegian coaster. Bridge protection fitted. 4 light machine guns fitted. Accommodation altered. Additional ballast added.
Bertha and Metinda	Steam salvage vessels	Bridge protection fitted. Accommodation improved. 1 Oerlikon and 2 light machine guns fitted.
Confederate	Steam salvage vessel	Operating abroad throughout the war. 2 Oerlikons and 1 Lewis gun fitted.
Dapper	Steam salvage vessel	Protection fitted to wheelhouse. 1 Oerlikon and 2 light machine guns fitted.
Darda	Steam salvage tender	Foremast and 3 ton derrick fitted. 2 derricks fitted to mizzen mast.
Dormouse	Motor salvage tender	
Drudge	Steam salvage vessel	Concrete protection fitted round wheelhouse. 2 Oerlikons fitted.
Emblem	Steam salvage tender	Duties very similar to peacetime duties and no major modifications carried out.
First	Steam salvage tender	New 7 ton derrick fitted. Bow roller fitted. 2 Lewis guns fitted.
Foremost 17 and 18	Lifting craft	New 20 ton winch fitted. 20 ton and 5 ton derricks fitted. 1 Oerlikon and 6 light machine guns fitted. Wheelhouse protection fitted. Ramp and horn fitted.
Francois Tixier	Steam salvage tender	Chartroom protection fitted. No inclining but

		ship examined and stability said to be satisfactory.
Galleons Reach	Steam salvage vessel	Bow sheaves fitted. Accommodation altered. 1 Oerlikon and 4 light machine guns used.
Guide US	Steam salvage tender	4 Marlins fitted.
Innishowen	Motor salvage tender	2 Lewis guns fitted.
Iron Axe	Steam salvage vessel	3 Lewis guns fitted. Wheelhouse protection fitted. Further ballast added later.
King Lear	Steam salvage vessel	2 light machine guns fitted. Bridge protection fitted.
Lady Southborough	Steam salvage vessel	Wheelhouse protection fitted. 1 Oerlikon and 2 machine guns fitted. Mast and 10 ton derrick fitted.
Longtow	Steam salvage vessel	2 Hotchkiss fitted. Bridge protection fitted.
Maggie Lough	Steam salvage tender	Deck modifications carried out. Wheelhouse protection fitted.
Miss Elaine		2 light machine guns and 1 12pdr fitted.
Nessus	Steam salvage vessel	Bridge protection fitted. 1 Oerlikon and 2 twin Hotchkiss fitted.
Palmston	Steam salvage tender	Wheelhouse protection fitted. 1 Oerlikon and 2 twin machine guns fitted.
Ramier	Steam tug	Accommodation altered. New mast and 5 ton derrick fitted.
Ranger	Steam salvage vessel	4 Hotchkiss and 1 Strip Lewis fitted. Bridge protection fitted. No inclining but stability stated to be satisfactory.
Recovery of Leith	Steam salvage vessel	Bridge protection fitted. 1 Oerlikon and 2 light machine guns fitted.
Richard	Steam salvage vessel	Bridge protection fitted. 2 light machine guns fitted.
Roselyn	Motor salvage vessel	Twin Lewis fitted. Bridge protection fitted.
Salvage Chieftain	Steam salvage vessel	16 light machine guns fitted. Bridge protection fitted.
Storeton	Steam salvage vessel	
T H Tilly	Steam salvage tender	
Thistle	Steam salvage tender	1 Oerlikon and 2 fitted. Hotchkiss
Thoma II	Motor salvage tender	2 Lewis guns fitted. Inclined.
Valkyrien	Steam salvage vessel	Operating overseas.
Venture III	Harbour tug	Wheelhouse protection fitted.
Vine	Steam salvage tender	New mast fitted. 3 ton and 1 ton derricks fitted. Wheelhouse protection fitted.
Wayfarer	Motor salvage tender	Wheelhouse protection fitted.
Wm H Hastie	Steam salvage tender	2 twin Marlins fitted. Wheelhouse protection fitted. Mast and 4 ton derrick fitted. 2 bow rollers fitted. Accommodation altered.
Seehond	Diesel electric salvage vessel	7 ton derrick fitted. Accommodation altered. Bridge protection fitted. 2 Hotchkiss and 1 6pdr fitted.
Zeeleeuw	Motor salvage tender	Inclined and 2 tons ballast used.

Wreck Dispersal Vessels

Before 1939 the clearing of wrecks was the responsibility of Trinity House, but when the war started all salvage firms, plant and equipment were taken over by the Admiralty as Trinity House could not possibly cope with the task of clearing wrecks, the number of which by the end of 1940 very nearly brought East Coast traffic to a standstill.

The Wreck Dispersal organisation was then formed and the first question was to decide the best type of vessel suitable for this service which would meet the staff requirements. In brief these vessels were to be capable of hoisting and stowing one or two diving cutters; providing accommodation for crew of approximately thirty-five; carrying sufficient armament to allow of vessel working alone without escorts; having sufficient storage space for depth charges and other demolition stores; minimum endurance of seven days' steaming; special DG arrangements to enable these vessels to work in unswept areas (this item invariably involved the fitting of additional generators). Later Asdics were added to assist in the location of wrecks.

It was also necessary at this stage to decide on the best type of craft for the diving boat to work directly over the wreck. The one selected was the 32ft service pulling cutter fitted with auxiliary engine and echo-sounding apparatus. Reports on sea experience has proved that no better craft could have been found for this work.

The scarcity of tonnage in late 1940 and early 1941 made it very difficult to find vessels to suit even these limited staff requirements. Early in

Wreck Dispersal Vessel general arrangement

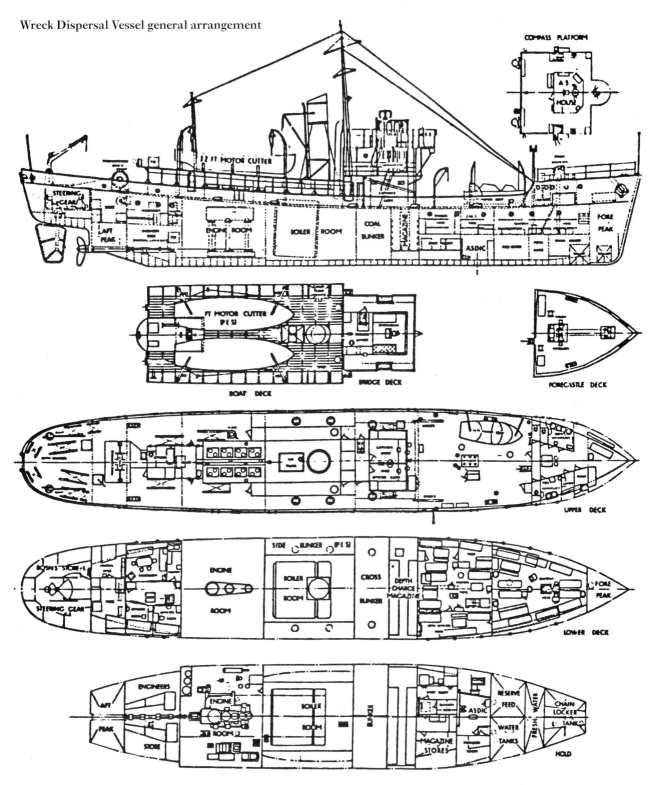

1941, however, it was approved for *Dalriada* to be fitted for this service.

Dalriada was a cargo passenger vessel, on cross-Channel service, dimensions 230ft 10in x 34ft 6in x 15ft 6in (moulded) – gross tonnage 758. The conversion involved providing stowage for depth charges and other demolition stores, fitting davits,

etc. for two 32ft cutters, protecting crew and fitting armament.

The work of wreck dispersal was now becoming very urgent and the search was still going on for suitable vessels. In August 1941 it was approved for two further vessels to be allocated for this work. One of these was *Felixstowe* (renamed

Colchester in December 1941) and the other an ex-German trawler *Maria*. *Felixstowe* was a single screw, coal-burning cargo and cattle transport, gross tonnage 892, dimensions 215ft lbp x 33ft x 17ft moulded depth, and was converted into practically the same staff requirements as *Dalriada*. She went into service about the end of January 1942 but remained under the management of her former owners. All other vessels converted for wreck dispersal duties after this were manned and run by RN crews.

The *Maria*, 165ft bp x 25ft 10in x 14ft 6in moulded depth, was converted to practically the same requirements as the two former vessels, except that for reasons of seaworthiness only one 32ft cutter was carried.

In April 1942 a report and recommendation was prepared by the Director of Wreck Dispersal indicating the policy for dealing with wrecks and requesting approval for the provision of three new wreck dispersal vessels.

The staff requirements laid down were briefly: relatively light draught not exceeding 10ft; a large hold and hatchway for stowing large pieces of ship's structure; to be capable of lifting at least 50 tons at her bow and of steaming with the weight suspended; to have a deadweight capacity of 150/200 tons; speed about 8kts; two masts placed abreast to facilitate the handling of large and awkward pieces of scrap.

The Director of Salvage at this time also required extra craft and after seeing the sketch design prepared by DNC for DWD suggested it would make very suitable craft for general salvage work and requested at least four of these vessels.

In view of the equally urgent requirements for salvage vessels it was approved in April 1942 that seven vessels should be built to requirements that would be a compromise, so that they could be used with equal facility for either salvage or wreck dispersal work. A design was prepared by DNC and nine ships were eventually built but the commitments of the Director of Salvage were such that he was able to substantiate his claim for more ships and all nine were allocated to him, leaving DWD without any of the new ships. A condition was that if DWD required any heavy lifting done D of S/V would assume responsibility.

In the latter half of 1942 and 1943 four ships were converted to wreck dispersal vessels, viz. *Ary*, *Empire Sentinel* (renamed *Rampant*) and two M/S trawlers *Jacinta* and *Yezo*. The vessels varied in length between 130ft bp and 180ft bp but were converted in much the same was as *Colchester* except that *Jacinta* and *Yezo* were only allocated one diving cutter and their depth charge complement limited to approximately forty.

In January 1944 approval was given for six M/S trawlers to be converted for wreck dispersal duty. This was necessary in order to cope with DWD's

Lundy, an Isles *class trawler, as converted to a wreck dispersal vessel, in 1949.*

commitments which might arise as a result of Operation Overlord. These vessels were:

Name	Length bp	Beam	Moulded Depth
Admiral			
Sir John Lawford	134ft 6in	25ft 0in	14ft 3in
Burke	130ft 9in	24ft 6in	14ft 0in
Clyne Castle	135ft 0in	24ft 9in	14ft 3in
Laurel	140ft 0in	24ft 6in	14ft 3in
Lune	145ft 0in	24ft 0in	14ft 0in
Tehana	130ft 4in	24ft 0in	14ft 0in

Arrangements were made on these vessels to carry only one diving cutter, trawl winches were landed and boat hoisting carried out by windlass on fore-castle head. A part of the coal bunker had to be taken to provide accommodation space, a steel WT bulkhead being erected athwartships and a flat built in. The space underneath the new flat was used for stowage of demolition stores. The DG equipment had to be brought up to the standard of former ships; this required extra power and involved the fitting of an additional generator in each case. Asdics were omitted.

The number of wrecks off the Normandy beaches was small and these were soon dealt with, but the liberation of the continental ports provided a big task for the Wreck Dispersal Organisation, the harbours of Ostend, Boulogne, Calais, Zeebrugge, Flushing and others having to be cleared of a number of wrecks of vessels of all sorts and sizes.

Towards the end of the war DWD sought and obtained approval for eighteen *Isles* class A/S–M/S trawlers (Admiralty designed) to be converted for wreck dispersal duty. The dimensions of this class were: 150ft bp x 27ft 6in beam x 15ft 0in moulded depth.

Being generally 15ft longer and 3ft to 3ft 6in more beam than the trawlers previously used, they were much more suitable craft. A boat deck was built to provide stowage space for two 32ft diving cutters, radial davits being used for hoisting, leads being taken to the M/S winch, which was retained.

DWD requested that 200 DCs be carried for demolition purposes. Part of the bunker space was taken to make a DC magazine. A WT bulkhead was built athwartships and racks erected, with runways over for lifting blocks, to carry 120 DCs. Deck stowage was provided for a further forty, making the total number carried 160. Flooding and spraying arrangements were provided for this magazine off the firemain.

All the armament was removed and the existing magazine used for the stowage of demolition explosives. As these vessels came into service, the first one in October 1945, the requisitioned ones were released for return to trade.

Experience with wreck dispersal vessels showed that the Admiralty-designed trawlers were the most suitable of all the vessels used for this work, the requisitioned trawlers generally being too small, endurance and demolition store carrying capacity having to be sacrificed to make them seaworthy.

Owing to lack of space on these vessels, Welin-type quadrant davits would have been much more convenient for hoisting the diving cutters with a spreader such as 'T' bar being fitted to enable the existing boat-slinging arrangements to be used. Welin-type davits were considered but the additional time required for their manufacture due to pressure of orders for higher priority work precluded their use.

A small boat-hoisting winch would have ben a great asset on these vessels as the using of M/S winch or windlass for this purpose was inclined to be clumsy.

In the converted trawlers which were of smaller dimensions, it was necessary to keep the top-weight to the absolute minimum in view of armament carried. The cutter davits, therefore, were limited to 7ft 0in outreach and consequently the heels of the davits had to be sited outboard. This was a disadvantage as the davits were liable to damage and also to damage ships and boats coming alongside. With the allocation of *Isles* class trawlers, which were much bigger, the outreach was increased and davit heels sited inboard.

CHAPTER 23

Tugs

Editorial Note
The Admiralty had a considerable number of tugs at the outbreak of war though some dated back to the first World War. A large number of new ships were built, mainly to existing commercial design, or acquired including some from the USA.

Admiralty tugs may be divided into four distinct classes by virtue of the work they carry out:
1. Rescue tugs – these are large ocean-going tugs.
2. Towing and reberthing tugs – employed on target towing, towing heavy ships into harbour and reberthing.
3. Tugs for coastal and harbour work.
4. Small harbour service tugs.

Rescue Tugs

The general requirements for rescue tugs were that they should possess good sea-going qualities, large endurance, sufficient power for 13-16kts, free speed, good freeboard, and be fitted with suitable rescue gear such as fire and salvage pumps, towing hooks, self-rendering winch, powerful capstan aft, etc. Further, these tugs required a good standard of habitability to conform to Ministry of Transport requirements.

At the outbreak of hostilities in 1939, the only Admiralty ocean-going tugs classed as rescue tugs in Home waters were six *Saint* Class, three *Resolve* Class and two fleet target towing tugs of the *Brigand* Class.

Saint Class
These were built as ocean-going tugs, during the 1914-18 war, to Board of Trade requirements and Lloyds or British Corporation classification.
The general particulars of this class were:

Length overall	142ft 9in (over fenders)
Length between perps	135ft 0in
Breadth (moulded)	29ft 0in
Depth (moulded)	16ft 0in
Displacement (deep)	870 tons
Draughts (deep) F	14ft 3in
A	14ft 5in
mean	14ft 4in
Speed (max) (deep displacement)	12kts
Endurance	1700 miles at 9kts

Machinery
The machinery consisted of two coal-fired cylindrical boilers – 180lb/sq in, and triple expansion main engines developing 1200ihp at 130rpm. Coal carried was 230 tons, restricted to 180 tons. One 13kW generator was fitted in each ship.
Propeller particulars:

diameter	10ft 7in
pitch	12ft 0in
developed blade area	34sq ft
4 blades – bronze	

Towing Equipment
Two towhooks and a steam-warping capstan.

Armament for war purpose was:
2-Oerlikon guns
2-twin Brownings
or 1-12pdr gun
1-twin 0.5in m/c gun
2 Lewis guns

When arming these tugs it was found necessary to ballast and also restrict the amount of coal carried to 180 tons.

Stability Particulars	*Light Condition*	*Deep Condition*
Metacentric height	1.20ft	1.65ft
Max GZ	0.60ft	0.45ft
Angle of max GZ	29°	19°
Range	58°	59°
Displacement	667 tons (ie with ballast and 40 tons coal)	870 tons

Forty-four tugs of this class were completed between October 1918 and June 1920.

Resolve Class
These were built as twin-screw ocean-going and dockyard tugs in 1918-19. The general particulars were:

Hesperia, a very powerful - and handsome - wartime built tug.

Length overall	186ft 1in (over fenders)
Length between perps	175ft 0in
Breadth (moulded)	34ft 0in
Depth (moulded)	18ft 6in
Displacement (deep)	1360 tons
Mean draught (deep)	14ft 0in
Speed (max)	13kts
Complement	28 officers and men

Machinery consisted of four coal-fired cylindrical boilers and two triple expansion engines giving a total of 2400ihp at 140rpm.

350 tons of coal was carried in these ships, of which 70 tons were kept in a reserve bunker.

Propeller particulars:

diameter	10ft 8in
pitch	13ft 0in
developed blade area	36sq ft
4 blades – originally bronze	

Towing Equipment
Two towhooks and steam-warping winch.

Armament for war purposes consisted of one Oerlikon gun and Lewis guns.

Stability Particulars

	Light Condition	Deep Condition
Metacentric height	2.68ft	2.62ft
Max GZ	1.60ft	1.40ft
Angle of max GZ	38°	32°
Range	66°	67°
Displacement	1007 tons	1361 tons

Six *Resolve* class tugs were completed from September 1918 to May 1919.

Assurance Class

To overcome the shortage of tugs, a number were requisitioned for rescue service; in addition, the tug *Salvonia* was inspected with a view to the placing of orders for repeat vessels for this service. It was decided to modify slightly the design of the *Salvonia* and build four similar tugs to Admiralty requirements.

The vessels built were known as the *Assurance* class and subsequent orders brought the total built to twenty-one.

General particulars were:

Length overall		156ft 6in
Length between perps		142ft 6in
Breadth moulded		33ft 0in
Depth moulded		16ft 0in
Displacement (deep)		1006 tons
Draughts (deep)	F	12ft 4in
	A	15ft 11in
	mean	14ft 2in
Speed (deep)		13kts
Endurance at 10kts		5000 miles

The modifications and improvements made on the original *Salvonia* design included arrangements for fitting armament and ammunition, a larger capstan aft, steam hydraulic or electro hydraulic steering gear, and the siting of all accommodation forward.

The vessels were built under the survey of Lloyds Register and were classes 100 A1 for tow-

ing services. Navigation lights and life-saving appliances conformed to Ministry of War Transport regulations.

Protection

About 7 tons of bulletproof plating were fitted in

General arrangement of
Assurance **class rescue tug**

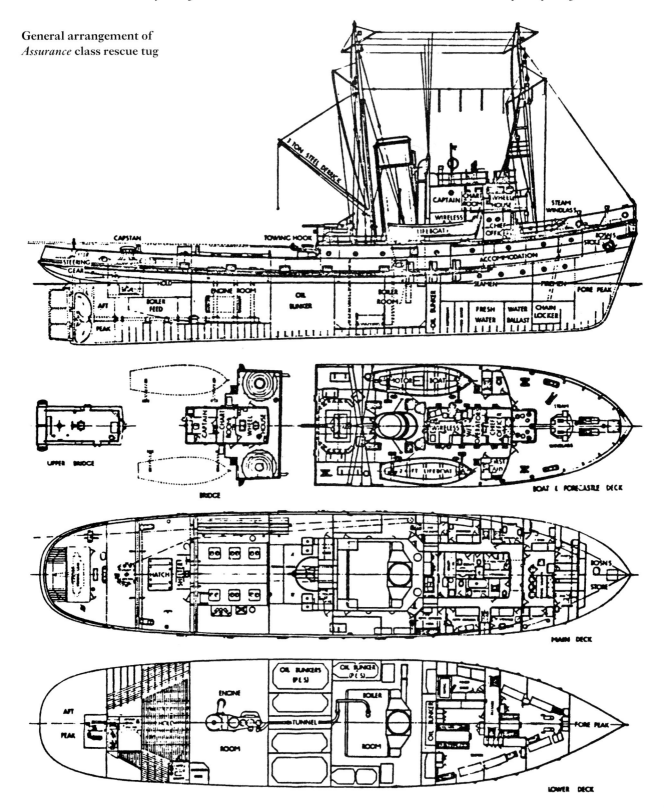

each of these ships, mainly around the bridge structure and over the steering position.

Machinery
Boiler – 17ft diameter, tubed and working at 210lb/sq in with a steam reciprocating triple expansion main engine developing 1350ihp at 122rpm. 262 tons oil fuel was carried.

Propeller particulars:

one 4-bladed cast iron propeller
diameter   11ft 9in
pitch   12ft 0in
developed blade area   52sq ft

In vessels with electro hydraulic steering gear the generators fitted were either:

1-20kW and 1-5kW or
1-20kw and 1-10kW

with the steam hydraulic steering gear

1-15kW and 1-7½kW or
1-15kW

Towing equipment originally fitted consisted of towhook and bitts; later the ordinary towhook was replaced by a special shock-absorbing hook with a view to reducing the wear and tear on the wire hawsers. On trials a Bollard pull of 13½ tons was obtained. Other equipment included a combined steam and hand double gipsy windlass.

Armament
As the ships were designed during the war, they were built with their full war armament of:

1-12pdr gun
2-twin Lewis guns

No important changes were introduced before the completion of the first order of four vessels, but as a result of sea experience it was found necessary to carry out certain modifications in the later vessels.

Included as modifications were:
(a) Increase in scantlings of frames forward, and general stiffening of the fore end to withstand excessive panting in heavy seas.
(b) One of the ordinary towhooks replaced by a Monarch shock-absorbing towhook with a view to saving steel wire hawsers.
(c) Increase in the scantlings of the tow beams.
(d) Rearrangement of the vessel and sleeping quarters.

Later modifications included increase in armament to:

1-12pdr
2-Oerlikons

and 2-Hotchkiss, and removal of the 3 ton derrick on the foremast to facilitate handing of gear from the hold.

In order to maintain freeboard and stability, it was found necessary to reduce the oil fuel carried and to fill the water ballast tanks in the light condition.

Stability Particulars
These particulars are for a typical ship of the class after the various modifications and additions had been carried out.

	Light Condition	*Deep Condition*
Metacentric height	1.04ft	2.33ft (fl)
Max GZ	0.54ft	0.60ft
Angle of max GZ	28°	35°
Range	53°	65°
Displacement	764 tons	1056 tons

Complement   31 officers and men

Cost   About £69,000 per vessel.

The *Assurance* class tugs proved to be very suitable for carrying out rescue duties and in all twenty-one vessels to this design were built by Messrs Cochrane and Son Ltd of Selby, as follows:

1939 Programme	1940 Programme
Assurance	*Frisky*
Tenacity	*Jaunty*
Prudent	
Restive	

1941 Programme	1942 Programme
Adept	*Saucy*
Adherent	*Stormking*
Charon	*Allegiance*
Hengist	*Antic*
Dexterous	*Assiduous*
Griper	*Earner*
Prosperous	*Sesame*
Horsa	

The time taken to complete one vessel varied from about 11 to 15 months.

Bustler Class
In April 1940 approval was given for orders to be placed with Messrs Henry Robb of Leith for two diesel rescue tugs, based on a design prepared by the firm in conjunction with the Overseas Towage and Salvage Co Ltd, London. The scantlings were in accordance with Lloyd's Rules and all wartime economies were incorporated.

Bustler class general arrangement

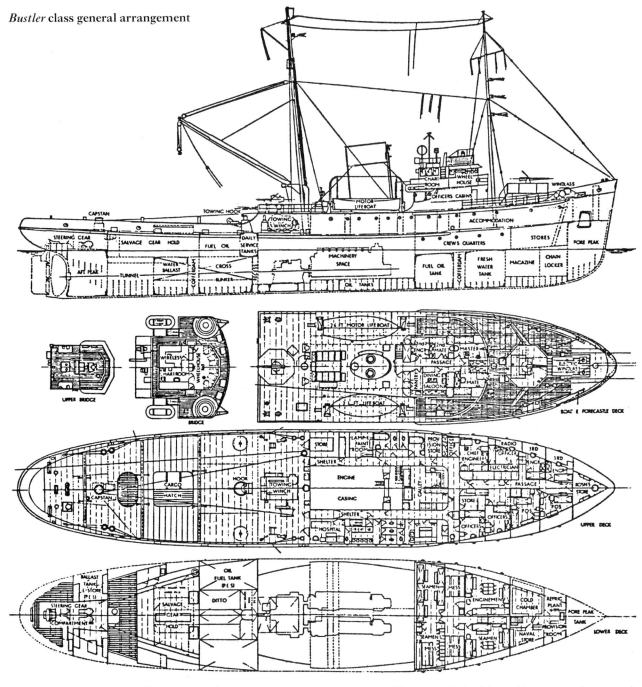

General particulars were:

Length overall		205ft 0in
Length between perps		190ft 0in
Breadth moulded		38ft 6in
Depth moulded		19ft 0in
Displacement (deep)		1618 tons
Draughts (deep)	F	14ft 0in
	A	16ft ½in
	mean	15ft 0in
Speed (deep)		15kts
Endurance		14,000 miles at 12kts

The upper deck of these ships was continuous and the forecastle deck ran from the stern head to abaft amidships; stem raked and forefoot well rounded. Stern was of semi-cruiser type to accommodate the steering gear.

All ships of this class were equipped with a hospital on the starboard side at the after end of the bridge structure.

Protection

6½ tons of bulletproof protective plating was fitted per ship, mainly around wheelhouse and over the engine room.

Machinery

Two Atlas diesel engines, each of 1600bhp at 320rpm, were geared to main shaft, giving a total of 3020bhp at 145rpm. 340 tons of diesel oil was carried.

Propeller particulars:
one 4-bladed propellers

diameter	12ft 9in
pitch	12ft-9.6ft (varying)
developed blade area	63.5sq ft

Generators fitted were two 100kW and one 19kW.

Towing Equipment etc. consisted of a self-rendering winch 40hp (50hp on later vessels), a Monarch towhook and an ordinary towhook. Other equipment included an electric windlass giving 8 tons at 30ft/min and an electric capstan of 5 tons at 50ft/min.

A bollard pull of 29 tons was obtained on trials.

Firefighting equipment consisted of a 100 ton fire pump and a total of 400 tons salvage pumps.

Armament
1-12pdr gun
2-Oerlikon guns
1-2pdr pom-pom
4-stripped Lewis guns

Stability	Light Condition	Deep Condition
Metacentric height	2.37ft	3.31ft (fl)
Max GZ	1.78ft	2.24ft
Angle of max GZ	47°	47°
Range	81°	over 90°
Displacement	1080 tons	1618 tons

Complement   42 officers and men

Cost   About £146,000 per vessel.

General

The *Bustler* class tug was a successful design and in all eight vessels were built by Messrs Henry Robb Ltd of Leith, as follows:

1940 Programme   1942 Programme

Bustler	*Mediator*
Samsonia	*Reward*
	Turmoil
	Warden

1941 Programme

Growler
Hesperia

Time taken to build each vessel varied from 12 to 20 months.

Envoy Class

These vessels were ordered by the Ministry of War Transport through the Director of Merchant Shipbuilding in 1943, to be handed over to the Royal Navy on completion. The design was limited by the building capacity of Messrs Cochrane's and the size of machinery that could be produced by Messrs C D Holmes. *Envoy* class was generally similar to *Assurance* class except that the dimensions were slightly increased. General particulars were:

Length overall		174ft 6in
Length between perps		160ft 0in
Breadth moulded		34ft 6in
Depth moulded		16ft 6in
Displacement (deep)		1318 tons
Draughts (deep)	F	14ft 2in
	A	16ft 3in
	mean	15ft 3in
Speed (deep)		13kts

These vessels were built under the survey of Lloyd's Register and classed +100 A1 for towing services. Life-saving appliances were to Ministry of War Transport Regulations.

Machinery

Two cylindrical boilers at 225lb/in with steam reciprocating triple expansion main engine developing 1600ihp at 124rpm. 370 tons oil fuel were carried.

Propeller particulars:
one 4-bladed propeller

diameter	11ft ½in
pitch	12ft 0in
developed blade area	53sq ft

Generators fitted: two 20kW

Towing equipment etc fitted consisted of two towhooks, one Monarch type and the other of the builder's own make. The double purchase steam warping capstan was capable of 8 tons at 25ft/min and 2 tons at 120ft/min. Other equipment included a combined steam and hand double gipsy windlass, a 150ton/hr fire and salvage pump and a portable salvage pump of the same capacity.

Armament
1-12pdr
2-Oerlikons
2-0.5in Colt guns

Stability Particulars	Light Condition	Deep Condition
Metacentric height	1.52ft	3.06ft (fl)
Max GZ	0.87ft	1.10ft

Envoy class general arrangement

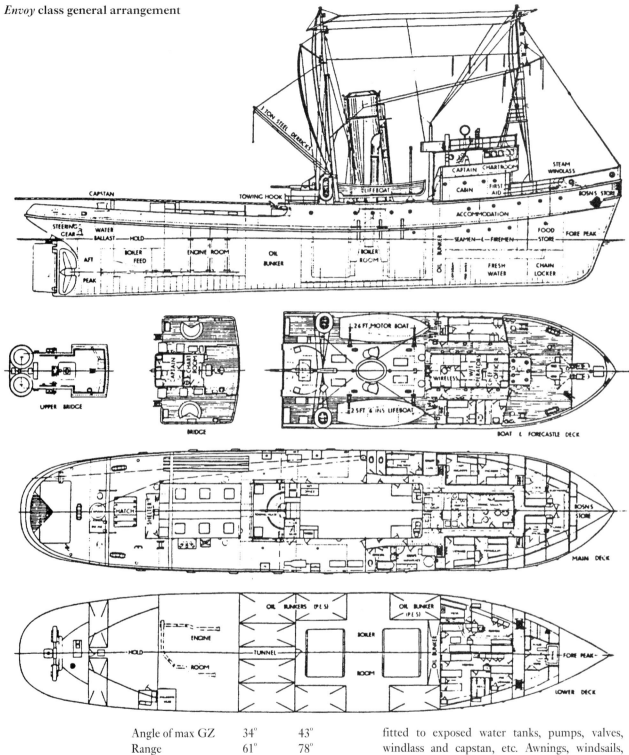

Angle of max GZ	34°	43°
Range	61°	78°
Displacement	851 tons	1318 tons

Complement 8 officers and 26 men

Cost   About £85,000 per vessel

General

All the vessels of this class were fitted for service in cold climates; steam supply and lagging were fitted to exposed water tanks, pumps, valves, windlass and capstan, etc. Awnings, windsails, light-excluding ventilators, etc. were provided for service in the tropics.

Experience in service showed that very high temperatures were reached in the boiler room which was ventilated by the Howden system of freed draught to the boilers. This was improved by fitting 12½in fans and trunking and additional lagging to steam pipes, uptakes, etc.

A total of six *Envoy* class tugs were handed over to the RN – all built to the 1943 programme, viz.

| *Envoy* | *Enigma* | *Enchanter* |
| *Enticer* | *Enforcer* | *Encore* |

The time to build each vessel was 8 to 9 months.

BATs and ATRs

These tugs were built in the USA to a design produced by the Americans, but based on the *Assurance* class tug; drawings of the *Assurance* class were sent to the USA for this purpose.

The ATRs (auxiliary tugs repeat)[1] were repeat orders of the BATs (British auxiliary tugs).

The general particulars of the BATs and ATRs were:

Length overall	143ft 0in
Length between perps	134ft 6in
Breadth moulded	33ft 0in
Depth moulded	17ft 0in
Displacement (deep)	800 tons
Draughts (deep) F	11ft 10½in
A	13ft 7½in
mean	12ft 9in
Speed (deep)	14.3kts
Endurance	7200 miles at 13.5kts

Structure etc.

Vessels were welded throughout and 15lb ST8 splinter protection bulwarks were fitted around the forward part of the bridge.

Machinery

Two diesel electric engines, geared to a single shaft. The main engine generator sets consisted of two diesels each 950bhp, 750rpm driving two 605kW 560 volt generators. Rated horsepower was 1500shp at 200rpm. 173 tons of diesel oil was carried.

Propeller particulars:

one 3-bladed Manganese bronze propeller	
diameter	9ft 9in
pitch	7ft 4in
developed blade area	40sq ft

Electric generators fitted consisted of one 60kW and one 30kW diesel, giving a total of 135hp.

Towing equipment in these ships included a self–rendering electric towing winch and a towhook of the Monarch type.

Armament was arranged in the original design and consisted of one 3in HA/LA and two 20mm single Oerlikons.

Stability Particulars

	Light Condition	Deep Condition
Metacentric height	1.59ft	2.78ft (fl)
Max GZ	0.76ft	0.93ft
Angle of max GZ	28½°	26½°
Range	56½°	+90°
Displacement	556 tons	800 tons

Complement

35 officers and men. The officers' quarters in these ships were well fitted out, but the crew's accommodation was rather below British Standards.

General

Reports on behaviour of these vessels at sea varied considerably; some COs stated that they rolled badly and recommended larger bilge keels, whilst others were satisfied and reported them as being superior sea boats to either the *Assurance* or *Saint* classes.

[1] This is as originally written. ATR actually stood for Auxiliary Tug Rescue.

Favourite, *one of a number of US built tugs.*

A total of twenty-four vessels, ie fourteen BATs and ten ATRs, were allocated to the RN under Lease-Lend arrangements; three of the former were subsequently handed over to the RAN. The time taken to build one vessel varied from 5 to 10 months.

Wooden ATRs

These tugs were also built in America and, except for weather deck hatches, engine casings and deck houses, were of all-wood construction.

General particulars of the wooden ATRs were:

Length overall		165ft 0in
Length between perps		155ft 0in
Breadth moulded		33ft 0in
Breadth moulded over planking		34ft ¾in
Depth moulded		19ft 0in
Displacement (deep)		1298 tons
Draughts (deep)	F	15ft 1½in
	A	16ft 3in
	mean	15ft 8½in
Speed (deep)		12kts
Endurance at 10kts		3240 miles

Structure

The hull construction as double skin, each thickness being worked fore and aft with a good shift of butts. Frames were of double white oak.

Protection was fitted in the form of 10lb HTS shields to guns and 10lb HTS to wheelhouse and chartroom.

Machinery

Each vessel of the class was fitted with a single reciprocating main engine 1600ihp at 185rpm powered by two watertube type boilers. 247 tons of oil fuel were carried.

Propeller particulars:

one 4-bladed Manganese bronze propeller	
diameter	9ft 1in
pitch	8ft 2½in
developed blade area	30sq ft

Two 60kW TGs giving 120 volts DC were also fitted.

Towing Equipment

Spring towhook, towing bollard and an electric winch. These tugs, unlike their steel counterparts, were not fitted with self-rendering gear.

Armament consisted of:

1–3in HA/LA gun
2–20mm single Oerlikons

Stability Particulars	Light Condition	Deep Condition
Metacentric height	2.07ft	2.23ft (fl)
Max GZ	1.22ft	0.95ft
Angle of max GZ	34°	30°
Range	60.5°	57°
Displacement	1016 tons	1298 tons

Complement 9 officers and 23 men

As in other American small vessels, the accommodation was very good for the officers but cramped for the crew, where accommodation was fitted with 3-tier bunks.

General

Reports from American experience showed that the seakeeping qualities were excellent and the wooden ATRs were preferable to the steel ATRs and BATs in this respect.

Four vessels, viz. *Director, Emulous, Freedom* and *Justice*, were allocated to the RN under Lease-Lend arrangement.

Time taken to build one vessel was about 15 to 16 months.

Tugs for Towing and Reberthing

The general requirements for these tugs were similar to those for rescue duties except for a requirement for greater manoeuvrability, for which reason twin screws were fitted.

The dockyard tugs available prior to the war for these services consisted mainly of the *Saint* class and *Resolve* class; various paddle tugs twenty to forty years old were also used for towing ships in harbour and reberthing.

The grounding of *Nelson* at Portsmouth in 1934 brought out the necessity for more powerful tugs for efficient berthing of the larger warships and provision was made in the 1936 estimates for the construction of three twin-screw tugs for both target towing and dockyard service. The design produced was known as the *Brigand* class.

Brigand Class

General particulars:

Length overall		174ft 0in
Length between perps		165ft 0in
Breadth moulded		32ft 0in
Depth moulded		18ft 6in
Displacement (deep)		1225 tons
Draughts (deep)	F	12ft 8in
	A	15ft 11½in
	mean	14ft 4in
Speed (deep)		15.7kts
Endurance		3500 miles at 15.7kts

Freebooter, *in November
1946, one of a pre war
design of large tug.*

Structure etc.

These tugs were of Admiralty design and were built to Lloyd's survey and classification.

Machinery

Two watertube oil-fired boilers at 250lb/sq in and two steam reciprocating main engines, each giving 1500ihp. Contractors: Fleming & Ferguson Ltd, Paisley.

A total of 400 tons of OF were carried, including 113 tons in reserve tanks.

Propeller particulars:

two 4-bladed bronze propellers	
diameter	10ft 6in
pitch	12ft 3in
developed blade area	40sq ft

Electric generators consisted of one 15kW steam generator per ship.

Stability Particulars	*Light Condition* (with water ballast)	*Deep Condition*
Metacentric height	1.0ft	2.36ft (fl)
Max GZ	1.36ft	2.26ft
Angle of max GZ	59°	60°
Range	over 90°	over 90°
Displacement	908 tons	1225 tons

Towing Equipment, etc.

Two slip hooks and a steam-driven self-rendering towing winch.

A bollard pull of 32 tons was obtained on trials. Other equipment included a steam windlass.

Armament for war purposes was:
    1-3in HA/LA gun
    2-Lewis guns

Complement   49 officers and men

Cost   £106,000 per vessel

Approval was given in 1938 for a repeat vessel, viz. *Marauder*, and in 1939 for a further vessel, *Freebooter*. The *Brigand* design was slightly modified for these two vessels by increasing the beam by 9in for improved stability. In addition, the ships were provided with a 15kW diesel generator to increase the dynamic power, so that electric heating and lighting could be used in harbour, without having to maintain steam.

A total of five vessels were built by Messrs Fleming & Ferguson and the time for building of one vessel varied from 10 to 14 months.

Brigand and *Marauder* were taken over for use as rescue tugs.

1936 Programme	1938 Programme	1939 Programme
Brigand	*Marauder*	*Freebooter*
Buccaneer		
Bandit		

Nimble Class

Provision was made in the 1940 programme for the construction of a new dockyard tug, the *Nimble*. The lines were similar to the *Marauder*, etc. but with beam increased to 34ft 0in. The general arrangement also differed from *Marauder* on the following lines.

(a) The two boiler rooms were made into one with a common stocking space.

(b) Forecastle deck carried over half the length of the ship to provide additional space for accommodation.

(c) Funnel moved to provide room for mounting a small gun on the bridge deck aft.

(d) Inner bottom fitted in engine room for use as a ballast tank.

Other general improvements were also incorporated as a result of war experience.

The general particulars of *Nimble* were:

Length overall	175ft 9in
Length between perps	165ft 0in
Breadth moulded	34ft 0in
Depth moulded	18ft 6in
Displacement (deep)	1216 tons
Draughts (deep) F	12ft 6in
A	14ft 10in
mean	13ft 8in
Speed (max)	15kts
Endurance	3600 miles at 10kts

Structure etc.

The vessels were built to British Corporation rules. No mainmast was fitted but two 3 ton derricks on derrick posts were fitted in order to lift the salvage anchors as stated above, the boilers were placed in one boiler room with a common stoking space.

Machinery

Two watertube boilers at 250lb/sq in with two steam reciprocating engines developing a total of 3000ihp at 140rpm.

A total of 412 tons of OF was carried.

Propeller particulars:

two 4-bladed propellers	
diameter	10ft 6in
pitch	12ft 3in
developed blade area	40sq ft

Generators fitted were one 25kW steam generator and one 25kW diesel generator.

Towing equipment etc. consisted of two towhooks with a special nipper, and a winch for stowing the towing wire. A tow post was also fitted at forecastle head for vessel to act as a trailer. The bollard pull was measured as 28 tons. Other equipment included windlass, capstan, 190ton/hr fire and salvage pump, and two 75ton/hr electric pumps.

Stability Particulars

	Light Condition	Deep Condition
Metacentric height	0.93ft	2.79ft (fl)
Max GZ	1.25ft	2.56ft
Angle of max GZ	48°	55°
Range	88°	over 90°
Displacement	844 tons	1216 tons

Armament for war was:

1-3in HA/LA
1-0.5in twin machine gun } in
2-Oerlikons } *Nimble*
3-Oerlikons } in repeat
2- stripped Lewis guns } vessels

Complement 44 officers and men

General

Approval was given in 1943 for the construction of three repeat vessels of the *Nimble* class. These repeat vessels were built under Lloyd's rules and slight modifications to scantlings were made as well. They were completed to the original scheme for *Nimble* except that two ships, viz. *Expert* and *Careful*, were fitted for service in hot climates. No armament was fitted due to the cessation of hostilities.

Arrangements were made to fit a rope guard with wire cutter, and a special wire cutter on the propeller of *Careful* as an experiment. Approval was also given for *Capable* to be used for trials with Rotol's variable pitch propeller for increased manoeuvrability.

Incidentally, *Capable* gave a max. bollard pull of 36 tons while on trials with the variable pitch propeller.

Four vessels only were built to this design and the time for building of each was about 10 months.

1940 Programme	1942 Programme
Nimble	*Careful*
	Capable
	Expert

Nimble herself was fitted out for duties as a rescue tug on her completion in 1942.

Coastal and Harbour Tugs

The general requirements for coastal and harbour tugs were:

(1) ihp of 800-1000 for a free speed of 10-11kts.
(2) Two towhooks, heavy bollards and fairleads.
(3) Seagoing qualities.
(4) Good habitability.
(5) Moderate endurance.

In 1938 a requirement arose for a tug for local harbour work at Rosyth and, as no suitable vessel was available for purchase, a design was developed for a small tug mainly for harbour use, but also capable of occasional seagoing service.

This first tug to this design was laid down in 1939 and was named *Impetus*, which, with the repeat orders in 1940 and 1942, became the class name.

Impetus Class

General particulars:

Length overall		98ft 0in
Length between perps		90ft 0in
Breadth (moulded)		28ft 0in
Depth (moulded)		14ft 0in
Displacement (deep)		465 tons
Draughts (deep)	F	9ft 9in
	A	13ft 0in
	mean	11ft 4½in
Speed (max)		11kts
Endurance		950 miles at 11kts
Metacentric height in deep condition		3.02ft (fl)
Complement		4 officers, 9 men

The vessels were fitted with steam reciprocating main engines developing 800ihp.

A total of five tugs were built by Messrs Alexander Hall, Aberdeen, to this design. The time for building each tug varied from 7 to 10 months.

Empire Class

This class was built by Director of Merchant Shipbuilding for Ministry of Transport and twelve were allocated for dockyard service. They were of slightly varying sizes, typical vessels having moulded dimensions 105ft 10in x 27ft 1in x 11ft 8in. Main engines, which were reciprocating, gave 800-1100ihp with oil-fired and coal-fired boilers.

Revue Class

Approval was given in 1939 for the building of four tugs of Messrs Cochrane No 1202 (*Revue*) type. In view of the urgent demand for tugs at various dockyards, however, it was decided to requisition Messrs Cochrane's No 1202 and No 1206 as they completed, and build a further two vessels only, viz. *Alligator* and *Crocodile*.

These last two vessels were built by Messrs Richard Dunstan to the Rules and survey of Lloyd's Register and incorporated several features of the *Impetus* class as well as other features which were particular Admiralty requirements.

The moulded dimensions were 105ft 0in x 26ft 6in x 13ft 0in. Machinery gave a maximum speed of 11kts at 1000ihp.

These tugs were eventually fitted out for service in the tropics.

Small Harbour Service Tugs

The general requirements for tugs in this service were:

(1) ihp about 350.
(2) Speed 9kts.
(3) Towhook.
(4) Accommodation for crew to sleep on board if necessary.
(5) Low freeboard acceptable.

TID Tugs

TID utility-type tugs were designed by Director of Merchant Building for harbour and river work, and a number were loaned to the RN. Their dimensions were 65ft x 17ft x 8ft x 6ft draught (98 tons displacement) and construction was all-welded and built up of prefabricated sections under the survey of British Corporation; machinery was steam reciprocating ihp 220 with coal-fired and oil-fired Scotch boiler working at 140lb/sq in.

Minion Class

This design was produced in 1938 and a total of five tugs were built for harbour service work. Their general particulars were:

Length overall		71ft 6in
Length between perps		66ft 0in
Breadth (moulded)		18ft 6in
Depth (moulded)		8ft 6in
Displacement (deep)		114 tons
Draughts (deep)	F	5ft 5in
	A	7ft 10in
	mean	7ft 7in
Speed (max)		9kts
Endurance		1600 miles
Complement		6 officers and men
Metacentric height in deep condition		2.28ft (fl)

One vessel was completed for service in the tropics.

A number of commercially owned tugs was requisitioned for dockyard service and some vessels ordered by the Director of Merchant Shipbuilding for Director of Small Vessels Pool were handed over to the Royal Navy. Included amongst these were the Canadian-built *Tanac* tugs of wood construction, moulded dimensions 65ft x 16ft 9in x 7ft 6in draught aft and 300bhp diesel engine, and steel vessels 60ft x 16ft 6in x 7ft 6in draught aft with 200bhp diesels. In addition some *Empire* class tugs built by Director of Merchant Shipbuilding for Ministry of Transport were allocated for harbour service.

CHAPTER 24

Netlayers

Editorial Note

The complicated defence of a port in World War II required a considerable number of specialised ships, *netlayers, controlled minelayers, indicator loop laying ships etc., described in this chapter.*

In 1939 there were two netlayers in commission, *Protector* and *Guardian*; these ships had been in service since 1936 and 1933 respectively and were fitted out for the laying of the heaviest type of anti-submarine nets.

The general particulars of these ships were:

	Protector	*Guardian*
Length overall	338ft 1½in	343ft 8½in
Length between perps	309ft 11¾in	310ft 1¼in
Breadth extreme	53ft ½in	53ft ⅜in
Depth (moulded)	26ft 6in	26ft 6 ⅜in
Deep displacement	3610 tons	3664 tons
Max speed (deep)	20kts	18kts
Endurance	4150 miles at 10kts	5590 miles at 10kts
Oil fuel	707 tons	734 tons
Nets carried	370 tons	370 tons
Complement	9 officers 168 men	9 officers 161 men
Armament	2-4in guns in a twin mounting 7-20mm single Oerlikons	

These ships were powered by geared turbines driving twin screws at a total of 9000shp at 210rpm for *Protector* and 6500shp at 250rpm for *Guardian*.

The stability particulars for the ships in deep conditions were:

	Protector	*Guardian*
Metacentric height	7.3ft	6.9ft
Max GZ	4.84ft	4.54ft
Angle of max GZ	45°	45°
Range	over 90°	over 90°
Displacement	3610 tons	3664 tons

Following upon a Board approval in 1940 for the production of 100 miles of anti-boat net defence, it became necessary to make provision for the rapid laying of this equipment as it became available. Approval was given in May 1940 for the conversion of two ships for this purpose and a pleasure steamer, SS *Atalanta* and a paddle minesweeper *Kylemore* were selected.

The conversion work consisted of extending the top or boat deck right aft, maintaining the full width of deck of 27ft 0in (23ft 0in in *Atalanta*). 3ft 3in steel troughs were fitted each side for the sinkers and floats, the wood deck being retained for the centre or net trough which was 15ft 6in wide. A 2ft 6in gangway was arranged each side of the deck. The length of clear deck required was 110ft 0in. This allowed one lay of half-a-mile of nets to be laid from the net deck. The fore hold was fitted for stowing the component parts of a further half-mile of nets. A 2 ton winch and davits were fitted for hoisting this lay on to the net deck for assembly, after the first half-mile had been laid. Stowage for the 1 ton net anchors was arranged at each quarter. One 12pdr HA/LA, two Lewis and two Maxim guns were fitted. Existing accommodation was largely used. The conversions were completed in four weeks and netlaying trials were carried out satisfactorily in July 1940.

In view of the mileage of nets necessary for the defence of the country, approval was given in the conversion of a further two vessels to anti-boat netlayers and the steamers *Tonbridge* and *Minster* were selected. The conversions were generally similar to the previous ships, but a sloped ramp was arranged port and starboard in the fore hold with a 2 ton winch port and port and starboard on the net deck. This enabled the spare lay of nets to be hauled up from the hold straight on to the net deck for assembly. Ramps and stowage for netlaying anchors were fitted aft on the main deck. Two 2pdr, two Lewis guns and two Holman projectors were fitted. Additional accommodation, stores, etc. were fitted as required.

The loss of *Kylemore* and *Tonbridge* by enemy action led to the conversions of the steamer *Brittany* and *Ringwood*, a sister ship to *Minster*, to netlayers.

In July 1941 *Protector* was seriously damaged by enemy action in the Far East and it was decided to replace her by *Guardian*. This resulted in the necessity for finding an efficient substitute for *Guardian* for duty in Home waters. The vessel

Kylemore as converted

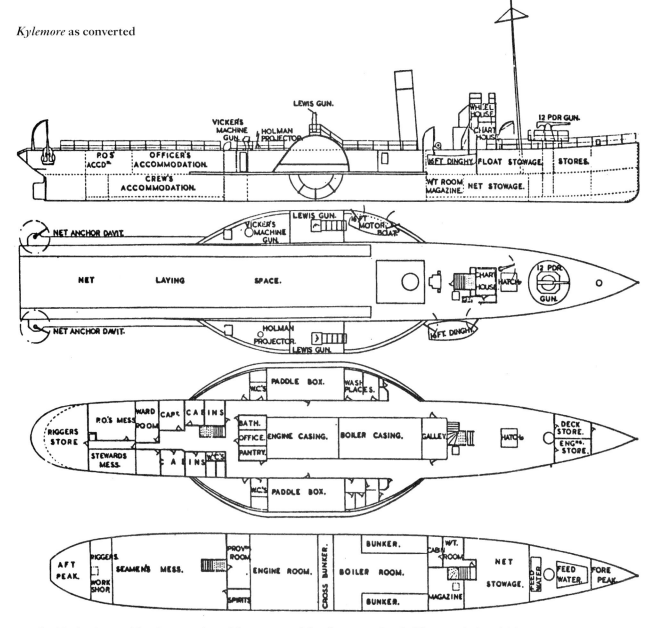

required had to be capable of ocean going with an endurance of not less than 2500 miles and capable of laying the heavier anti-submarine nets. Failure to find a suitable additional vessel which could be economically converted resulted in the decision to modify *Brittany* to meet the requirements.

The following work was carried out on the vessel:

Additional oil fuel stowage was arranged utilising existing FW and RFW tanks for oil fuel, constructing cofferdams as necessary and using the after peaks for FW and RFW. The loss of stowage of RFW was compensated for by fitting an additional 10ton/day distilling plant. Additional stringers were fitted at the fore end of the ship. The hatch to the fore hold was reduced in size and

steel hatch covers fitted. The net deck, which consisted of wood planking secured to the beams, was plated in between the stringer plate and the engine and boiler casings and the wood deck relaid. Sidelights below the main deck were blanked watertight. The large ship-side doors on the main deck were plated in and a small WT door with strong-back fitted. A 5 ton derrick was fitted over the fore hatch and the vessel was fitted for Arctic and tropical service.

At the end of the European war, *Brittany*, *Ringwood* and *Atalanta* were released from naval service and returned to the Ministry of War Transport.

The leading particulars of these later ships were as follows:

	Tonbridge, Minster, Ringwood	Kylemore	Atalanta	Brittany
Length between perps	220ft 0in	220ft 0in	210ft 0in	250ft 0in
Breadth	33ft 7in	40ft 0in	30ft 0in	39ft 0in
Deep displacement as netlayer	1430 tons	603 tons	723 tons	2102 tons
Deep mean draught	12ft 9in	7ft 1½in	8ft 1½in	12ft 10½in
Complement:				
officers	5	4	4	9
ratings	74	34	36	85
Machinery	Twin screw reciprocating	Paddle wheel	Triple screw turbines	Twin screw turbines
Oil Fuel	–	–	–	247 tons
Coal	115 tons	90 tons	38 tons	–
Nets carried	63 tons of A/B nets on deck and 105 tons in hold	35 tons of A/B nets on deck and 35 tons in hold	35 tons of A/B net on deck and 35 tons in hold	90 tons A/S nets on deck and 180 tons in hold
GM	2.0ft	1.5ft	1.75ft	2.11ft

Netlayer *Tonbridge* general arrangement

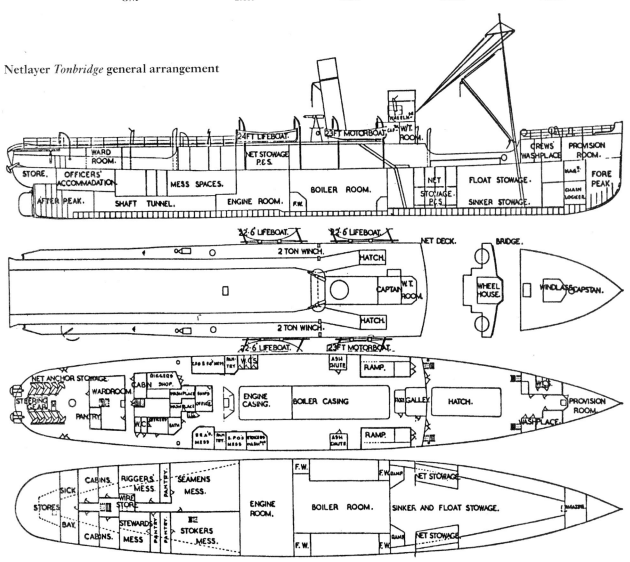

Brittany as converted

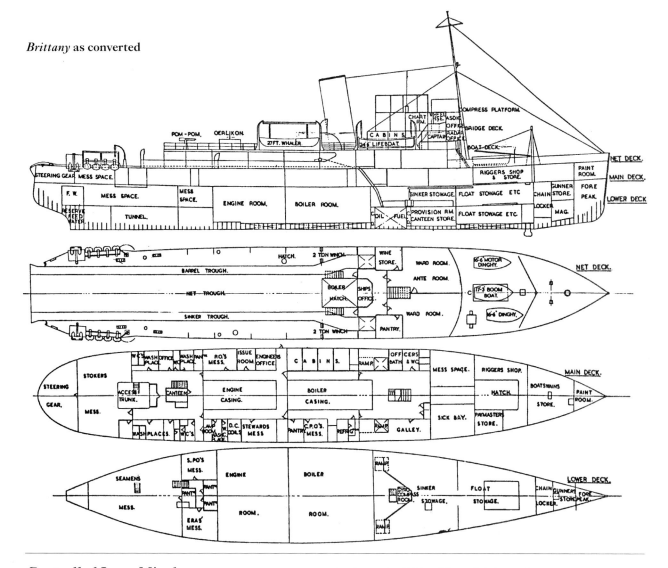

Controlled Loop Minelayers

In 1936, staff requirements for a controlled loop minelayer were laid down and a design worked out to meet those requirements.

The principal particulars of the design were:

Length overall (including bow sheaves)	163ft 9in
Length between perps	145ft 0in
Breadth moulded at upper deck	27ft 0in
Depth moulded	14ft 0in
Deep displacement	585 tons
Mean draught (deep)	8ft 11in
Oil fuel	60 tons
Power	400ihp
Maximum speed	10kts
Endurance at 8kts	3000 miles
Complement	47 (total)

The vessel was capable of carrying twenty L-type mines and sinkers on the upper deck and was provided with the necessary equipment for laying a twenty mine loop minefield and for weighting and relaying the loop minefield when necessary. Provision was made for carrying 10 miles of tail cable and 1600 yards of loop cable.

Machinery consisted of one oil fired watertube boiler and two reciprocating engines developing 200ihp on each of two shafts at 160rpm.

Propeller particulars:

diameter	6ft 0in
pitch	7ft 0in (3 blades)
developed blade area	10sq ft

To meet the requirement for manoeuvrability consideration was given in the design stage to the fitting of Voith-Schneider propellers. However, as these to date had not been proved, it was decided to keep to the normal types of propeller and rudder.

No armament was provided for in the original design, but during the war the ships built to this design were fitted with two Lewis guns.

Stability Particulars
These were based on inclining experiment carried out on *Linnet* in June 1938.

	Deep Condition	Light Condition
Metacentric height	2.15ft (fl)	2.3ft
Max GZ	1.21ft	1.16ft
Angle of max GZ	32°	39°
Range	67°	64°
Displacement	608 tons	411 tons

No strength calculations were made. The dimensions of *Linnet* were practically the same as *Basset*, which was built to Class 100 A1 trawler, Lloyds, and the same scantlings were adopted.

The first of the class built was named *Linnet*; she was followed by *Redstart* and *Ringdove*.

Ship	Builder	Laid down	Launched	Completed
1936 Programme				
Linnet	Ardrossan Dockyard	28 Apr 1937	24 Feb 1938	18 Jun 1938
1937 Programme				
Redstart	Henry Robb	13 Sep 1937	3 May 1938	28 Oct 1938
Ringdove	Henry Robb	25 Sep 1937	16 Jun 1938	5 Dec 1938

Controlled Minelayers Converted from A/S, M/S, Trawlers

Further ships were needed for controlled minelaying and in April 1942 approval was given to convert *Mackerel* and *Turbot* (subsequently renamed the *Corncrake* and the *Redshank*), two coal-fired trawlers of the *Fish* class (*Gullfoss* type) which were building as A/S, M/S trawlers. Their principal dimensions were:

Length overall	162ft 0in
Length between perpendiculars	146ft 6in
Breadth (moulded)	25ft 0in
Depth (moulded)	14ft 0in
Displacement (deep)	910 tons

Maximum speed was 10kts; endurance with 202 tons coal at 8½kts 5000 miles; endurance with bunkers limited to 149 tons of coal (to maintain minimum freeboard of 1ft 6in for ocean voyages) 3800 miles.

They were converted to carry sixteen L-type mine units, 10 miles of tail cable, 1600 yards of loop cable, and to lay and maintain a standard sixteen-mine loop; this included laying the mines, the loop and the tail cable, and weighing and relaying the loop minefield when necessary. In March 1943 approval was given for *Fish* class and *Isles* class and other converted trawlers to carry twenty L-type mine units.

The *Corncrake* was completed in November 1942 and the *Redshank* in February 1943. *Redshank* cost £49,000.

It had been hoped to build two modified *Linnets* in 1942 but, owing to the extra work and the loss of time which would result in incorporating the modifications, together with the consequent dislocation in the already approved trawler programme, it was decided to allocate two coal-fired *Isles* class trawlers, the *Sheppey* and the *Thorney*, renamed the *Blackbird* and the *Dabchick*, originally intended for A/S, M/S work, for controlled minelaying service. As the ships at the time were not due to be laid down for two or three months, the builders had time in which to revise their plans. *Blackbird* cost £61,000.

They were chosen in preference to two further *Fish* class conversions because they drew less water, an advantage when laying mines close inshore.

Principal dimensions:

Length overall	164ft 0in
Length between perpendiculars	150ft 0in
Breadth	27ft 6in
Depth moulded	15ft 0in
Displacement (deep)	790 tons

Maximum speed was 12kts; endurance at 10kts with 184 tons of coal ex-mines, tail cable etc., 4500 miles.

They were converted to perform the same duties as the *Corncrake* and *Redshank*.

The *Blackbird* was completed in June 1943 and the *Dabchick* in July 1943.

In April 1943, two of twelve *Isles* class trawlers in the 1943 programme were earmarked for service as controlled minelayers: the *Whitethroat* for the Canadian navy and the *Stonechat*. They were built to the same specification as the *Blackbird* and *Dabchick* except that they were oil-fired and in addition the *Whitethroat* was fully fitted for Arctic service and with a pressure system for fresh water and sanitary arrangements.

The *Stonechat* was completed in November 1944 and the *Whitethroat* in December 1944.

Controlled Minelayers (Conversions from Merchant Types)

Additional controlled minelayers were made available by converting three commercial trawlers and one inter-island diesel-driven passenger ship. They were equipped for laying twenty L mines in a standard mine loop.

One other vessel – *Spindrift* – an ex-German trawler captured in 1940, was converted for controlled minelaying.

The service of these ships rendered was generally satisfactory though the performance of *Lochnevis* was limited during rough weather due to the lightness of her construction.

The vessels requisitioned from trade were returned at the end of the war.

Ship	L	B	D	Tonnage Gross	Converted
Sandmartin (ex *Jay*), trawler	140ft 4in	24ft	12ft 10in	311	1941
Alsey, trawler	150ft 4in	25ft 1in	14ft 1in	368	1940
Snakefly (ex *Fane*), trawler	131ft 0in	24ft 6in	13ft 5in	273	1940
Lochnevis (inter-island)	175ft 0in	31ft 0in	10ft 5in	568	1941

Indicator Loop Laying Ship

Early in 1936 staff requirements were finalised for indicator loop layers. They were, briefly, for vessels able to proceed overseas and lay indicated loops (stationary asdics) at the entrances to harbours which were, or might be required to be used as fleet anchorages. The laying of such loops were to include also the laying and landing of the tail cables and the weighing and relaying of the loops.

The minimum requirement was fixed as being the laying in one operation of one loop with a front of 5 miles, ie about 15 miles of loop cable and 5 miles of tail weighing approximately 120 tons and occupying 1600cu ft exclusive of stowages cones, working spaces, etc. Ships of larger capacity were to be arranged to stow and work in multiples of the 5 mile front unit; these vessels would thus be capable of laying at one operation one, two, three or four such loops. To make for economical working and rapidity of loading and operating, two separate cable cones were desired, though not specified as essential.

The vessels were required to have a minimum endurance of 3000 miles at 11kts and a maximum speed of 13kts.

To fulfil the minimum requirements a twin screw oil-fired steamship was designed and included in the 1936 new construction programme. She was built to Lloyd's rules and eventually named *Lasso*.

General particulars of the design were:

Length overall (over bowsheaves)	205ft 0in
Length between perps	180ft 0in
Breadth (moulded)	35ft ¼in
Depth (moulded)	23ft ⅜in
Deep displacement	1105 tons
Mean draught deep	11ft 1in
Power	1100ihp
Max speed (standard)	13kts
Oil fuel	160 tons
Complement	7 officers, 39 men

Provision was made in this ship for the carrying of 15 miles of loop cable and 10 miles of tail cable on separate cable cones. The vessel was also provided with the usual cable fittings, including double bow sheave, cable winch and dynamometer, whilst space had to be provided for the stowage of one indicator loop control station (HDA) unit to be carried on board during passages.

Lasso was armed during the war with 1-4in LA gun and an Oerlikon gun.

Machinery consisted of two sets of reciprocating engines driving twin screws at 150rpm.

Propellers were 3-bladed and had the following dimensions:

diameter	7ft 6in
pitch	11ft 0in

The auxiliary machinery included a 50kW steam-driven generator situated in the engine room and a 50kW diesel generator in its own compartment on the lower deck, forward of the boiler room.

An inclining experiment carried out on *Lasso* in May 1938 gave the following results:

	Deep Condition	Light Condition
Metacentric height	2.42ft (fl)	2.63ft
Max GZ	2.48ft	1.65ft
Angle of max GZ	54°	59.5°
Range	over 90°	89°
Displacement	1125 tons	731 tons

Lasso was laid down in 1937, launched in March 1938 and was completed ready for service in June of that same year.

Conversions

On the outbreak of war it was apparent that further new construction could not be expected to meet the requirements for these ships, so various small ships, capable of being easily and quickly converted, were taken over by the Admiralty for the purpose of maintaining and repairing the loops at certain fixed bases.

The following gives a complete list of the vessels converted:

Small Cable Ships

Ship	Gross Tonnage	L	B	D	Date of taking up
Eldorado (ex *Ophir*)	469 tons	155ft	26ft	13ft	Nov 1941
Aquilla	469 tons	155ft	26ft	13ft	Dec 1941
Sprayville	466 tons	152ft	25ft	12ft	Sept 1943
Cecile Mapleson	440 tons	142ft 6in	26ft 6in	11ft 3in	Feb 1942
Mead	606 tons	170ft	29ft 10in	16ft 6in	May 1942
Straide	326 tons	131ft 7in	23ft 1in	10ft	July 1940
Castlerock	259 tons	124ft 6in	22ft 1in	10ft	Aug 1940
Mondara	359 tons	135ft	23ft 6in	11ft	Aug 1940
Emile Baudot	1050 tons	222ft 6in	32ft 3in	19ft 3in	Aug 1940
May	257 tons	124ft 6in	22ft 1in	9ft	Jun 1940
Dunavon	235 tons	125ft 3in	21ft 1in	9ft	Aug 1940
St Oran	249 tons	122ft	21ft 6in	9ft 4in	Jan 1941
Plymouth Trader	142 tons	98ft	20ft	8ft	Apr 1940
X 216	142 tons	98ft	20ft	8ft	Mar 1940
Lady of the Isles	166 tons	130ft 6in	18ft 6in	9ft 4in	Mar 1940
Bankville	339 tons	150ft 2in	24ft 5in	11ft 8in	May 1942
Retriever	863 tons	210ft	32ft	19ft 5in	Oct 1942

These ships, most of which were coasters, were chosen specially in order that their conversion for cable work would interfere as little as possible with the designed function, clearly evidenced by the rapidity with which they were converted back for use in trade.

Great difficulty was experienced in finding suitable ships which could be spared from their normal functions and the conversions were carried out by small yards throughout the country.

A number of these conversions included the fitting of a gun – usually an Oerlikon.

The success of harbour defence throughout the war largely depended on the equipment laid and maintained by these small vessels which operated under greatly varying conditions.

Self-Propelled Minelaying Lighters – MINERS

In 1937 it was approved to build five self-propelled minelaying lighters for duty as either controlled loop minelayers or as indicator loop layers attached to a harbour or an anchorage, the *Linnet* class being reserved for operations as controlled loop minelayers which necessitated working away from a base.

A design was worked out for a diesel-driven vessel and the principal dimensions were:

Length overall	118ft 6in
Length between perps	110ft 3in
Breadth (moulded)	326ft 5in
Depth (moulded)	12ft 0in
Displacement	368 tons
Mean draught (deep)	7ft 7in

The vessels were equipped to lay twenty mines in a standard wire loop and for recovering mines and cable exactly as in the *Linnet* class. With no mines or tail cable on board, stowage was available for about 16 miles (100 tons) of indicator loop cable.

If required to lay indicator loops, the mine recovery winch was used for laying and recovering the cable.

These lighters were fitted with twin screws and two sets of diesel-driven propelling machinery giving a total of 350hp. The power for the minelaying winches and davits was supplied by two 50kW diesel generators. The oil fuel stowage was sufficient for 5 tons of diesel oil which gave an endurance of about 500 miles at the maximum speed of 10kts.

Special manoeuvring ability was provided by keeping the vessel as short as possible, fitting twin screws, cut-away stern contour and twin-balanced rudders.

Being employed on minelaying duties from a base, no provision was made for sleeping and living quarters for the crews, but a mess equipped with tables and seating accommodation for taking meals, together with an oil cooking stove for boiling water and warming food was provided. Limited provision was made for a washplace, WCs and water services.

The first five of the class, ie M1–M5, were completed as shown below and approval was given to build a further three.

By 1941, however, the *Miners* were employed on duties beyond their designed function, namely the laying of mine loops working independently of a base. It was decided, therefore, to construct the three new *Miners* as self-contained units and to bring the earlier *Miners* into line as soon as possible.

The ships were now no longer required to function as indicator loop layers, there being sufficient ships (mainly conversions) to perform the neces-

A minelaying lighter, Miner *VI, taken on 12 Aug 1957 and little changed.*

sary duties as such, and thus the after cable hold, together with other stowage space, was released for use in providing accommodation for the ships' new function. Cabins were provided for the CO and his 2nd in command, sleeping and living arrangements for the crew with a space allotted as an emergency sleeping space for the mining party; a galley was built and the endurance of the ships extended by increasing the diesel oil stowage from 5 tons to 10 tons and the fresh water stowage from 1½ to 5 tons.

The *Miners* acquitted themselves admirably throughout the war, working efficiently even when they were called upon to perform more than their designed function under improvised conditions.

Ship	Builder	Laid Down	Completed
1938 Programme			
Miner I	Philip & Son	21 Nov 1938	26 Oct 1939
Miner II	Philip & Son	22 Dec 1938	16 Mar 1940
Miner III	Philip & Son	18 Jan 1939	16 Mar 1940
1939 Programme			
Miner IV	Philip & Son	10 Feb 1940	12 Nov 1941
Miner V	Philip & Son	22 Apr 1940	26 Jun 1940
1940, 1941 & 1942 Programme			
Miner VI	Philip & Son	22 Apr 1941	30 May 1942
Miner VII	Philip & Son	31 Mar 1943	31 Mar 1944
Miner VIII	Philip & Son	28 Mar 1942	15 May 1943

CHAPTER 25

Armed Merchant Cruisers

[1] Osborne, R. (Ed). Conversion for War. World Ship Society, Kendal, 1983

[2] Brown, D K. Armed Merchant Ships - A Historical Review. Symposium 'Merchant Ships to War', RINA, London, 1987.

[3] On the problems of wartime travel see also; Brown, D K. A Century of Naval Construction. London, 1983.

[4] Norbury-Williams, L. Ships with Steel Skirts. WARSHIP 1989, London, 1989.

Editorial Note

There are few accounts[1,2] of the modern history of armed merchant ships and, with the exception of Refs 1 and 2, these tend to concentrate on disasters and derogatory descriptions such as 'Admiralty Made Coffins'. Between the wars, the Admiralty was very concerned - perhaps too much - over the threat to shipping from surface raiders. As described in the text, planning began in 1920 with arrangements for suitable ships to be stiffened to carry guns. In 1937 detail plans were made for conversions in three stages with ships allocated to specific yards for conversion. These plans worked well and armed merchant cruisers entered service speedily.

As the war went on, the better ships were given improved guns and shells, radar, aircraft etc but the threat from raiders diminished as air patrols became more extensive and the armed merchant cruisers were transferred to other duties, mainly as Landing Ships Infantry. The effectiveness of empty oil drums as torpedo protection is notable. It was suggested for use during the Falklands campaign but the arrangement of the merchant ships concerned made it impractical.

The problems of fitting defensive armament to cargo ships are even less well known and are described in great detail here. It is a more personal account than in most chapters with references to the difficulties of dealing with obstructive owners and the "parsimonious" Treasury. There was clearly a very heavy work load whose effects were made worse by the problems of wartime travel.[3] As well as guns, ships were fitted with paravanes and Asdic with led to further problems. It is surprising that no mention is made of the ACTAEON net defence (AND) which involved a great deal of effort by DNC department and saved a few ships.[4]

In 1920 approval was given for fifty large passenger ships to be stiffened to take six, seven or eight 6in guns and two 3in HA guns in preparation for conversion to armed merchant cruisers in the event of war. This stiffening was either fitted permanently or, where it would interfere with the peacetime function of the ship, was made portable and carried on board. It was later decided that an additional twenty-four ships should be converted on the outbreak of war but, due to lack of suitable ships, this number was never achieved and the actual number of ships fitted out being fifty-six, including those to Canadian, Australian and New Zealand account.

In 1936 standard plans, based on the P&O liner *Carthage*, were prepared for conversion of a passenger liner to an AMC, and a specification containing instructions for three stages of conversion,

Rawalpindi, *famous for her gallant fight against* Scharnhorst *and* Gneisenau.

ie emergency equipment, semi-complete equipment and complete equipment, was also prepared. This specification, the general arrangement drawing of HMS *Carthage*, together with detailed plans of the necessary packing rings, shell racks, depth charge arrangements, etc. were forwarded to all LWPSs at home and dockyards abroad. The ships earmarked for conversion were each allocated to a particular port of dockyard for the conversion to be carried out, and immediately on the outbreak of war the vessels were sailed to their allocated port and the work commenced.

It was originally estimated that the time occupied in the emergency conversion would be three weeks, five weeks for the semi-complete and two and a half months for the complete equipment. In the early months of the war certain of the vessels were fitted out with the semi-complete equipment at their first conversion. Others were given the emergency conversion, and later had their equipment improved to the semi-complete or complete stage.

The following is a list of the vessels concerned, together with the owners, and firms which carried out the work:

Ship	Owners	Dimensions	Conversion carried out by	Length of time
Alaunia	Cunard White Star	519ft x 65ft x 43ft	Gibraltar Dockyard	5 weeks
Alcantara	Royal Mail	639ft x 78ft x 44ft 9in	Malta Dockyard	About 3 months
Andania	Cunard White Star	519ft x 65ft x 43ft	Cammell Laird	10 weeks
Arawa	Shaw Saville	530ft x 68ft x 43ft 6in	Sydney, Australia	7 weeks
Antenor	A Holt	490ft 9in x 62ft x 39ft	Calcutta	11 weeks
Ascania	Cunard White Star	519ft x 65ft x 43ft	Cammell Laird	6 weeks
Asturias	Royal Mail	639ft x 78ft x 44ft 9in	Harland & Wolff, Belfast	4½ weeks
Aurania	Cunard White Star	519ft x 65ft x 43ft	Swan Hunter	5 weeks
Ausonaia	Cunard White Star	519ft x 65ft x 43ft	Vickers-Armstrongs Walker	8 weeks
Bulolo	Burns Philp	390ft x 58ft x 30ft 9in	South Africa	3¼ months
California	Anchor Line	550ft x 70ft x 42ft 9in	Fairfields	3½ weeks
Canton	P&O	530ft x 73ft x 46ft	A Stephens	7 weeks
Carinthia	Cunard White Star	600ft x 73ft 6in x 45ft 1in	Vickers, Barrow	3½ months
Carnavon Castle	Union Castle	645ft 7_in x 73ft x 45ft 6in	Simonstown	6 weeks
Carthage	P&O	518ft 6in x 71ft x 37ft	Calcutta	3¼ months
Cathay	P&O	522ft 2in x 70ft x 46ft	Bombay	8 weeks
Cheshire	Bibby Line	482ft x 60ft x 36ft 3in	Calcutta	8½ weeks
Chitral	P&O	524ft 7in x 70ft x 46ft	A Stephens	4½ weeks
Cilicia	Anchor Line	480ft x 66ft x 35ft 6in	John Browns	5½ weeks
Circassia	Anchor Line	480ft x 66ft x 35ft 6in	Fairfields	9 weeks
Comorin	P&O	522ft 2in x 70ft x 46ft	South Africa	4 months
Corfu	P&O	518ft 6in x 71ft x 37ft	Harland & Wolff, Belfast	10 weeks
Derbyshire	Bibby Line	482ft x 66ft x 36ft 6in	Fairfields	7 weeks
Dunnottar Castle	Union Castle	530ft x 71ft 6in x 35ft	Hawthorn Leslie	7½ weeks
Dunvegan Castle	Union Castle	530ft x 71ft 6in x 35ft	Harland & Wolff, Belfast	3 months
Esperance Bay	Aberdeen & Commonwealth	530ft x 68ft x 43ft 5in	Durban	5½ weeks
Forfar ex Montrose	CPR	546ft x 70ft x 43ft 3in	Fairfield	5½ weeks

Hector	A Holt	490ft 9in x 62ft x 39ft	Bombay	3 months
Jervis Bay	Aberdeen & Commonwealth	530ft x 68ft x 43ft 6in	Harland & Wolff, London	4 weeks
Kanimbla	McIlwraith, McEacharn	468ft x 66ft x 36ft	Sydney	10½ weeks
Laconia	Cunard White Star	600ft 6in x 73ft 6in x 45ft	Portsmouth	4½ months
Laurentic	Cunard White Star	575ft x 75ft x 45ft	Devonport	6½ weeks
Letitia	Donaldson Atlantic Line	518ft x 66ft x 42ft	Canada	8 weeks
Maloja	P&O	600ft x 73ft x 43ft 6in	Bombay	10½ weeks
Monowai	Union SS of NZ	500ft x 63ft x 37ft 6in	Wellington, NZ	–
Montclare	CPR	546ft x 70ft x 43ft 3in	Vickers, Barrow	4 weeks
Mooltan	P&O	600ft x 73ft x 43ft 6in	Harland & Wolff, Belfast	4 months
Moreton Bay	Aberdeen &	530ft x 68ft x 43ft 6in	Sydney	7 weeks
Patroclus	A Holt	490ft 9in x 62ft x 39ft	Harland & Wolff, Liverpool	3¾ months
Pretoria	Union Castle	560ft x 76ft x 37ft	Harland & Wolff, Belfast	10 weeks
Queen of Bermuda	Furness-Withy	550ft x 76ft 6in x 43ft 3in	Harland & Wolff, Belfast	8 weeks
Rajputana	P&O	547ft 2in x 71ft x 38ft 6in	Esquimalt, Canada	12 weeks
Ranchi	P&O	547ft x 71ft x 38ft	Bombay	9½ weeks
Ranpura	P&O	547ft x 71ft x 38ft	Calcutta	11½ weeks
Rawalpindi	P&O	547ft 2in x 71ft x 38ft 6in	Green and Silley Weir	–
Salopian ex *Shropshire*	Bibby Line	482ft x 60ft x 36ft 3in	Cammell Laird	5½ weeks
Scotstoun ex *Caledonia*	Anchor Line	550ft x 70ft x 42ft 9in	Harland & Wolf, Belfast	4 weeks
Transylvania	Anchor Line	550ft x 70ft x 42ft 9in	Fairfield	3½ weeks
Voltaire	Lamport & Holt	520ft x 64ft x 43ft	Swan Hunter	–
Wolfe ex *Montcalm*	CPR	546ft x 70ft x 43ft 3in	John Brown	11 weeks
Worcestershire	Bibby Line	482ft x 64ft x 36ft 6in	John Brown	–

Circassia in 1941.

Jervis Bay *(1940) whose
fight with the* Admiral
Scheer *enabled most of her
convoy to escape.*

These vessels, with the addition of *Westralia* and
Manoora, which were converted in Australia for
the Australian Navy, and *Prince Robert, Prince
Henry* and *Prince David*, which were converted in
Canada for the Canadian Navy, give the total
number of AMCs which were actually fitted out
in the very early days of the war.

The work involved in fitting out these vessels
consisted of:

(a) Installing six, seven or eight 6in guns and two
3in HA guns.

(b) Building and fitting out magazines for the
stowage of the necessary ammunition and
arranging supply to the guns, including the
RU lockers.

(c) Arranging adequate accommodation and
messing arrangements for a crew of approximately 230, in addition to the normal engine
room personnel, which were retained on
requisitioning of the ship.

(d) Ballasting as necessary for satisfactory
stability.

Armament

Of the fifty-one ships listed previously, forty-two
were fitted originally with Mk VII guns on PIII,
PIV or PVIII mountings with a light type director. Two vessels, *Cilicia* and *Circassia*, were fitted
with Mk XII guns on PXIII* mountings and
seven ships, *Canton, Derbyshire, Dunnottar Castle,
Dunvegan Castle, Pretoria Castle, Queen of
Bermuda* and *Wolfe* were fitted with Mk XII guns
on PVII or PVII* mountings, these nine ships all
having full director firing.

As a result of *Alcantara*'s engagement with a
German raider in July 1940, it was decided that
the range of AMCs' guns should be increased.
Increased charges and 6in c.r.h. shells were introduced in all ships with suitable guns. In addition,

at later refits certain of the ships either had the
whole or part of their main LA armament
replaced by more modern guns, or additional
guns fitted; the inconvenience caused by carrying
two types of ammunition for the LA guns had to
be accepted.

Where possible during the re-armament of
AMCs, the broadside was increased from four to
five by fitting the new guns on the centre line forward or aft, in lieu of having the gun sided.

As regards the HA armament, opportunity was
taken on *Chitral, Laurentic* and *Montclare* when
the main armament was being altered, to substitute three 4in HA guns with fuse-keeping clock
for the two 3in HA guns originally fitted. On
Canton and *Corfu* two twin 4in were fitted.

The close range armament of the majority of
the ships when originally converted consisted of
two Lewis guns, and this was gradually augmented by a heterogeneous collection of weapons consisting of Hotchkiss guns, twin and quadruple .5
machine guns, single Mk VIII 2pdrs and Harvey
projectors. With the introduction of Oerlikons,
these were substituted so far as the supply position warranted. Eventually some ships had up to
sixteen Oerlikon guns fitted.

Magazines

The positions usually selected for the magazines
and shell rooms were in nos 2 and 5 holds. The
layout consisted of a magazine, shell room and
handing room for the 6in ammunition, and an HA
magazine. In the emergency stage, it was specified
that these magazines could be constructed of
wood, but in only six ships was advantage taken of
this relaxation. In some ships the 6in magazine
was built in the hold and the remaining space
utilised as the 6in shell room without building
additional bulkheads.

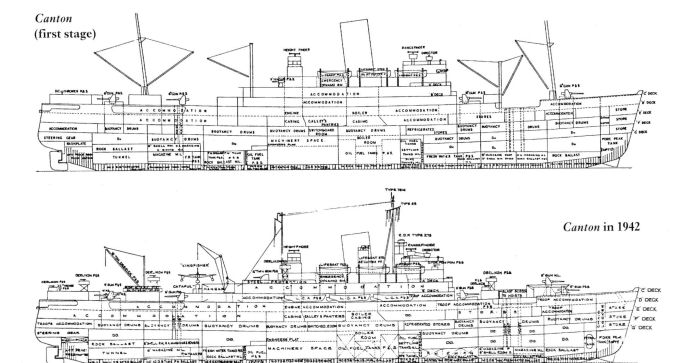

Canton
(first stage)

Canton in 1942

The necessary ammunition trunks, flashtight scuttles, bollard hoists, davits, etc. for supplying the ammunition to the guns were also fitted.

During the semi-complete conversion, the tops and sides of magazines and shell rooms were fitted with 40lb mild steel protection; flooding and spraying arrangements were also fitted to the magazines. Although the magazines and shell rooms were specified to be watertight, no test was carried out, as it was considered that this might materially delay the completion.

Accommodation

In the emergency conversion, it was arranged that officers and men should occupy the existing cabin accommodation, but in the semi-complete conversion arrangements were made to fit out open messes for the ratings and enclosed messes for CPOs, POs, etc.

As the vessels were originally passenger liners, it was seldom necessary to interfere with the cooking arrangements or washing arrangements. In fact it is stated that *Queen of Bermuda* was the only vessel in the Royal Navy where every officer had his own bathroom!

An attempt was made in later refits to reduce the amount of woodwork in the ships, but this was found to be beyond practical limitations.

Ballasting

With the inevitable increase in topweight during the conversion of these ships, it was found that the vessels would not stand two adjacent main com-

partments being flooded without capsizing. To improve stability a considerable amount of permanent ballast had to be stowed in all these ships.

In the majority of the vessels this amount varied between 1500 and 3000 tons, although a few ships such as *Bulolo*, *Laurentic* and *Monowai*, the amount was considerably less.

This permanent ballast consisted of primarily of rock and road metal, but in a few instances sand was used and, in the vessels fitted out in India, pig iron. The sand was not a success, as it was found that it gradually filled up the bilges and prevented the bilge suctions from working. Due to the amount of work involved, it was impossible to have the sand completely removed and replaced by rock, but where the ballast had to be removed for any other purpose, it was replaced by rock. In 1942, when the shortage of pig iron in this country became acute, it was considered worthwhile removing the pig iron from vessels when they were in for refit and replacing it with rock. In this way a considerable amount of pig iron was added to the country's stock.

Prior to the start of the Second World War financial approval was sought to purchase a nucleus of 250,000 oil drums to be used in AMCs as buoyancy drums.

This proposal was not approved, with the result that it was impossible to provide Armed Merchant Cruisers with the protection afforded by these drums when it was urgently required in the early months of the war. As drums became available, however, they were fitted in the conversions then in hand, and at each succeeding refit the number of drums gradually increased to the full requirement.

The method of drum stowage was briefly thus:

The 'tween deck spaces at the 'damaged' waterline were stowed first to preserve stability, and later the stowage was extended to the holds working from forward and aft towards amidships. As a result of the stowage of these drums in the amidship tween decks, thereby reducing the free surface effect on the bilged waterline if damaged, it was possible to reduce the intact GM and thus produce a steadier gun platform. In those ships fitted with buoyancy drums therefore, the amount of permanent ballast could be slightly reduced.[5]

A total of 1,200,000 drums was actually stowed in Armed Merchant Cruisers.

Due to the non-availability of drums in the early stages, wood was used to a certain extent as buoyant material. In view of the fire risk, this wood was later removed so far as was possible in the time available at refits and drums were substituted, but this was not fully achieved, with the result that some of the AMCs had this wood stowed for the whole of the time they were in service.

Troop Carrying Capacity

Early in 1941 it was decided to increase the accommodation provided on AMCs in order to carry troops as passengers. Thus troop carrying became a secondary function of the AMCs.

This requirement necessitated the removal of drums from the upper tween decks spaces so that they could be converted into messes, etc. It was pointed out that this would reduce the margin of stability in the event of damage, but this increase in risk was accepted. D of ST was called in to collaborate on the fitting out of the spaces concerned.

Altogether sixteen ships were fitted out as troopers and the numbers which could be carried, in addition to the Naval complement, varied from ten officers and 100 other ranks in *Cheshire*, to 180 officers and 1,780 other ranks in *Queen of Bermuda*.

Landing Craft

Late in 1941 it was decided that those vessels which could carry more than 500 troops should be fitted to carry LCA for possible use in landing operations. The necessary gallows davits were designed, and the appropriate electric winches ordered. It was proposed to carry six LCA on each ship and *Carthage*, *Canton* and *Corfu* were so fitted out. In early 1942 it was decided that AMCs should gradually revert to trade and trooping so that this scheme was not proceeded with, beyond the three ships mentioned above.

Catapults and Aircraft

Although the original specification for the conversion to AMC contained the necessary clauses for the installation of the catapult and crane for the handling of aircraft, no catapults or aircraft cranes were available when the vessels were converted.

Early in 1941, five SIII(L) or similar fixed-type catapults and cranes ex cruisers became available, and *Alcantara*, *Queen of Bermuda*, *Pretoria Castle*, *Asturias* and *Canton* were the five vessels selected for the installation of this equipment. Three vessels, *Alcantara*, *Canton* and *Pretoria Castle* were fitted out in the UK during 1941, the other two being fitted out in the USA. Each vessel carried two Seafox, one on the catapult and one in a hangar which was constructed in the vicinity of the after mast, the mast being removed. Bulk stowage of petrol in No 1 hold was arranged on the later vessels, but *Alcantara* originally had the petrol stowed in quick-release tanks on deck.

[5] The importance of this point may not be recognised. Without drums, which preserve stability after damage, it was necessary to have a large initial metacentric height (GM). Roll period is inversely proportional to the square root of the metacentric height and the lower GM of ships with drums would make them much steadier platforms.

Canton in her early configuration. (See plan)

Canton *later when she was the most powerful AMC. Note the seaplane (Kingfisher) and catapult, tripod mast. Her guns were more modern than those of most AMC and fired the longer range 6 crh shell.*

[6] Some of the incidents involving drum fitted ships follow:
Cheshire. Hit on 14 Oct 1940 by a torpedo which made a hole 36ft x 20ft, flooding 2 & 3 holds and their double bottoms. Even though the flooding spread slowly into 4 hold the ship remained upright and could steam slowly to port.
Patroclus was hit by 4 torpedoes in the initial attack on 3 Nov 1940. She was then shelled by the submarine which scored two hits.

The Seafox aircraft went out of production, and the SIIIL catapults fitted to AMCs would not take a heavier aircraft so that, when American P6 fixed catapults became available in mid-1942, twelve of these catapults were obtained. They were suitable for Kingfisher aircraft, and seven further AMCs were selected for the installation of these catapults, together with the five ships already fitted with the British catapult. Late in 1942 three ships were taken in hand, *Cilicia*, *Corfu* and *Canton*, the first two ships to be fitted with catapult, crane and hangar, and the last ship to have the SIII(L) catapult replaced by a P6 catapult. The hangar of *Canton* had also to be rebuilt to take the larger Kingfisher aircraft.

Before any further ships could be taken in hand, it was decided to return the AMCs to trade, although it was April 1944 before *Canton*, the last to revert to trade, was actually paid off.

Radar

In 1941 radar was introduced on AMCs and eventually nearly all the ships were fitted with a surface warning set, and an aircraft warning set, types 273 and 286 being the usual equipment.

General

Merchant ship lifeboats were removed and replaced by service cutters, both pulling and motor, by 25ft and 16ft FMB and by Carley Floats.

There were a number of serious damage incidents involving Armed Merchant Cruisers, but it is of note that only one vessel actually capsized as a result of damage sustained in action. The remainder of the vessels, where they were sunk, foundered – a tribute to the effectiveness of the ballasting and buoyancy drums.[6]

On operations the vessels were employed on the Northern Patrol, Freetown Convoy Escort, Halifax Escort, Cruiser Duties South Atlantic, East Indies Station, New Zealand Station, America and West Indies Station, and Australian Station.

Alaunia, *Ausonia* and *Aurania* (re-named *Artifex*) were later converted to base repair ships, *Ranpura* to repair ship, *Montclare* to destroyer depot ship and RAFT flagship, *Wolfe* to submarine depot ship, *Pretoria Castle* to auxiliary aircraft carrier and *Bulolo* to the first CO headquarters ship LSH(L).

Cheshire, typical of many AMCs.

All the other ships were reconverted for trade and trooping by D of ST.

DEMS
1939–45 War

The provision of defensive equipment for merchant ships may be divided into three periods:

1st period	August 1936 to September 1939
2nd period	September 1939 to August 1941
3rd period	August 1941 to conclusion of war

1st Period

In August 1936 a section of the Naval Construction Department was formed to investigate certain aspects of war work, such as the earmarking of trawlers for A/S and M/S duties, liners for AMC duties and as auxiliary aircraft carriers, etc.

In 1937 numerous conferences were held with the view of arranging for gun stiffening to be fitted on merchant ships and to decide who should bear the cost of such work. It was ultimately decided that selected ships of over 500 tons (gross) under construction, or to be constructed, and ships selected by the Admiralty, Board of Trade and Ship Owners from existing tonnage of over 1600 tons (gross) and not more than twelve years old, should be stiffened. The age restriction was relaxed in certain exceptional cases.

Priority of fitting gun stiffening on existing tonnage was to be as follows:

(a) Tankers
(b) Large fast passenger ships (15kts and upwards)
(c) Large intermediate passenger – cargo ships
(d) Large cargo ships

The Admiralty bore the cost of stiffening selected ships of over 500 tons (gross) under construction on or before 30 November 1937 (that is, shops for which contracts had actually been placed); stiffening of existing tonnage was also an Admiralty liability. Ship owners were made responsible for the cost of stiffening new tonnage ordered after 30 November 1937.

The armament allowed for was:

Ships under 1600 tons (gross) – one 12pdr HA/LA;

Ships over 1600 tons and under 7000 tons (gross) – one 4in LA and one 12pdr HA/LA;

Ships over 7000 tons (gross) – one 4in or 4.7in LA and one 12pdr HA/LA;

Fast ships (including cargo liners of 15kts and 11,000 tons (gross) or over) one 6in or 5.5in LA and one 3in HA.

The preparation of stiffening drawings by DNC Department was well under way in January 1938. In deciding positions for the mountings, six points had to be taken into consideration.

(a) The mountings had to be fitted abaft amidships to satisfy international law.
(b) The owner's wishes.
(c) General arrangement of the ship.
(d) Amount of disturbance to ship's fittings.
(e) Arcs of fire.
(f) Strength of existing structure.

It was very difficult to satisfy all the above conditions and item (e) frequently had to suffer. Matters were not made any easier by the attitude of some owners who considered the whole matter an unmitigated nuisance. On the majority of ships, however, the mountings were sited to the best advantage.

Where guns were not sited to the best advantage, opportunity was taken, after the war started, to resite them at new positions. This, of course, used labour and material which could have been more usefully employed elsewhere.

When designing stiffening for existing tonnage every endeavour was made to utilise existing structures to minimise interference with ship arrangement. The fitting of stiffening for 6in guns entailed a considerable amount of work as in all cases the stiffening had to be carried down through three between decks and, as the majority of the ships in this class had crew accommodation aft, it was not possible to carry out the work without considerable interference to ship's fittings.

At the commencement of all this work the ship owners were supplied with a DNC drawing which showed typical armament positions. When they had made themselves conversant with the information given on the drawing they informed Trade Division regarding specific ships which they would make available for stiffening in the near future. If the ships were in the approved categories the matter was then referred to DNC. This procedure was ultimately modified and the owners dealt direct with DNC. The arrangement then was for owners to bring direct to the Naval Construction Department general arrangement drawings of the ships which they wished stiffened. Gun positions were arranged to mutual satisfaction and some indication of the stiffening required was given. The owners then arranged with their contractors to have detailed stiffening drawings prepared which, on completion, were submitted to DNC for concurrence. Copies were then sent to the WPS concerned and the owner was in a position to put the work out to tender. The price was vetted by the local WPS and subject to his verdict Admiralty approval was given for the work to be put in hand at the first convenient opportunity. It should be appreciated that, although the Admiralty were liable for some of the expenditure, the owners in every case placed the contract and were later reimbursed when it was an Admiralty liability.

It was soon found that the constructor of the section concerned spent most of his time interviewing owners' representatives and little time was left for administering the remaining work in the section. It was then arranged for the owners to send in general arrangement drawings of their ship and from these DNC prepared detailed drawings of Admiralty proposals. When time did not permit of drawings being made, the stiffening arrangements were indicated on the general arrangement drawings for the guidance of the owners' contractors. This method was unsatisfactory as a copy of the arrangements proposed could not be kept for reference. The stiffening of new construction vessels did not offer many difficulties as proposals for defensive equipment were incorporated in the design stage.

In addition to the preparation and 'vetting' of drawings, a considerable amount of travelling was done by DNC staff in visiting ships and giving verbal instructions regarding the design of stiffening required. These visits were necessary as sometimes only 18 hours' notice was given of a suitable opportunity to carry out stiffening work on a ship for which drawings had not been prepared.

During this time it was not unusual for individual draughtsmen to have as many as thirty/forty ships awaiting their attention. This involved a tremendous pressure of work on the section and constructor, and latterly a sub-section (within the section) consisting of ten draughtsmen and a senior draughtsman was formed to deal with DEMS work alone. The normal time taken to prepare a fully detailed stiffening drawing was 1½ days.

An 'as fitted' drawing, which illustrated in colour the stiffening fitted, was supplied by the contractors. Prints were retained on the ship, by the owners and by the Admiralty.

The experience gained during this work showed the necessity from economic and efficiency points of view of having gun stiffening embodied in ships' structures during building. When this was done the cost was at least halved and the best positions for the guns were assured.

By September 1939, stiffening drawings covering 500 specific ships of different types had been prepared by DNC. In addition, twenty drawings for general guidance had been prepared, such as: typical stiffening arrangements; ready use shell lockers, etc.; teak packing rings etc.

The teak packing ring consisted of a minimum of 3in teak (after planing), a 30lb top plate and a ⅜in thick circumferential steel band to prevent splitting. They were fitted under all heavy mountings up to and including those for 4.7in guns. It was found that these packing rings were quite suitable and, although thousands were fitted, very few failures were reported. In the early days the top plate was rolled two ways before fitting and, providing due care was taken when bolting it down, there was no distortion, but latterly it was decided to lightly machine both sides of the top plate.

Approximately 760 ships were stiffened before the war. More ships could have been stiffened but for the parsimony of the Exchequer.

2nd Period

This period was more or less a repetition of the first period. One advantage was that it was possible to site the armament to the best advantage from a defensive point of view. Some members of DNC's staff still did a considerable amount of travelling in arranging positions for guns and advising on design of gun stiffening. Owing to pressure of work all this travelling had to be done at night and was to the physical detriment of those concerned. With the outbreak of war, work of greater urgency had to be manned and the staff engaged on DEMS work had to be reduced. As the experience of the technical staffs at the ports increased, the preparation of stiffening drawings eased off and finally ceased. The 'vetting' of stiffening arrangements was then left to the discretion of the WPS staffs. Age and tonnage restrictions were removed but the former priorities were still adhered to. Instructions were given that magazines with batten stowage were to be improvised in redundant cabins and storerooms or any other suitable spaces, but as the average merchant ship did not have redundant spaces the ammunition was carried in lockers of any type.

Prior to May 1941 .30in and .303in machine guns, Holman & Harvey projectors were fitted for close-range A/A fire. The positions for those weapons were arranged by the local 'fitting-out' staffs. It became apparent that owing to the multiplicity of weapons which were becoming available some effort would be required to standardise the layout of weapons.

The first typical armament arrangement was agreed in May 1941 and on it was illustrated the following points:

Ocean-Going Cargo Ships
1-4in LA aft
2-2in UP (gymbal mountings) and sight, or 1-

2in UP pillar box or 1-12pdr HA/LA mounted just forward of and superimposed on the 4in LA

2-twin M/Gs (1 port and 1 starboard) on for ward outboard corners of the poop deck

2-twin M/Gs (1 port and 1 starboard) on wings of the navigating bridge

2-2in UP trough mountings (1 port and 1 star board) mounted amidships with the UP sight on the wheelhouse roof

4-FAMs (2 port and 2 starboard) mounted amidship

1-Oerlikon mounted on wheelhouse roof

4-PACs (D) mounted on wheelhouse roof

A similar drawing was made in July 1941 for oil tankers, but with the following armament:

1-4in LA

1-12pdr HA/LA or 2in UP pillar box mounted just forward of and superimposed on 4in LA

2-Oerlikons (1 port and 1 starboard) mounted abreast of and at the level of the wheelhouse roof

4-FAMs or 6-PACs (D) mounted on wheel house roof

2-M/Gs (1 port and 1 starboard) on wings of the navigating bridge

The stowage of ammunition was now a problem and deck space was at a premium owing to the number of ammunition lockers which had to be carried.

During this time stiffening drawing for 270 specific ships and numerous drawings of general interest were prepared.

Up to the end of July 1941 2304 ships (exclusive of war casualties) had been armed.

3rd Period

To date there had been very little contact between the various Admiralty departments concerned with DEMS, but a conference held in London on 1 August 1941 initiated a very close liaison between DTD, DMB and DNC.

This conference was principally concerned with the arrangements which should be made for the defensive equipping of new construction tonnage. It was decided that:

(i)   There should be more co-ordination between the departments concerned;

(ii) The Admiralty and not 'fitting out' officers should decide the positions for the weapons – there were still diverse opinions regarding the best positions; and

(iii) That the layout of armament on existing tonnage should follow arrangements to be made for new construction tonnage – previously it had been the reverse.

DMB proposed that the co-ordinating authority should be DNC and that DNC should appoint an officer for liaison duties. This was concurred in and the conference was adjourned until 7 August to allow of a new armament layout being prepared. In the interval DNC appointed a Liaison Officer.

At the adjourned conference, the arrangements shown on the new armament layout drawing (DNC 24/A 1240), which was based on 'B' type standard merchant ship, were very fully discussed and the following arrangement agreed upon:

1-4in LA aft

2-2in UP gymbal mountings and sight, or 2in UP pillar box or 12-pdr HA/LA. Positioned about 26ft 0in forward of and superimposed on the 4in LA. The latter weapons to be fitted on pedestals of sufficient height to give horizontal fire over the LA gun

2-M/Gs (1 port and 1 starboard) mounted on deckhouse at after end of boat deck

2-M/Gs (1 port and 1 starboard) mounted on the wings of the navigating bridge

4-FAMs (2 port and 2 starboard) mounted on the boat deck

2-2in UP troughs (1 port and 1 starboard) mounted amidships with the sight on the wheelhouse roof

1-Oerlikon mounted on the wheelhouse roof

4-PACs (D) (2 port and 2 starboard) mounted on the wheelhouse roof

It was found that the wheelhouse roof was not large enough to accommodate the armament to be mounted and the area had to be increased considerably. DMB stated that he was prepared to modify the superstructure of new construction tonnage to suit our wishes, provided sufficient warning was received. This in effect gave DNC a free hand.

The conference was of the opinion that UP weapons should not be mounted on tankers, irrespective of whether they carried crude oil or petroleum, in view of fire risk. It was finally decided that ocean-going tankers should be armed with the following:

1-4in LA aft

1-12pdr superimposed on and just forward of the 4in LA

2-M/Gs (1 port and 1 starboard) mounted on the after end of the boat deck

2-M/G (1 port and 1 starboard) mounted on the wings of the navigating bridge

2-Oerlikons mounted on the wheelhouse roof

4-PACs (D) mounted on the wheelhouse roof

It was agreed that DNC in collaboration with DMB and DTD should develop typical arma-

[7] AND originally stood for Actaeon Net Defence but later the A was understood to stand for Admiralty. See Ref 4.

ment layout drawings for smaller ocean-going ships, also for coasters, tugs and other small craft as quickly as possible. The new layout drawing DNC 24/A 1240 was modified to suit the wishes of the conference and with further slight modifications was approved at a further conference held in London on 19 August 1941. Copies of the drawing were circulated to 'fitting-out' officers on 26 August 1941.

No sooner was this done than the amidship arrangements had to be scrapped owing to the advent of AND (Admiralty Net Defence)[7]. The topping lifts of this gear interfered seriously with the arcs of fire. After protracted discussions it was decided that the after armament could remain as already arranged but that the amidship layout should be on the following lines: the two M/Gs at the after end of the boat deck to be mounted at the ship's side on pedestals about 8ft 0in high. This height ensured at least horizontal fire over the lifeboats' davits.

Positions of the 2in UP troughs, trough sight and PACs (D) to remain as already arranged.

Bridge Arrangement for AND Ships
   2-0.5in Colts mounted on the wheelhouse roof. The wheelhouse roof to be extended to the ship's sides immediately over the navigating bridge wings. 2-Oerlikons (1 port and 1 starboard) to be mounted on the wings of the wheelhouse roof.

Bridge Arrangements for Non-AND Ships
   2-Oerlikons mounted on the wheelhouse roof
   2-.0.5in Colts (1 port and 1 starboard) mounted on the wing of the navigating bridge

Alternative to
   2-0.5in Colts mounted on the wheelhouse roof
   2-Oerlikons (1 port and 1 starboard) mounted

on the wings of the navigating bridge
A new drawing (DNC 24/A 1246) was prepared on the above lines, and circulated to 'fitting-out' officers at home and abroad on 16 October 1941.

Concurrently with the above a similar drawing (DNC 24/A 1250) was being prepared for ocean-going tankers and illustrated the following layout:

   1-4in LA aft
   1-12pdr HA/LA mounted just forward of and superimposed on the LA gun
   2-0.5in Colts (1 port and 1 starboard) mounted on pedestals erected on the after outboard corners of the boat deck

Bridge Arrangement for Admiralty Net Defence Ships
   2-0.5in Colts mounted on the wheelhouse roof
   2-Oerlikons (1 port and 1 starboard) mounted on the wings of the extended wheelhouse roof
   4-PACs (D) mounted on the wheelhouse roof

Copies of this drawing were circulated to 'fitting-out' officers at home and abroad during the latter days of November 1941.

All 0.5in Colt emplacements were made large enough to accommodate Oerlikons. Although the drawings were primarily for use on new construction ocean-going tonnage, they were also used for guidance on existing tonnage.

With the publication of the above drawing it was possible to take an interest in coasters and similar small craft. These ships offered problems of their own as so little deck space was available for mountings and lockers and the general arrangements of the ships differed so much. An attempt was made to give each one individual treatment but time did not permit this. About a dozen drawings were prepared, covering as large a field as possible, and, although the drawings were for specific ships, they were issued for general guidance. The maximum armament allowed for was:

Empire Pacific in 1945, one of a class of 1200 ton coasters specially built for the Ministry of War Transport for service in the Far East.

The tanker SS Regent Hawk *on 29 June 1945, showing the late-war armament fitted to merchant vessels.*

(i) *Large Coasters*
1-12pdr HA/LA aft
1-2in UP pillar box
1-Oerlikon
2-0.5in colts or 2-.303in/.30in machine guns
4-PAC (J)

(ii) *Small Coasters*
1-12pdr HA/LA
1-Oerlikon
2-0.5in colts or 2-.303in/.30in machine guns
2-PAC (J)

Matters were rather hectic at this time and it was becoming increasingly difficult to find opportunities to prepare armament layout drawings. To ensure standardisation of armament layouts it was arranged that DMB should instruct shipbuilders to send drawings of all new construction tonnage to the DNC Liaison Officer through their local WPSs; the positions for the weapons were then indicated on the drawings and they were returned. The covering letters stated in detail the exact locations of the armaments and copies were sent to DMB and DTD. This arrangement, wherein the Admiralty issued explicit detailed instructions for the arming of new construction tonnage, was adhered to until the conclusion of hostilities. Between August and December 1941 every armament layout prepared was submitted to DMB (Glasgow), DNC (Bath) and DTD (London) at fortnightly meetings. DMB returned to London in December 1941 and these meetings were then held weekly. Early in 1942 an arrangement was made with DTD wherein DNC issued instructions regarding the armament to be allowed for on new ships, without prior discussion with DTD.

Magazines fitted with batten stowage and water spraying arrangements were now being fitted. Stowage was arranged for normal requirements but at a later date it was increased to accommodate

operational requirements which required a deck area of about 200sq ft for a combined 4in/12pdr/Bofors magazine at the after end of the ship. Subsequently, when it was agreed to fit a gun forward, an additional magazine of about 90sq ft was fitted forward.

In February 1942 it was decided to accelerate the mounting of Oerlikon guns and conserve shipyard labour by prefabricating Oerlikon gun pedestals and platforms. A design was prepared, and orders were placed with firms not engaged in either shipbuilding or ship repairing. These prefabricated seatings were so well received that it was decided to prefabricate 12-pdr HA/LA and Bofors pedestals and platforms. The prefabrication policy fully justified itself as 250,000 man hours per 1000 Oerlikon pedestals were saved.

Exclusive of war casualties 2525 British ships were armed up to the end of March 1942.

In view of changes in war conditions and also in the supply of weapons, the normal scale of arming was revised in March 1943 and more latitude was given in the interpretation of the tonnage demarcation, ie a 2000 tons coaster was treated as an ocean-going ship and a 14,000 tons transport was armed on the same scale as a 16,000 tons ship, space and weight permitting. The armament on ocean-going (new construction) tonnage and ships on operational service was now to consist of:

1-4in LA aft
1-2in UP pillar box (12pdr HA/LA on tankers) or Bofors or 12pdr HA/LA mounted just forward of and superimposed on the 4in LA
2-Oerlikons (1 port and 1 starboard) mounted on pedestals erected on the after outboard corners of the boat deck
2-Oerlikons (1 port and 1 starboard) mounted on pedestals erected on the forward outboard corners of the boat deck. (Ships of over 15kts only)

2-Oerlikons (1 port and 1 starboard) mounted on the wings of the wheelhouse roof
2-0.5in Colts mounted on the wheelhouse roof
1-12pdr HA/LA mounted on a pedestal erected on the forecastle deck. (Ships of over 15kts only)
2 to 4-FAMs mounted amidships
2 to 4 PAC (J) mounted amidships
2-PACs (D) mounted on wheelhouse roof
Existing ship on operational service were also armed as above but those engaged on trade routes had two Oerlikons fewer and no 12pdr HA/LA forward.

Coasters (1000 gross tons and above)

1-12pdr HA/LA
0 to 1- 2in UP pillar box
2 to 3-Oerlikons
2-0.5in Colts
4-PAC (J)

Coasters (500-1000 GT)

1 to 3-Oerlikons
2-0.5in Colts
2 to 4-PAC (J)
2-PAC (D)

Coasters (under 500 GT)

0 to 2-Oerlikons
2-twin 0.5in Colts

Shortly after this it was decided that all weapons should be fitted at the ships' sides and the practice of mounting 0.5in Colts on the roofs of wheelhouses was discontinued. They were mounted on sponsons, built out on the fore side of the navigating or bridge decks.

It was now standard practice to position weapons, on all ocean-going ships (new construction) as previously arranged for AND ships.

The arrangement and fitting-out of gunner's accommodation was the responsibility of Ministry of War Transport but DNC notified the shipbuilders regarding the number of gunners to be provided for. The number of gunners per weapon was as follows:

LA gun two gunners
HA/LA gun one gunners (two where no LA gun)
Bofors gun four gunners
Oerlikon gun one gunners
UP pillar box one gunner

Machine guns were normally manned by the ships' crew. When engaged on operational service the above numbers were doubled.

In February 1944 the arming policy was again revised and the fitting of FAMs (except in operational ships), PACs (J) in ocean-going ships, and 2in UP pillar boxes in coasters was discontinued. The speed demarcation on the arming of new construction ocean-going tonnage was dropped, and the fitting of an Oerlikon aft instead of a 2in UP pillar box commenced; this position aft was also prepared to take a Bofors, to facilitate the changeover of weapons at a later date. It was now becoming apparent that the ideal weapon for coasters was the Oerlikon, and in most cases, although the official policy was to fit a 12pdr aft on the larger ones, two sided Oerlikons were fitted instead.

In March, owing to the increasing scarcity of 12pdrs and gunners, the mounting of this gun forward, except on operational ships and ships of 15kts, had to be discontinued. The fitting of the pedestals and platforms and magazines continued so that when a ship was taken up for special service she was ready to mount a gun forward. When a 12pdr was not available a Bofors was fitted instead.

The last of the typical armament drawings were prepared at this time which showed the undernoted weapons arranged to best advantage on six ships varying between 6000 and 10,000 GT.

1-4in LA aft
1-Oerlikon mounted on a Bofors pedestal, aft
6-Oerlikon, amidships
2-0.5in Colts, amidships
4-PACs (D) amidships
1-12pdr HA/LA forward

Another drawing showed the undernoted weapons arranged to best advantage on three tankers varying between 8000 and 12,000 GT.

1-4in LA aft
1-Oerlikon mounted on a Bofors pedestal aft
2-Oerlikons on the boat deck
2-Oerlikons in the after well and 2 amidships or 4-Oerlikons amidships
2-0.5in Colts amidships
4-PACs (D) amidships
1-12pdr HA/LA forward

Those emplacements were made large enough to accommodate Oerlikons.

The armament fitted on operational ship was as above with the exception that a Bofors was mounted aft instead of an Oerlikon. Existing tonnage engaged on trade routes had two fewer Oerlikons and no 12pdr forward.

In November 1944, to save shipyard labour it was decided that only gun stiffening integral with ship's structure should be proceeded with until about six months from the completion date. The shipbuilder then communicated with the Admiralty with regard to the remainder of the work. If the ship was scheduled for sailing in a non-belligerent area only the minimum of work was done, otherwise she got the full DEMS equipment for her tonnage.

Seven thousand British Ships and 2500 Allied ships were armed by Britain during the war.

Immediately upon the collapse of Germany, disarming of merchant ships (except those sailing in the Far East) commenced.

Note

From experience gained during the Second World War it is considered advisable that the following points should be borne in mind:
1. Schemes of arming should be decided upon in peacetime.
2. All gun stiffening integral with ships' structures should be done during building.
3. All drawings relevant to the defensive equipping of merchant ship should be prepared and should be circulated to all concerned in peacetime so that they may know what is required in an emergency.
4. Immediately on the outbreak of war, or preferably before, a constructive officer should be appointed for liaison duties and given the authority to attend all conferences relating to DEMS and if necessary be in a position to arrange for conferences. He should be released, as far as possible, from office duties so that his services may be put to better use by personally contacting 'fitting-out' officers, and arranging the best and quickest means of overcoming their troubles.
5. In arranging positions of and stiffening for weapons the ultimate arming should be borne in mind, ie arrange for the weapons which may be fitted at a later date, not only the ones which are to hand at the commencement of hostilities.

The Fitting of Asdic Equipment in Merchant Ships

In April 1942 it was decided that it was desirable to fit in new construction vessel a listening equipment for submarine detection and shipowners were informed that approval had been given to incorporate this in ships building to Government and private account.

The conditions of fitting this equipment to privately owned vessels under construction were that the supply, installation and maintenance of the listening set should be an Admiralty liability, but that the cost of any necessary structural work estimated at £300–£600 should be borne by the owners as for other defensive equipment. The equipment would only be fitted to new construction ships with a speed of 15kts and over

Four operators were required and where possible they were made available from the merchant navy crew of the vessel. It was necessary for them to attend a course of instruction at the Hydrophone School at Greenock lasting two weeks, with an extra week for the ratings who were to be in charge of the maintenance. In cases where the ratings could not be provided from the crew, it was necessary for them to be carried as extra DEMS ratings and additional accommodation was required.

Owners who agreed to fit the equipment acquainted the Admiralty two months before the date of the launch so that the necessary equipment could be made available.

The fitting of the equipment necessitated the building of the directing gear compartment in the forward hold with a watertight trunk for access, a small asdic office on the navigating bridge usually adjoining the wheelhouse with a sliding window allowing the instruments to be sighted by the officer in the wheelhouse and small cupboard about 4ft x 3ft on the boat deck level for instruments. The asdic directing compartment was fitted with a fan ventilation supply and a natural exhaust but it was found necessary in vessels where this compartment was situated adjacent to a heated oil fuel tank to lag the bulkheads and trunk with 3in block asbestos to reduce the temperature and condensation. On the earlier vessels the asdic office and instrument cupboard were fitted with natural ventilation but it was later found necessary to fit artificial ventilation to these compartments, especially in vessels operating in tropical waters.

In April 1943 it was decided to fit asdics in existing ships, the entire cost being borne by the Admiralty, and the structural alterations being arranged and supervised by WPS in conjunction with the owners' superintendent.

Instructions to cease fitting asdics to merchant ships were issued in December 1943, and of the forty-five vessels which were approved to be fitted only twenty-eight were completed, twenty-six with type 136 and two with type 128A.

Fitting of Radar Equipment in Merchant Ships

In May 1942 the question of fitting radar type 271/273 on independently routed merchant ships of over 15kts was raised and a good case was put forward by the Director of Anti-Submarine Warfare in view of the increased number of sinkings by submarines of this type of vessel.

It was proposed to use superseded earlier marks of type 271 ex HM Ships, and that they should be reconditioned and fitted in prefabricated huts for fitting at Home ports. It was considered that the initial requirements would be for about five or six ships a month so that the provision of personnel (four per ship), which was one of the difficulties, could be spread over a period.

It was later approved to fit radar type 273 and type 286PQ or 291 on nine monster liners, that is vessels of over 25,000 tons, and the first of these vessels was equipped early in 1943. About thirty existing vessels were selected to be equipped, practically all of them of the large passenger liner class and in January 1943 all Warship Production Superintendents were informed that these vessels were to be equipped, together with all new construction vessel with a speed of over 15kts.

The prefabricated huts were manufactured by Messrs Smiths of Trafford Park, Manchester, and the fitting of the equipment was carried out under the supervision of Warship Production Superintendents in conjunction with the Port Radar Officer and Defensively Equipped Merchant Ships Staff Officer.

The siting of the set was subject to the following requirements: to be outside an 11ft radius from the standard compass, the centre of the lantern to be at least 11ft from the signal mast and the bottom of the lantern to be either above the top of the funnel or at least 20ft from it.

In addition, some vessels which used the Manchester Ship Canal had the further restrictions of keeping the top of the lantern below the bridges under which the vessels passed. It was found possible in most cases to site the set on the monkey island before the funnel although it was sometimes necessary to move the standard compass forward and the signal mast aft.

In November 1943 the drawings and instructions for fitting were forwarded to ports abroad with a view to equipping vessels which rarely visited the United Kingdom.

Most of the vessels which were fitted with radar were equipped with a mercantile aircraft beacon and in February 1944 it was approved to fit a gyro repeater in the radio office.

Early in 1945 it was decided to fit type 268 in merchant ships but in June 1945, after the end of the European war, the fitting of sets was confined to vessels which were going to the Far East.

Up to the end of the war over 220 merchant ships had been equipped with either type 271, 273 or 269 radar sets.

In November 1945 it was decided to allow shipowners to have type 268 fitted if they were prepared to pay the cost of prefabrication, the cost of delivery and fitting and an annual charge for the hire of the set, the shipowners to be allowed to retain the sets for at least three years or until a satisfactory commercial type of radar was available. Arrangements for installation and any necessary stiffening were to be made by the owners, who were also responsible for service and maintenance which was carried out by W H Smith of Manchester.

Owners of ships fitted with type 268 before this date were to pay for the hire of the set if they wished to retain it and shipowners who decided not to fit 268 and whose vessels already had type 271 or 273 fitted were to be allowed to purchase these sets outright.

Merchant Ships – Bow Protection Against Moored Mines (1918-45)

At the end of the 1914-18 war all paravane equipment was removed from merchant ships. Certain unused gear was already in store and the addition of the removed equipment called for a redistribution of stocks at ports at home and abroad so that the gear would be readily available for fitting in an emergency.

It was stated that approximately 120 sets of clump and chain, and four sets of planing shoe equipment were available for armed merchant cruisers and fast liners in addition to the 500 incomplete sets of hinged boom gear available for vessels up to 16kts.

In 1935 it became apparent that the modern practice with regard to the underwater form of new construction merchant ships tended more to render ineffectual the protection afforded by the standard methods of towing paravanes and in consequence it was decided in February 1937 to set up a Shipping Defence Advisory Committee to consider the defence of merchant shipping in an emergency.

The first meeting of this committee was held in March 1937 to discuss the possibilities of constructing merchant vessels with bows suitable to take paravanes in time of war and of the steps to be taken in the case of vessels not so suitably constructed. One definite conclusion reached was that the perfect bow shape from the point of view of towing paravanes to give maximum protection was not entirely acceptable to the Merchant Navy due to certain losses in efficiency and difficulties that must be experienced in ship handling and navigation.

As a result it was decided that existing ships were to be dealt with as was found most practicable with the types of equipment then available and that shipowners should have their attention drawn to the importance of adapting the shape of the bow to suit paravane requirements in future new construction, at the same time being requested to supply drawings to the Admiralty of stems of their vessels for consideration as to the type of gear for which they were suitable. A circular letter was issued by the Chamber of Shipping of the United Kingdom and the Liverpool Steam Ship Owners Association at the request of the Admiralty in September 1937 and the owners were given sketches and descriptions of the various types of towing equipment, it being pointed out that the point of tow was desired at keel level and that the Admiralty type of stem was the most suitable for bow protection to be fitted, when required, without docking the vessel.

About this time endeavour was made and with some success to build up the stocks of paravane equipment both at home and abroad and, as though to encourage this increase of reserve, improvements to HM Ship paravanes gave redundant stocks, which were now transferred for use in merchant ships. Orders for new hinged booms were placed as this gear had proved highly efficient in the 1914-18 war and a consequent amendment to the 1934 scheme of distribution took place as the need arose to protect a greater number of fast liners.

Investigations of the Shipping Defence Advisory Committee had emphasized the extreme importance of developing some form of bow gear for merchant ships which could be fitted without delay and without docking. Difficulty had been experienced with the planing shoe in keeping it down under seagoing conditions to give a reasonably low point of tow. On the other hand the hinged boom had as previously mentioned, in the majority of cases, been the only standard type of equipment that could offer anything approaching a reasonable degree of protection. The immediate reaction to this latter gear, however, was the apparent necessity of docking involving expense, quite apart from the boom and its attendant fittings. Furthermore, the hinged boom did not offer a sufficiently submerged point of tow with the modern form of stem.

It was clear also that the clump and chain method had several disadvantages such as the probable damage to the hull when docking or when working anchors and cables due to the proximity of the chains.

It was agreed that the question of developing a simple and efficient towing arrangement for paravanes in merchant vessels could most rapidly be solved by informal discussion at a place where the date concerning paravanes and towing ropes was at hand.

Suggestions for overcoming the difficulties with the planing shoe were put forward by DNC but with little effect. The need for a definite downhaul for this type of equipment was by now evident. The main features of DNC's suggestions centred around maintaining a low point of tow without the necessity of fitting a stem extension (involving docking) in ships with cut-up or a rounded forefoot.

The informal discussion already referred to took place at *Vernon* in November 1937 and as a

SS Empire Toiler *in June 1942, showing the bow protection gear.*

result it was decided that typical lines of merchant ship stems should be supplied to the Mining School for models to be made and experiments carried out.

The response to the circular letter of 1937 to shipowners was most encouraging and upwards of 2400 drawing were received in DNC. Early in 1938 work commenced on the analysis of the various types of stems, each ship being dealt with individually or as a class and consideration given as to its suitability for hinged boom, clump and chain, or planing shoe.

By July of the same year this analysis and classification was completed. Eighty-eight per cent of the vessels were found suitable for the planing hoe or hinged boom, the remaining 12 per cent being suitable only for clump and chain.

At this same period a wood 'mock-up' of the hinged boom for merchant ships was rigged on the stem of HMS *Dauntless* in Portsmouth Dockyard for trial. The purpose of the trial was to ascertain if sufficient data could be obtained to enable hinged booms to be prepared to such a degree as to be ready for immediate fitting and thus avoid drydocking.

Visualising the success of this trial it was decided in order to avoid future dry-docking on merchant ships (except where a bearing stop was required) to take advantage of a ship's periodical survey in dry dock for the purpose of 'marking-off' for hinged boom. This enabled relative cost with *Dauntless* trial to be assessed and in consequence the amount of financial assistance to contractors for 'marking-off' was agreed upon. Seventy selected owners were later informed that DNC's analysis showed that a large number of their ships would require hinged booms and they were asked to co-operate in arranging for 'marking-off' to be done during the normal survey period in dry dock.

Charts were prepared in DNC (based on information lifted from HMS *Dauntless* etc.) on which data for hinged booms was to be inserted and these were issued to fitting-out authorities at home with instructions to send duplicate copies of completed charts to DNC who would be turn forward one copy to the owners of the vessel for their information, retaining the other for reference so that the data could be easily communicated to any fitting-out area if the need to fit a new hinged boom arose due to damage or other causes. Instructions were also issued that one copy of the completed chart was to be placed on board in possession of the Master.

All drawings, together with fitting-out and working instructions for all types of paravane towing equipment were now condensed into one common Confidential Book and copies circulated to all fitting-out authorities at home and abroad. Furthermore, a series of wood mock-ups similar to that used for trial purposes on HMS *Dauntless* were made for distribution to certain Naval stores for general use in those areas when fitting-out vessels with hinged boom equipment.

Discussion now took place as to the practicability of fitting cross-Channel steamers having bow rudders with paravane protection. The speed of these vessels as a whole placed the hinged boom out of the question and it was at that time not considered advisable to lock the bow rudders as these would probably be required, even in an operation, for navigational purposes.

With the need to protect every selected vessel, whether in or out of convoy, no limit as to the minimum speed had up to this time been laid down. It was sufficient if a vessel could maintain a speed equivalent to that required for dropping paravanes (about 6-7kts). Limits were, however, imposed at a later date and these will be dealt with when that stage is reached.

The need for the adoption of the Admiralty stem in merchant ships again presented itself in November 1938. Examination of the 2400 drawings previously referred to had shown that very few existing vessels had a stem that could take the planing shoe without the need for a stem extension. Trials were carried out on RFA *Olna* in the same month in which a planing shoe was veered past the forefoot by means of double bridles. This method was given a further trial later under service conditions and was then discarded. It was probable that a large number of future new construction merchant ship would be of a speed outside the limits of the hinged boom and therefore it became obvious that there was a need to incorporate structure in the forefoot to take planing shoe or clump and chain.

Paravane parties familiar with all details as included in the Confidential Book already referred to and who were to assist in the 'lining off' of hinged booms and recording of the necessary data, were at that moment being assembled in vital areas preparatory to hostilities breaking out.

The demand for some other form of protection that would dispense with dry docking has already been mentioned and in February 1939 we find the introduction by DNC of a type known as the 'A' frame. Its main advantages were its ability to maintain a point of tow abreast or forward of the fore side of stem and as low down as necessary and its simple topping lift as compared with the numerous leads required on the other known system.

It was obvious at that time that the 'A' frame, as well as achieving a forward low point of tow, could also be satisfactorily applied to vessels having a considerable cut-up or round of forefoot and it was even applied to the Maier form bow with relative ease. With this gear no elaborate forgings or castings were required as for the other types and it could be easily assembled and fitted at the ship.

Furthermore, it was apparent that a definite point of tow could be maintained through the 'A' frame remaining in contact with the stem under all seagoing conditions.

Consideration had been given in the design stage to the width necessary between the main channels to clear the anchors when the frame was being raised or lowered, and a lot of time and thought was given to the question of watertightness of the hull where the connecting shaft pierced the ship's side, and streamlining was to be applied to the whole frame as far as practicable to overcome water resistance.

A model of the frame was made based on the lines of RFA *Olna* and following this an experimental frame was made and fitted to RFA *Oleander* in March 1939 for sea trials under bad weather conditions and through a dummy minefield and these were highly successful.

It had been decided by the Shipping Defence Advisory Committee in October 1938 to carry out full-scale trials of the various types of towing gear and to invite shipowners' representatives to attend. Admiralty officers were to supervise the fitting-out of the gear on selected ships and instruct the personnel in its use. The owners were to consider leaving the gear on board for, say, six months to enable the crews to have routine exercise in handling. War broke out, however, before the expiry of this time and the gear remained as fitted for trial. The trials gave the personnel experience in handling of paravanes with the various standard forms of towing gear.

Trials were carried out in May 1939 on *City of Bedford* with clump and chain, and on *Carelia* with planing shoe and in July 1939 *Somme* was also fitted-out with hinged boom. (This vessel had previously been 'marked-off' whilst undergoing periodical survey in dry-dock.) Previous reference to 'A' frame trials on RFA *Oleander* will indicate why the gear was not tried out on this occasion.

It should be noted at this stage that a considerable number of vessels had been 'marked-off' for hinged boom and the charts showing the recorded date distributed as already described, and 'A' frame drawings, fitted out and working instructions had been prepared and issued to all fitting-out authorities at home and abroad.

August 1939 saw a completed list of vessels so recorded, published, whilst in September the first publication was made showing the types of equipment for which each ship was suitable (based on DNC's analysis of stem drawings). In addition, this latter publication indicated whether a vessel had been recorded for hinged boom and/or whether a stem extension had been fitted for planing shoe. This information was of considerable value to fitting-out authorities a sit enabled preparatory work to be put in hand in anticipation of a vessel's arrival.

All this time experiments on lengths of paravane wires had taken place, the short towing wire of 10-15 fathoms being finally accepted as offering the maximum possible protection to most forms even whilst the vessel was under helm. This, of course, meant the repositioning of paravane handling arrangements in vessels already fitted with long towing ropes. With the introduction of larger vessels, the need to maintain a standard length of 15 fathoms arose as it was vital to protect the stern when steaming in a cross tide through the ordinary type of minefield under small helm.

Vessels with broad contour plate stems were now arriving at arming ports abroad at a time when despatch of 'A' frames had not yet been arranged. In view of the possible need to fit planing shoe to these vessels, a curved plate to be welded to the fore edge of the contour plate and of sufficient radius to permit easy movement of the shoe up and down the stem was designed in DNC, and copies circulated to all ports concerned.

In December 1939, in order to settle finally the question of stocks of the various types of equipment to be held in store at home and abroad, it was decided to make provision for the protection of 3224 merchant vessels. Provision was made for 3300 sets comprising 2000 'A' frames, 830 hinged booms, 240 clump and chains and 230 planing shoes.

Trouble now arose in HM Ships (when steaming at slow speeds) in that the planing shoe was tending to ride up and off the stem, bad tending of the backhauls accelerating the trouble and in March 1940 we find the planing shoe completely replaced by the clump and chain method in Naval vessels. Anticipating similar trouble in merchant vessels so fitted, it was decided as a first measure to use up the available planing shoe sets on existing and new construction vessels but to place no further orders for this gear. Any ships already fitted experiencing trouble to be replaced at the first available opportunity by the 'A' frame or hinged boom (preferably the former).

The question of suitable paravane protection for future new construction merchant ship was now of paramount importance and it was decided in April 1940 to advise shipowners to construct their vessels with the straight bow and to incorporate a clump casting in the forefoot enabling clump and chain or planing shoe to be fitted (planing shoe still had to be considered in case of any future change in policy). This casting became generally known as the 'new pattern' clump casting. Until these castings could be mass produced, shipbuilders supplied fabricated castings for individual vessels. In general the straight stem was from this time favourably accepted.

In the subsequent circular to shipowners informing them of the above change they were also advised to fit 'A' frame gear to existing vessels ass this type was, wherever practicable, to replace hinged boom. The relative information, together with copies of the drawings referred to in the preceding paragraph, was incorporated in the Shipowners Handbook.

The limitation as to minimum speed etc. at which paravanes were to be fitted was now laid down as 9kts loaded with a maximum draught aft of at least 12ft.

By April 1940 quantities of 'A' frames were available and, in view of the fact that 706 ships had been 'marked-off' for hinged boom and only 330 vessels had been fitted, it was decided to cease 'marking off' until the remaining 376 vessels had been fitted. In the meantime 'A' frames, wherever practicable, should be adopted.

One inch chain cable was now in very short supply due to demand made on this item in fitting out vessels with clump and chain equipment, and orders were placed for 400 lengths in the USA, having regard to the introduction of 'new pattern' clump castings referred to above.

Acoustic mines were now being encountered and, as a counter-measure, several hundreds of trawlers were fitted with the 'A' frame and at the apex a hinged conical hammer box was incorporated. A DNC drawing shows how this 'A' frame and hammer box were generally fitted, little difficulty being experienced in its fitting.

It is interesting to note that by September 1940 approximately 700 merchant ships had been fitted with paravane equipment.

As a result of sea experience, various modifications were found necessary to the original 'A' frame as designed and these were finally incorporated in a drawing which was circulated to all authorities at home and abroad in June 1941. It embodied the main essentials of the original frame with the addition of such features as extra steamling, pressed plate collars and breakwaters. With regard to the breakwaters, severe damage had been caused to 'A' frames, when vessels were pitching, due to the clearance necessary between the 'A' frame and the ship's side to avoid fouling anchors when raising and lowering, in addition to local conditions necessitating a maximum extension where the spindle left the ship. These breakwaters had, where fitted, been found to fulfil their purpose in preventing a rush of water between the frame and the ship's side. Lack of welders and insufficient time led to these breakwaters seldom being fitted.

It was obvious by August 1941 that the smaller types of vessels were experiencing difficulty in working their paravane equipment, due to congested and short forecastle decks etc., and in consequence instruction were issued that as convenient all such gear was to be removed from vessels with fewer than six deck hands but that all permanent fittings such a clump castings, cleats, fairleads, eyeplates, etc., welded or riveted to ship's structure, were to remain in case the need to reequip these vessels arose.

In September 1941 the *Prince Baudouin*, a cross-Channel steamer with bow rudder, was successfully fitted with clump and chain equipment. The bow rudder was efficiently locked by welding filling-in pieces between the rudder and the hull. Plate were connected each side of the rudder of shape to form a false stem to take the 'new pattern' clump castings and to prevent any stresses being brought on thefrail stem bar.This method was later applied to several other cross-Channel steamers.

Lack of time and docking facilities prevented a lot of vessels from being fitted about this period with one of the standard types of paravane equipment available. In consequence an emergency type of gear, to be known as the 'chain harness', was introduced and first fitted to the *Empire Plover* at Hull about January 1942. Briefly it consisted of a continuous chain passing round the forefoot and connected at the extremities to the ship's structure at a convenient position aft of the steam head. Another chain bridle was passed round the stem bar and connected to the continuous chain, its purpose being to endeavour to maintain a correct towing position when paravanes were streamed. The chain bridle was later replaced by a plate shoe. A maximum speed of 16kt was laid down for this equipment.

February 1942 saw several proposals put forward for the introduction of an internal tube for paravanes similar to that being used in HM Ships. These were turned down on account of the difficulty anticipated in getting shipowners to incorporate the involved casting necessary at the forefoot and on the deck, together with the problem of inserting the tube whilst the vessels were building.

For some time past tank tests on the resistance to vessels due to the presence of paravane chains had been carried out and in May 1942 Messrs J L Thompson, Shipbuilders, Sunderland, reported that the loss of speed due to chains alone when 10kts was being developed was about ½kt.

By May 1942 approximately 1300 merchant ships had been fitted with paravane equipment.

Difficulty was now experienced with paravane arrangements on monster liners. *Queen Elizabeth* arrived in June 1942 with broken chains. A form of solid plate extension had been fitted to the forefoot well aft of the stem, but the chains had been permitted to chafe on the deck edges on passage to and from the capstan. Wood rubbing pieces had been fitted at these position but movement of the chains had made these useless. *Queen Mary* later experienced the same trouble. The troubles were attributed to high speeds maintained by these vessels coupled with the long lengths of chain between deck edge and clump and insufficient slack in the chains.

It was decided to fit the standard DEMS arrangement with some major modification as regards the size of chain cable at the earliest opportunity and, in the case of *Queen Elizabeth*, a merchant ship clump casting, special deck edge fairleads and 1½in chain cable (in lieu of the 1in chain cable fitted at that time) were to be placed on board. The broken links of existing cable were renewed for further service until these arrangements could be fitted. Instructions were issued that the new casting was to be fitted at a position a far forward a possible having regard to the dimensions laid down in O.U. 6299. Owing to repeated difficulties, however, with these vessels, the Masters were instructed not to stream paravanes unless specially ordered but to keep the gear rigged.

The fitting of clump and chain equipment on new construction merchant ships was from this time discontinued. As a result of the tank tests already mentioned, hinged boom became the standard for new construction and existing ships, subject to speed limitations. Where the 2½in plate had been incorporated in the forefoot to take the 'new pattern' clump castings, it was to be retained but the castings were not to be fitted.

Vessels with congested forecastles and tankers specially fitted with sparred decks for carrying additional cargo etc. were in February 1943 requested to land their paravane equipment and no similar vessels were in future to be fitted. One of the major difficulties was the failure to find suitable positions for gallows cranes etc.

The running of paravanes had for some time been possible on vessels fitted with short torpedo defence nets but, with the introduction of extended nets, it was doubtful if the two systems could be worked together. However, in May 1943 a drawing was prepared and it was estimated that with a short paravane towing rope of 12½-13 fathoms, no fouling of the fore-end of the net would occur. Vessels with short nets were still to complete with two ropes of about 15 fathoms.

The previous limitation a to the speed etc. at which paravanes were to be fitted was now amended to apply to new construction ocean-going ships only, existing ships being considered only at 15kts or over unless engaged on operational or special duties.

Sea trials were carried out on *Empire Symbol* in September 1943, with extended nets and trial paravane towing ropes fitted of 12½ and 14½ fathoms respectively. Gallows cranes were arranged at break of forecastle as in drawing referred to above. As a result of these trials it was decided that all future vessels fitted with extended nets should be provided with towing ropes not exceeding 12½ fathoms in length and that 'A' frames wherever practicable should be fitted, as it was found that the short tow rope could be more readily worked with this arrangement.

November 1943 saw the introduction of a system to be known as the 'endless chain'. It was applicable to the known system of clump and chain but dispensed with the familiar long leads of chain and tailing wires along the forecastle deck. The introduction of this gear was very beneficial as it came at a time when the chain position in this country was very acute.

At the same time HMS *Vernon* introduced a system known as the 'chain necklace' to be applied to monster liners. Copies of the arrangement were placed on Board-selected vessels for fitting this gear at the first opportunity. Briefly the system comprised an endless chain suspended at intervals along the deck edge such that when released it fell against the clump at the forefoot from which the towing wires operated. The clump was to be faired to prevent chafe of the bridle and masters were informed not to fit this gear unless the existing system failed.

March 1944 saw trouble with 'A' frames on merchant aircraft carrier grain ships. These vessel had to be down to the loaded draught to form a stable and level platform for flying and in consequence the 'A' frames dipped deeply into the head sea causing damage to the heel fitting and in some cases flooding of the chain locker. On the other hand, the hinged boom was unsuitable as it protruded too high for flying off. Planing shoe and clump and chain were also unsuitable for reasons already stated. Fitting of these vessels was therefore discontinued.

In September 1944 it was decided that paravanes should no longer be fitted to new construction ocean-going merchant ships below 15kts unless detailed for special operations and further, where removal of gear already fitted would delay a ship's completion date, the fitting was to be completed.

The post-war policy regarding the laying apart of stores for any future was was fully discussed and it was decided to reserve stocks in Dockyard Naval Stores of 300 sets of equipment comprising 150 'A' frames, fifty hinged booms and 100 clump and chain.

Instructions were issued in November 1945 that paravane equipment could now be removed from all merchant ships and that gear so removed (except chains in serviceable condition) was to be brought to produce.

In conclusion it is interesting to note that, of the 3224 merchant ships due for protection, approximately 2150 had been fitted up to the time of the general removal.

CHAPTER 26

RFA Tankers

Editorial Note

The Admiralty owned a number of tankers at the outbreak of war but many were old and small and even the modern ones were slow. They could only refuel at sea by the astern method which with the small hoses used, was very slow. This short chapter has little to say about the efforts made to develop equipment and procedures for abeam transfer, as used in the USN. Tankers were in short supply during the war and only in 1943 did the Admiralty manage to get faster ships which could work with a task force and even the best of the wartime ships were still slow, both in ship speed and in replenishment time.

Royal Fleet Auxiliaries

Ranger Class Tanker

The *Ranger* class of Royal Fleet Auxiliary tankers – cargo capacity 3000 tons – were intended to replace the old 2000 tons class *Belgol*, *Celerol*, *Fortol*, etc. In all six *Rangers* were built but, due to the shortage of tankers throughout the war, the 2000 tons class were retained on service.

These ships were of the single deck type with poop and forecastle, straight stem raked forward, cruiser stern, and machinery and all accommodation aft.

The ships were built to Lloyds requirements and classified 100 A1* for carrying a full cargo of petroleum in bulk.

The main dimensions of the individual ships varied slightly.

Leading particulars for *Gold Ranger* were:

Length overall	355ft
Breadth extreme	48ft 0in
Displacement	6704 tons
Mean draught	20ft 2½in
Freeboard	2ft 5¼in
Speed	13kts
Endurance	6000 miles at 13kts
Power	4000ihp
Cargo capacity	3213 tons
Complement (total)	12 officers, 28 men

Cargo Capacity etc.	Oil fuel	2582 tons
	Diesel oil	541 tons
	Petrol	90 tons

Pumping capacity was provided by two 350ton/hr pumps for the oil fuel, and one 20ton/hr pump for the petrol.

Pyrene air foam fire-fighting equipment was installed in the petrol pump room to supply foam to the petrol tanks, etc. The installation was capable of producing 200 gallon of foam per minute for nearly 15 minutes.

Protection

Protective plating 100lb D1 quality steel was fitted over the petrol tanks and petrol pump room. It was worked as doubling over the upper deck plating.

The wheelhouse was protected by 4in thick plastic armour on the sides, front and ends and 2½in on the top.

Armament was in accordance with DEMS practice. Originally one 4in LA, one 12pdr HA/LA and two Lewis guns were fitted. From time to time throughout the war, and from ship to ship, the armament was changed until finally a typical armament for a *Ranger* consisted of one 4in LA, a single Bofors and four single Oerlikons.

Increased complement was necessary to man the armament.

Machinery

The Black *Rangers* were fitted with propelling machinery built by Harland & Wolff. This consisted of one reversible single-acting diesel engine giving 4000ihp to drive a single screw.

Propeller particulars:

diameter	14ft 6in
pitch	12ft 6in
developed blade area	62sq ft

The Gold *Rangers* had Doxford diesel engines, giving 400ihp and single propellers.

Propeller particulars:

diameter	14ft 0in
pitch	12ft 1in
developed blade area	78sq ft

Two auxiliary boilers of the multi-tube type were fitted, burning oil fuel with forced draught and providing steam at 180lb/sq in.

The ships were designed for a speed of 13kts, but on trials mean speeds from 13.8 to 14.1kts were obtained in a deep condition of 6200 tons.

Ranger class general arrangement

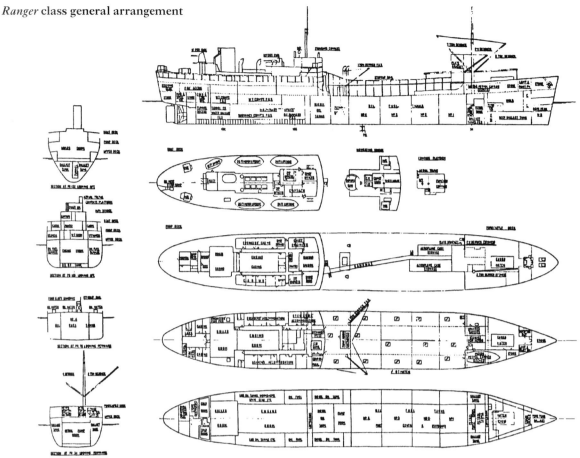

The distilling machinery installed provided 10 tons of water per day.

Stability

Typical stability figure for the class were as follows:

The worst condition is an intermediate load condition in which GM = 2.71ft (corrected for free surface in all tanks).

Maximum stability angle 44°

Maximum stability lever 2.2ft

Range of stability 81°

Draught forward 9ft 4in

Draught aft 19ft 11½in

In the light condition (GM – 4.18ft) the maximum stability angle was 32° and range of stability over 90°.[1]

General

For fuelling at sea these ships were fitted originally with the stirrup method of fuelling astern; the stirrup rail following the line of boat and well deck and accommodating 240ft of flexible metallic hose. No facilities were provided for abeam fuelling.

During the war the stirrup method was replaced by the buoyant hose method with one 5in rubber hose. In addition two 40ft derricks, one port and the other starboard, were fitted for the abeam method.

For supplying small quantities of petrol to other ships, arrangements were made for the stowage of a small motor petrol carrier in a compartment under the forecastle.

A sparred wood platform was fitted at the after end of the forecastle deck to accommodate a cased aeroplane.

[1] The *Rangers* were unusual tankers with armour over their petrol stowage and with the funnel off the centre line, presumably to get a good run of hose over the stern.

Ship	Builder	Laid Down	Launched	Completed
1939 Programme				
Black Ranger	Harland & Wolff	12 Oct 1939	22 Aug 1940	28 Jan 1941
Brown Ranger	Harland & Wolff	28 Oct 1939	12 Dec 1940	10 Apr 1941
Blue Ranger	Harland & Wolff	26 Oct 1939	29 Jan 1941	5 Jun 1941
Gold Ranger	Caledon Shipbuilding Co	14 May 1940	12 Mar 1941	4 Jul 1941
Gray Ranger	Caledon Shipbuilding Co	24 Jun 1940	27 May 1941	25 Sep 1941
Green Ranger	Caledon Shipbuilding Co	23 Sep 1940	21 Aug 1941	4 Dec 1941

Blue Ranger *in 1951. It is just apparent that the funnel is off centre to port. The Rangers were yet another of Rowland Baker's creations.*

Sprite Class (Petrol Carriers)

To increase the number of ships available for the transport of petrol in bulk, two petrol carriers were ordered early in the war. They were later named *Nasprite* and *Airsprite*.

They were of the single deck type with poop and forecastle, straight stem raked forward and cruiser stern; machinery and accommodation aft.

Cargo capacity of each ship was 533 tons petrol and 52½ tons lubricating oil; two pumps, each 50ton/hr were provided for pumping petrol and a 10ton/hr pump for the lubricating oil.

The general particulars of these two ships were:

Length overall	213ft 3in
Breadth extreme	33ft 2in
Displacement (deep)	1778 tons
Mean draught	12ft 9¾in
Freeboard	10in
Speed	10kts
Complement	7 officers, 23 men
Cargo capacity	160,000 galls petrol

Airsprite and *Nasprite* were fitted with triple expansion steam reciprocating propelling machinery developing 750ihp and driving a single screw.

On trials both ships exceeded the designed speed of 10kts.

Both ships were built to Lloyd's requirements and classified 100 A1* for carrying full cargo of petrol in bulk.

In accordance with DEMS practice these vessels were armed originally with a 12pdr HA/LA gun, two Hotchkiss and one Lewis gun. The only protection fitted was to the sides, ends and top of the wheelhouse and consisted of plastic armour.

Stability

The worst condition of these ships is 'arrival in ballast' and the best 'departure deep loaded'. Following are the corresponding metacentric heights of *Airsprite*:

	Metacentric height	Displacement
Arrival in ballast	0.68ft	1227 tons
Departure deep loaded	1.82ft	1778 tons

Ship	Builder	Laid Down	Launched	Completed
Nasprite	Blythswood	April 1940	December 1940	11 Feb 1941
Airsprite	Blythswood	September 1941	22 Dec 1942	16 Feb 1943

1500 ton Tankers

In April 1940 approval was given to build six 1500 ton fleet attendant tankers. Two were to replace two of the old 1000 ton tankers and the remaining four would release for freighting service some of the large tankers which it had been necessary to employ for fleet attendance and eventually replace four more of the 1000 tonners.

Leading particulars of the design were:

Length overall		263ft 0in
Breadth max.		38ft 6in
Depth		17ft 6in
Displacement (deep)		3200 tons
Draught (deep)		16ft
Power (steam reciprocating machinery)		1200ihp
Speed		10kts
Endurance		2000 miles
Cargo capacity	oil fuel	1500 tons
	diesel oil	100 tons
	petrol	50 tons

No slips were available in the United Kingdom for building these vessels and the capacity for building was sought in Canada. Shipyards in Canada could not, however, cope with the particular requirements of a fleet attendant tanker. It was therefore decided in May 1940 to abandon the idea of laying down these six ships.

Wave Class

At the beginning of 1943 it was decided to take up two 15kt tankers of standard design to augment the fleet of RFA tankers. Two such tankers were being built by Harland & Wolff at that time and arrangements were made to take them over on completion, the keel of the first having just been laid.

As RFAs, fuelling-at-sea was to be one of the main functions of these ships, consequently detailed consideration was given to the special arrangements needed. To expedite completion however, little alteration was made to the original design and fitting out.

For fuelling-at-sea abeam, each ship was fitted with two 60ft derricks, one port and one starboard in the after well, each derrick having a working load of 2 tons and carrying one hose trough at its head.

For fuelling by the astern method a clear passageway was made through the centre castle and poop accommodation, the accommodation being repositioned at the ship's side and taking up the side walkways. A fore and aft platform was fitted from forecastle to centrecastle and from centrecastle to poop to provide a straight lead from forecastle to the stern.

Two stern chutes were fitted and arrangements to enable two 5in rubber hoses to be streamed astern from the starboard quarter and one 3in petrol hose from the port quarter.

Later, other tankers of the same class were fitted during construction with fuelling-at-sea arrangements and, on completion, taken over as RFAs. The fuelling-at-sea equipment was in accordance with the practice at that time but was fundamentally the same as that fitted in the first two ships.

By the end of 1946 there were seven *Wave* tankers in service as RFAs – *Wave King*, *Wave Monarch*, *Wave Emperor*, *Wave Governor*, *Wave Regent*, *Wave Sovereign* and *Wave Chief*; two further tankers were still under construction. In addition there were eleven ships to the same basic design in service but under commercial management; it was the intention to take over these ship from commercial management as RFAs and rename them in the *Wave* series.

The main particulars of the *Wave* class were as follows:

Wave class
general arrangement

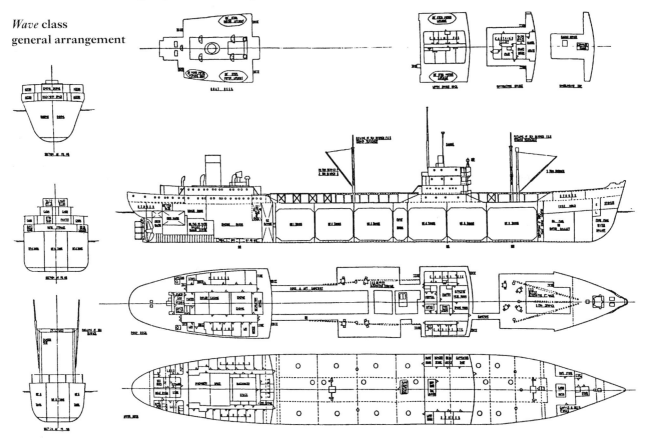

Wave Premier *on 9 June 1948. She is in wartime configuration except for removal of her guns. Note the long derricks for refuelling abeam.*

Length overall	492ft 5in
Breadth extreme	64ft 4in
Displacement (deep)	16,483 tons
Mean draught (deep)	28ft 6in
Freeboard	7ft 2½in
Machinery – steam turbines	6800shp
Oil fuel	1680 tons
Speed max (deep)	15kts
Cargo capacity { oil fuel	7950 tons
diesel oil	750 tons
spirit	980 tons
Cargo pumps	2-390ton/hr
	1-50ton/hr
	1-59ton/hr
Complement	14 officers, 47 men

General

All six ships were fitted for fuelling by the trough and stirrup methods for abeam and astern fuelling respectively. The first three for the astern method, were fitted with one stern chute and a stirrup rail which followed the line of the weather deck; while for the trough method two ship's derricks situated in the after well were used.

The fourth ship, *Eaglesdale*, was fitted with platforms over the forward and after wells on the starboard side to provide a level run from forward to aft. During the building of this ship a floating rubber fuel hose was produced, and arrangements made for her to operate either rubber or flexible metallic hose on her stirrup rail.

Apart from the modernisation of the fuelling-at-sea equipment from time to time, only minor alterations were carried out in these ships during the war.

Dale Class Tankers

In 1939 there were insufficient Royal Fleet Auxiliary Tankers to meet wartime needs, and in order to increase the RFA fleet with the least disruption to commercial shipbuilding, it was decided to take over some commercial tankers of standard design.

The standard design at that time was an 11½kts, 12,000 ton tanker and in the ensuing two years six such ships were. taken over. One ship, *Dinsdale*, was sunk on its maiden voyage.

General particulars of *Eaglesdale*, a typical ship, were:

Length overall	479ft 0in
Breadth extreme	61ft 2in
Depth	34ft 0in
Displacement (deep)	16,820 tons
Mean draught (deep)	27ft 1½in
Speed	11½kts
Power	3650ihp
Complement (total)	4 officers, 56 crew (native)

Cargo Capacity etc

These ships were fitted for the carriage of oil fuel and petrol in bulk and had a total cargo capacity of approximately 11,800 tons. Four pumps at 270ton/hr each were provided for oil fuel and two at 50ton/hr each for petrol.

Ship	Builder	Laid Down	Launched	Completed
Denby Dale	Blythswood	26 Dec 1939	19 Oct 1940	30 Jan 1941
Echo Dale	Hawthorn Leslie	8 Jan 1940	29 Nov 1940	4 Mar 1941
Dingle Dale	Harland & Wolff	11 Dec 1939	27 Mar 1941	10 Sep 1941
Eaglesdale	Furness		18 Nov 1941	10 Jan 1942
Easedale	Furness	15 Feb 1941	18 Dec 1941	12 Feb 1942
Dinsdale	Harland & Wolff	-	-	11 Apr 1942

These tankers, taken over during building, joined the existing seven *Dale* RFAs to form the complete *Dale* class of thirteen tankers.

The existing ships had been included in the 1936 and 1938 new construction programmes and consisted of *Abbeydale*, *Aldersdale*, *Arndale*, *Bishopdale*, *Boardale*, *Broomdale* and *Cairndale*.

The leading particulars were:

Length overall	480ft 0in
Breadth extreme	59ft 5in
Displacement (deep)	17,200 tons
Mean draught (deep)	27ft 6in
Power	3260shp
	(*Cairndale* 4000shp)
Max speed	13kts
Cargo	11,650 tons oil fuel
Pumping capacity	920ton/hr
Complement	12 officers, 30 men

RN Tankers

The Naval staff began thinking seriously of fast oilers as early as 1942, and broad staff requirements were prepared for an oil tanker capable of accompanying an assault force, at a speed of 18kts, from the main base to an advanced base a considerable distance, ie 4000 miles away. The oil tanker was then required to supply the assault force with oil fuel, lubricating oil, petrol, stores, etc. and return to the main base escorted by two destroyers. Discussion went on until he middle of 1943, and it was then considered necessary for the vessel to carry aircraft for her own defence, entailing the provision of a small hangar and arrangements for operating a small number of aircraft. The design of such a novel vessel would have meant considerable work at a time when there were more urgent commitments, so the project was abandoned.

In early 1944, however, discussions were still going on regarding the draft staff requirements but, in view of the difficulty of finding labour from either the Naval or Merchant side of the shipbuilding industry to build these ships when so many other vessels of more vital necessity had to be constructed, the oil tankers were not mentioned in the 1944 Naval programme. The draft staff requirements of February 1944 envisaged that the fast tanker would be required to attend on the fleet during long periods at sea, and be capable of fuelling these ships whilst steaming at a speed of 18kts. This entailed the tanker being capable of accompanying and manoeuvring with the fleet.

Olna *and* Oleander

In early 1944 it became evident that it would be essential to have two fast oil tankers for service with the Far Eastern Fleet, and it was considered that these ships would be needed for operation from mid-1945 onwards until the final defeat of Japan. These fast fleet tankers were to be capable of accompanying the fleet and to have a carrying capacity of 15,000 tons of fuel at a speed of 18-20kts.

As there was no likelihood of getting such tankers from America and building any in time, it was decided that two all-welded tankers which were being built by Messrs Swan Hunter for the Anglo-Saxon Petroleum Company should be completed for the Navy. It was anticipated that the first ship would be ready for service in January 1945 and the second hip at the end of that year. These tankers had a cargo-carrying capacity of 17,000 tons and a speed of 16kts under average weather conditions, but it was considered that by reducing the cargo capacity to 15,000 tons and making other minor modifications the vessels would be capable of about 17kts under average weather conditions. The acquirement of these two tankers, which were renamed *Olna* and *Oleander*, did not fully meet the draft staff requirements and were, therefore, regarded purely as a stop-gap.

Leading particulars of these ships were:

Length overall	583ft 6in
Length between perps	550ft 0in
Breadth (mld)	70ft 0in
Depth (mld)	40ft 6in
Deep displacement	25,096 tons
Mean draught (deep)	31ft 9in
Power	13,000shp
Speed (max)	17kts
Oil fuel (bunkers)	1650 tons
Endurance	6000 miles at 17kts

Group Weights

Hull & equipment	6368 tons
Propelling machinery	1208 tons
Light weight	7576 tons

Machinery in these ships was of turbo-electric type manufactured by the British Thomson-Houston Co. This machinery incorporated a double unit synchronous type propelling motor, operated by two turbo-alternator sets, the installation having been designed to develop 11,000shp at maximum economy, the maximum continuous rating being 13,000shp.

Armament fitted consisted of:
1-4in gun
4-single Bofors
4-single Oerlikons

Protection fitted consisted of 100lb total thickness on top and sides of petrol stowage, and plastic armour around wheelhouse and W/T spaces.

Olna general arrangement

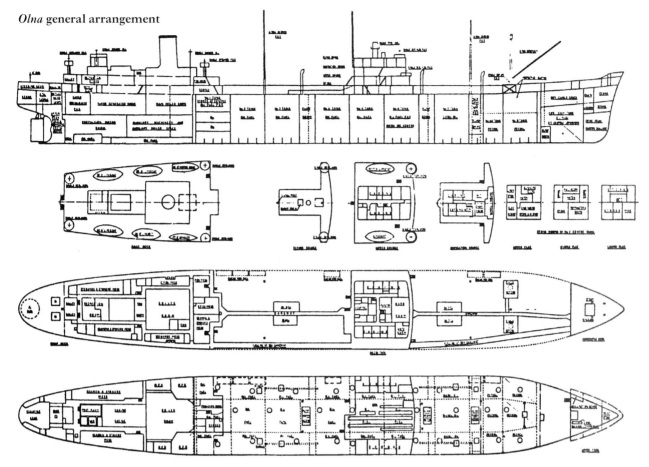

Cargo Capacity etc

Olna and *Oleander* as designed and built were the largest all-welded tankers ever constructed in the UK. The range of cargo oil tanks included nine sets of main tanks, each subdivided transversely by two longitudinal bulkheads in accordance with modern practice.

The cargo capacities were:

Oil fuel	9000 tons
Diesel oil	3000 tons
Petrol	2350 tons
Lubricating oil	240 tons

Two pump rooms subdivided the tanks into three groups so that the various grades of oil could be carried at the same time.

Pump fitted included:

4-390ton/hr for oil fuel
1-150ton/hr for diesel
2-200ton/hr for petrol

Stability Particulars

	Light Condition	Deep Condition
GM	10.62ft	4.86ft
Max GZ	3.54ft	2.92ft
Range	64½°	90°

A longitudinal strength calculation gave the following results:

	Hogging	Sagging
Max bending moment	302,000ton ft	346,000ton ft
Stress in deck	6.5ton/sq in	7.5ton/sq in
Stress in keel	6.4ton/sq in	7.3ton/sq in

Complement

As it was decided that these vessels would be sailing with a task force, a much larger complement was required for fuelling-at-sea etc. than would normally have been required for normal service as an RFA. Originally they were to be operated as RFAs and manned by a merchant crew, the accommodation being to Ministry of War Transport's requirements; however, in view of the increased complement it was decided to man the ships with naval crews and fly the White Ensign. This decision necessitated the crew's accommodation being completely redesigned, and the equipment of the vessel modified as far as possible to naval standards.

General

In the first vessel, *Olna*, much of the existing equipment and arrangements had to be accepted due to the advanced stage of the ship and the importance of not delaying the completion of the vessel. A number of modification were made however, the most important being in:

(i) Structural alterations to obtain the necessary subdivision for the fluid cargo and to accommodate the additional stores carried.

(ii) Alterations to gun platforms and sponsons for the new armament, and fitting protective plating over the petrol tanks.

(iii) Fitting of fuelling-at-sea arrangements for both 'abeam' and 'astern' methods.

(iv) Alterations to piping and additional pumps to handle the different types of cargo.

(v) Additional diesel generator capacity.

(vi) Alterations to accommodation and ventilation.

(vii) Amenities necessary for the comfort of the crew over extended periods at sea, ie canteen and soda fountain, recreation spaces, cinema installation, washing machines, etc.

Olna was completed in May 1945 and incorporated the majority of the latest ideas of that time on fuelling at sea. Operations in the Pacific proved the worth of the vessel and showed that she was a big advance on her predecessors – the *Wave* and *Dale* Class RFA tankers – and no difficulty was found in fuelling three ships simultaneously.

There were, however, several criticisms from sea and recommendations for future new designs which can be summarised as follows:

(i) The difficulty of maintaining constant speed with its consequent effect on station-keeping; this trouble might have been largely overcome by efficient ballasting. *Olna* was, however, a single screw ship with a very large propeller and therefore not so manoeuvrable as a twin screw vessel.

(ii) The necessity for a working deck on which the winches would be mounted to enable working personnel to be kept clear of the sea. This was introduced in a later RN tanker – *Northmark*.

(iii) In a tanker fuelling by the astern method, it was essential to keep the quarter deck clear and the 4in gun should therefore be raised above or removed entirely from the quarter deck.

(iv) Space available on the quarter deck for fuelling at sea was too small. In new designs every effort should be made to increase the area available.

(v) The rates of pumping avgas and avlub were far too low. These rates of pumping were largely governed by the limitation of 3in hoses.

At the time these two vessels were acquired the second ship, HMS *Oleander*, was in the early stages of construction, and as a result it would have been possible to include the majority of the requirements of the Admiralty. Before, however, the vessel could be completed, the Japanese war ended and the vessel was returned to her original owners, the Anglo-Saxon Petroleum Company. At the conclusion of hostilities HMS *Olna* was retained in the Admiralty service and converted as an RFA.

Northmark and Southmark

The end of the war with Germany enabled the Allies to obtain possession of two fast German oil tankers, the *Nordmark* and *Dithmarschen*. Since these tankers were capable of speeds of 21kts they would have been valuable additions in the operations against Japan. The vessels were, however, designed for the purpose of supplying submarines and surface raiders with stores and refrigerated provisions in addition to carrying oil fuel and consequently the oil cargo which could be carried was small in relation to the size of the ship.

The *Nordmark* (ex *Westerwald*) and *Dithmarschen* were built by Schichan Elbing, Schiffswerft, Danzig, and completed in 1938 and 1937 respectively. Brief particulars of the vessels were as follows:

Length overall	584ft
Length between perps	551ft
Max beam	72.3ft
Deep displacement	22,000 tons
Max draught	30ft 6in
Speed	21kts
Endurance at 20kts	7320 miles at 17kts
shp	22,000
Machinery	High pressure turbines and boilers with double reduction gearing

Cargo deadweight

Oil fuel	9400 tons
Lubricating oil	390 tons
Dry cargo stowage (inc. cooled and uncooled spaces)	920 tons

Pumping capacities

Black oil	900ton/hr
Lubricating oil	
90ton/hr	

Original Fuelling Arrangements

The vessels were originally designed and used for supplying oil fuel at sea over the poop, and oiling

Northmark profile and plans

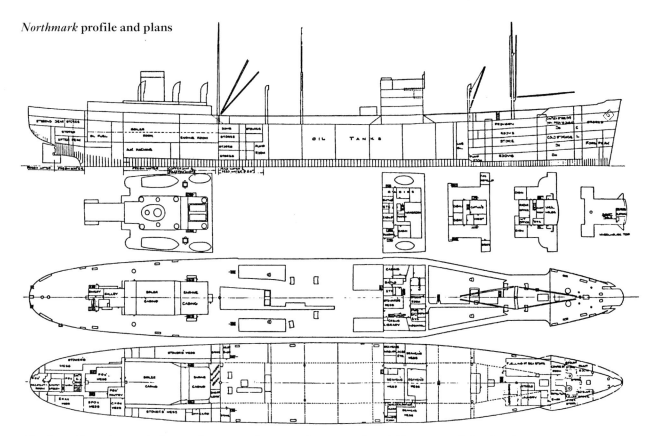

ship alongside and over the bows when stopped under harbour conditions.

Armament
The vessels were fitted with three 5.9in guns and a number of AA weapons of small calibre.

Amenities
A sick bay, operating theatre, laundry, canteen, cinema and SRE were provided for the wellbeing and comfort of the crew.

Navigational Equipment
Well fitted with modern equipment consisting of gyro-compass, echo sounding, D/F, radar (except *Dithmarschen*).

It was decided to convert *Nordmark* and *Dithmarschen* for service as RN fast fleet tankers. Since it was anticipated that the war with Japan would end at an early date, the work of conversion was restricted to a minimum and the limited amount of oil fuel cargo and lubricating oil which could be carried was accepted. The two tankers were renamed *Northmark* and *Southmark* respectively. *Northmark* was converted as Messrs Palmers, Hebburn-on-Tyne and *Southmark* at Messrs Deutche Weift, Hamburg. The principal modifications and alteration were:

(i) Modifying the large number of small cabins originally used for the German crew into large open broadside messes; fitting insulation to ships' side and generally adapting the accommodation and ventilation to RN standards and fitting for tropical service.

(ii) Fuelling-at-sea arrangements were fitted so that oil fuel and lubricating oil could be passed by the astern and abeam methods. This involved fitting two standard platforms and three standard stern roller fairleads for use with the astern method. ND posts and derricks were fitted in the aft well for transferring fuels by the abeam method. The winches were fitted on raised platforms so that personnel would be well clear of the sea. Two derricks on the foremast were fitted with ND rig for use as a secondary fuelling position and also for passing stores.

(iii) Removing existing German armament and fitting four single Bofors Mk III and seven single Oerlikons Mk VII A in lieu, modifying existing magazines as necessary.

(iv) Converting the space originally used for carrying torpedoes for the carriage of bombs.

Northmark was completed in December 1945, and placed in reserve, Category B. When the conversion of *Southmark* was nearly completed the Tripartite Commission in November 1945 reallocated the vessel to the US Government.

Index